A COURSE IN
NUMERICAL
ANALYSIS

HARPER'S SERIES IN MODERN MATHEMATICS

I. N. HERSTEIN AND GIAN-CARLO ROTA, EDITORS

HARPER & ROW, PUBLISHERS

NEW YORK, EVANSTON, AND LONDON

A COURSE IN
NUMERICAL
ANALYSIS

H. MELVIN LIEBERSTEIN

PROFESSOR OF MATHEMATICS, WICHITA STATE UNIVERSITY

DIRECTOR OF RESEARCH, THE MATHEMATICS AND BIOLOGY CORPORATION

A Course in Numerical Analysis
Copyright © 1968 by H. Melvin Lieberstein

Library of Congress Catalog Card Number: 68-10442

CONTENTS

FOREWORD
TO THE STUDENT
ON NOTATION

Logical notation is the mathematician's shorthand. It must be learned. Not only is it more precise than exposition, but it forces the author to make only very direct statements. For example, it may at first frighten a student to see the line

$$\forall \, \epsilon > 0 \; \exists \, \delta > 0 \ni 0 < |x - x_0| < \delta \Rightarrow |f(x) - f(x_0)| < \epsilon,$$

but once he has become accustomed to this shorthand, he will find it easier to master the materials written in this manner.

The style of notation in this book is standard to most American universities. (Admittedly there might be slight variations preferred by individual teachers and students.) It should be made clear, however, that we do not assume any background in symbolic logic. For this reason the early material in this book is kept simple, so that the student who has had no experience with logical notation has an adequate chance to accommodate it.

Unfortunately, there are some places in the book where our logical notation is clumsy. For example, how do we say in logical notation, 'x is between a and b' (often needed in referring to the Taylor theorem)? The answer is: for the open set between a and b, we use the notation (a, b) and we have

$$(a, b) = \{x \in R' \mid a < x < b\},$$

which is read '(a, b) is the set of all real numbers x such that $a < x < b$.' This of course assumes that a is less than b. If it is known to be true that $a < b$, then indeed we may write '$x \in (a, b)$' for 'x is between a and b.' Otherwise, we can write 'either $x \in (a, b)$ or $x \in (b, a)$' (i.e., ['$x \in (a, b)$ V $x \in (b, a)$']), for 'x is between a and b,' and this has been our choice whenever the Taylor theorem was involved.

One further note about the notation adopted in this book. Generally, exponents are used to fulfill a multitude of roles in mathematics, that is,

to indicate powers or roots,

to indicate arguments for functions where the argument behaves algebraically as though it were a power (e^x or a^x).

to indicate summation indices ($a^j x_j$ or $\sum_{j=1}^{n} a^j x_j$),

to indicate a set of ordered pairs or n-tuples, or a vector space (R^n, E^n, C^n),

to indicate a class of functions [$C^m(A)$],

to indicate a norm (L^p or l^p),

to indicate a higher-order derivative of a function [$f^{(m)}$].

We use exponents to fulfill one more role—to indicate elements of a sequence ($\{s^n\}$). Since iterative methods are rules for inductive definitions of a sequence, an iterate is an element of a sequence and is indicated by a superscript. An n-dimensional vector is written $x = (x_1, \cdots, x_n)$. Superscripts are therefore chosen as iteration indices in preference to subscripts, so that an iterate of a component of a vector will not look like an element of a matrix. Thus we write x_i^k for the k-th iterate of x_i, the i-th component of x, rather than x_{ik} or $x_{i,k}$.

The publishers have requested that we adopt a style of type to distinguish exponents used as iteration indices from exponents used as powers, but we believe that the student will find it easier to understand the difference from the context, than from the type style.

With the exception of iteration indices, summation indices when used as exponents, and other sequence indices, all formulas have been set in italics in accordance with modern practice. In order to make iteration indices, summation indices when used as exponents, and other sequence indices readily distinguishable from all other uses of superscripts, they have been set in roman type. This is consistently utilized here whether the exponent is a number or a letter, unless it is a letter from the Greek alphabet. Greek letters, when they appear as exponents, will always be powers or arguments of functions that behave algebraically like powers (i.e., ρ^γ), unless their use is immediately explained in the text. If an iteration index is referred to in the text, it will usually appear in roman type in order to avoid confusion as to the antecedent of the index. For example, we will usually write

$$x^k \, \forall k \in \Omega \qquad \text{not} \qquad x^k \, \forall k \in \Omega.$$

Finally, it should be noted that no special type has been used to distinguish vectors from other entities such as real or complex numbers. Here again, our choice of symbols, context, and explanatory phrases like '$\forall x \in V$' make such a type distinction unnecessary.

It is understood that a student undertaking this text has completed a semester of advanced calculus (introduction to analysis). Having done so, he should encounter no inordinate difficulties with style or notation, providing he is willing to learn the set of logical symbols. This book is as self-contained as possible and yet will, it is hoped, prepare a student in a year or less to use numerical analysis in the sciences.

For those students who wish to become more accomplished in numerical analysis, we recommend that you spend more time in those areas that will raise your general level of mathematics and on more advanced courses in numerical analysis that will prepare you for research in this area. Perhaps this text will encourage you to follow in these directions.

PREFACE

The intent of our title is to claim for numerical analysis the inheritance of the spirit of mathematical analysis as it flowered in the classical French school. We will try to demonstrate that the study of computation has matured to a point where it may justly begin to claim a place in this distinguished tradition.

To us a modern computor is a mathematician in a certain mood. Our objective, except for some original material, has been to write a book on 'what every young mathematician knows about computing.' Unfortunately, we think, most texts on numerical analysis have not been written in this vein, but have either tried to extend and modernize an outdated nonmathematical hand-computing tradition or to undertake the subject as though it were something apart from the task of computing. The former trend in matters of differential equations has caused an inordinate emphasis on round-off error as opposed to truncation error, without acknowledging that modern analysis often allows us to find a bound of the two together as an error of approximation. This tendency to consider round-off and truncation error separately has been accompanied with a tendency to identify numerical analysis with finite-difference methods, and it must be admitted that these two tendencies do seem inseparable.

On the other hand, the latter trend has encouraged some analysts to formulate their error bounds in real analysis without considering whether or not such bounds can be computed. In fact, the mathematically very difficult area of analysis of computational procedures—convergence of iterative methods and stability of marching schema—is usually ignored entirely in modern treatises on theories of approximation. We try to give a balanced account of techniques. If the balance sheet is unfavorable to finite-difference methods, we believe this is because the logic of the case leads in that direction and is not due to an unfounded prejudice on our part.

Finally, we regret the almost universal tendency for books on numerical analysis to treat the subject exclusively within its own mathematical framework without showing the excitement of the applications that bred the subject. For us a great richness in the subject arises from its uses in elucidating phenomena of nature or analyzing technological problems. Here lie our true motivations, and though it may cost us some of the space that we would like to devote to mathematical material, we will insist, wherever our limited breadth allows, on discussing the problems of science (as opposed now to mathematics) side by side with those computational techniques developed to treat them. In recent years, the advent of large-scale computing machines has caused numerical analysis to become of such primary importance in science and technology that we would feel justified in writing the same book under the title, *A Course in Applied Mathematics*. We believe that boundary value problems as mathematical models for scientific and technological phenomena will be with us in some form for all time. Only very rarely can we expect to find solutions of these models in a closed (finitely generated) form. Thus, besides formulation of the model, existence, and uniqueness of the solution of the model, we must make approximation of solutions for boundary value problems using finitely generated functions—the only ones we can compute—a basic concern in applied mathematics. This book is strongly oriented to that purpose.

This book is designed for a two-semester senior or first-year graduate course (or, with some omissions, as a one-semester graduate course) and has been developed over a period of five years. We have required a prerequisite of advanced calculus (introduction to analysis). Even this material could be acquired in a good first-year calculus course, but the book is intended to be such that almost anything a student knows about mathematics will help him to understand more numerical analysis. Research exercises are not artificially contrived, but are genuinely intended to entice advanced students into serious work in the field. Some elementary theory of analytic functions of a complex variable is used, but nothing to frighten even a beginning student. The background that would be most enlightening for an advanced student would be functional analysis, but such a background is clearly not expected. Principally, the advanced calculus requirement is intended so that a student will understand the nature of the real number system (especially the completeness property), some of the first continuity theorems, the implicit function theorem, the chain rule for differentiation, and the Taylor theorem (or Taylor polynomial). A thorough review of the essentials of linear algebra is included, but it is very compact and the student may wish to consider elementary linear algebra as a prerequisite course. The proof of the very theorem we use on the Jordan form is not included, but we do include the proof of the simpler diagonal form. Our review should equip the student to read a proof of the Jordan form in other sources should he insist on seeing it. No background in numerical analysis is required (or even desirable, perhaps), but subjects of interpolation and numerical quadrature are treated briefly in the Appendixes. The student may wish to study these in other sources.

We are deeply indebted to our students for their adamant stand that someone should try to make their training in applied mathematics more generally conform to modern training in mathematics.

H.M.L.

LIST OF LOGICAL AND SET THEORETIC SYMBOLS

$\exists$	there exist(s)	Ω	positive integers
$\forall$	for every	Ω_n	$=\{k \mid (k \in \Omega) \wedge (n \in \Omega) \wedge k \leq n\}$
$\therefore$	therefore	$f^{(n)}$	nth derivative of f
$\Rightarrow$	implies	P	P is true
$\Leftarrow$	is implied by	P'	P is not true
$\Leftrightarrow$	is equivalent to	$\subset$	is contained in
$\ni$	such that	$\supset$	contains
$\in$	belongs to, is an element of	$\cup$	union
σ	suppose	$\cap$	intersection
$\wedge$	and	$\{x^n\}$	sequence
$\vee$	or	x^n	element of $\{x^n\}$
R^1	real numbers	x^2	$= x \cdot x \quad x^n = x \cdot x^{n-1}, n \in \Omega$
R^n	n-tuples of R^1, $R^n =$	wlog	without loss of generality
	$R^{n-1} \times R^1$	$\subsetneq$	is properly contained in
$\{x \mid P(x)\}$	the set of all x such that the	$\supsetneq$	properly contains
	statement P depending on x	$\not\subset$	is not contained in
	is true	A	set
C^1	complex numbers	$\bar{A}$	closure of A
C^n	n-tuples of C^1	$\{a, b\}$	pair, set with two elements
$C^n(A)$	set of functions defined on		a and b
	A and n-times continuously	(a, b)	ordered pair, $\{\{a\}, \{a, b\}\}$
	differentiable in A, $\{f \mid (\exists B \ni f :$	$A \times B$	cartesian or cross product,
	$A \to B) \wedge \forall \ x \in A, f^{(n)}$ is con-		$\{(a, b) \mid a \in A, \ b \in B\}$
	tinuous at $x\}$	$\ln x$	logarithm of x
E^n	vector space on set R^n over R^1	$a^j x_j$	$= \sum_{j=1}^{n} a^j x_j$ finite sum of product
	with Euclidean norm		

CHAPTER 1

APPROXIMATE SOLUTION OF ONE NONLINEAR ALGEBRAIC EQUATION BY ITERATION

1. INTRODUCTION

In the computation of a solution of even one nonlinear equation, iteration is in general unavoidable. As every schoolboy knows, even the root of $x^2 - 2$ is not rational. Since we compute only with terminating decimals that are a subset of the rational numbers,[1] it is necessary to define Cauchy sequences converging to the solution. Iterative methods are rules defining the elements of a sequence inductively. If such a sequence of real numbers converges, it is because it is a Cauchy sequence, since a necessary and sufficient condition for a sequence of real numbers to converge is that it be a Cauchy sequence. The student will want to review the definition of real numbers as equivalence classes of Cauchy sequences of rationals where two sequences are equivalent if the difference of corresponding elements converges to zero. He should then be convinced that roots of nonlinear functions are, in general, sequences of rationals, and he must consider iterative methods to find them.

Two gaps still remain. First, the sequence as defined inductively by most iterative methods will be a sequence of real numbers. We do not compute even a finite number of its elements. Instead we compute terminating decimals. If, however, the sequence defined of real numbers

---

[1] All of which have repeating decimal representations, but do not necessarily repeat the zero decimal as required by termination.

$\{x^n\}$ is such that the error $|x^n - x|$, where x is the root, is reduced at every iteration, or even if this is true 'in the limit' or 'asymptotically,' then convergence of the sequence of real numbers $\{x^n\}$ will imply convergence of our sequence of terminating decimals $\{x^{*n}\}$.

Second, we must compute only a finite number of elements of our sequence of terminating decimals $\{x^{*n}\}$. It will be seen that for some iterative methods it is possible to bound $|x^n - x|$ in terms of x^0, for every n. We can apply this bound to the elements of the computational sequence $\{x^{*n}\}$ if we regard the element x^{*n-1} as the initial element x^{*0} and monitor the loss of significant digits in computing x^n from x^{n-1}.

We have seen, then, that 'finiteness' or the termination of sequences or series must be considered from the beginning in studies of computational mathematics. This necessity will become more urgent as we attack more difficult problems. Although we may often have to be satisfied with an imperfect world, our ability to overcome or circumvent the limitations of finite computations in handling necessarily infinite real analysis by the use of special convergence properties or error bounds will be a measure of our success in computational considerations.

Another method, due to Heine, of defining the real number system directly from the set of all nonterminating decimals is more immediately connected with computations than that of the Cantor equivalence classes of Cauchy sequences.[2] Actually, the two are equivalent, and we propose to use both viewpoints freely.

When approximation methods in differential equations come to be studied, it will be seen that we do not concede that current talk of 'round-off error' vs. 'truncation error,' etc., presents a rational basis for numerical analysis. In our framework, the two together are simply identified as the error of approximation. Tracing the round-off error in computations of any realistic complexity is still at this time rather unrealistic,[3] and, to the extent that error of discretization is unaccounted for by such techniques, they are not likely to be rewarding when used in problems of differential equations. Certainly we cannot accept a statistical treatment of round-off in the face of the possibilities for convergence and error bounds as discussed above. Our attitude is that the

---

[2] The Heine method is now being taught in high schools that use the School Mathematics Study Group materials, and mathematical interest in computing may receive an impetus from this.

[3] Although there are interesting developments in this area that will merit our attention, see Appendix C, p. 232.

first chapter of a book modeled on the basis of treating the round-off error vs. truncation error cannot be written. We circumvent such treatment insofar as is presently possible. This distinguishes our treatment as part of a definite school of thought in numerical analysis.

2. INVESTIGATION OF POSSIBILITIES

If we propose to an intelligent child the problem of finding the root of a given real-valued function f of one real variable, that is, of solving $f(x) = 0$, he may well propose graphing or the method of bisections. The method of bisections involves finding a point where f is positive and one where it is negative and halving. The method is reliable for continuous functions, but slow, especially if extended to functions of more than one variable. The army artillery officer, through information from a forward observer, uses a variation that might be called 'bracketing'. Success of the method depends on one of the most elementary existence theorems in analysis—one that an intelligent child senses —that between a positive and negative point for a continuous function of one real variable lies a root.

Finding a *root* of a function f is equivalent to finding a *fixed-point* of a function g such that

$$(1.1) \qquad\qquad x - g(x) = f(x),$$

since $f(x) = 0$ implies $x = g(x)$. Formulation of a problem as a fixed-point problem is more in conformity to modern tastes than formulation as a root problem because of the availability of some important general frameworks for fixed-point problems, but root and fixed-point formulations are equivalent. Again an intelligent child if asked to find a fixed point for a given real-valued function g of one real variable might try the following: Guess x^0, put $x^1 = g(x^0)$, $x^2 = g(x^1)$, thus successively 'improving' the guess. In fact, the great Italian mathematician Peano and, later, the great French mathematician Picard introduced this iterative method in the last century with universal success for the case where x itself is a real-valued function of one real variable and g is an integral with a variable upper limit. For the case of a real-valued function of a real variable, our child will have to be very lucky indeed to succeed; i.e., he will have to be lucky to find that he is actually improving his value and approaching the fixed point. He needs some analysis.

Let $g : R^1 \to R^1$, $g \in C^1(R^1)$, and let Ω be the set of positive integers. Let $x^0 \in R^1 \wedge x^{n+1} = g(x^n) \; \forall \, n \in \Omega$. ʊ $\exists \, x \ni x = g(x)$. Then

$$\varepsilon^{n+1} = x^{n+1} - x = g(x^n) - g(x).$$

From the Taylor theorem, $\exists \, \xi^n \in (x^n, x)$ or $(x, x^n) \ni$

$$\varepsilon^{n+1} = g'(\xi^n)(x^n - x) = g'(\xi^n)\varepsilon^n.$$

Therefore, if $|g'(x)| < 1 \; \forall \, x \in R^1$, the error is reduced at every iteration, and our child is indeed improving his value of x^n; otherwise, there may be no improvement. We have

$$\varepsilon^{n+1} = g'(\xi^n)\varepsilon^n = g'(\xi^n)g'(\xi^{n-1})\varepsilon^{n-1}$$

$$= \cdots = \left(\prod_{i=0}^{n} g'(\xi^i) \right) \varepsilon^0,$$

so that, if $|g'(x)|$ is not only less than one but actually bounded away from one,

$$\lim_{n \to \infty} |\varepsilon^{n+1}| = \lim_{n \to \infty} \left(\prod_{i=0}^{n} |g'(\xi^i)| \right) \varepsilon^0 = 0.$$

If, however, $|g'(x)|$ is, in general, very close to one, convergence will be slow. When we decide to do such an iteration on a computing machine, therefore, we will not want to print every iteration; perhaps we will want to print only every tenth one or even every hundredth iteration. Eventually, we will not want to compute every iteration but, looking down a column of iterates, we will try to extrapolate. Imagine what we see when we look down such a column:

	x^n		$g(x^n)$
	x^0		
	x^1	$=$	$g(x^0)$
	x^2	$=$	$g(x^1)$
	$\vdots$		$\vdots$
	x^k		
	x^{k+1}	$=$	$g(x^k)$
	$\vdots$		$\vdots$

$\omega = d/l$

To interpolate between x^k and x^{k+1}, we will form

$$(1 - \omega)x^k + \omega x^{k+1} \quad \text{or} \quad (1 - \omega)x^k + \omega g(x^k),$$

where ω is the proportional distance between x^k and x^{k+1} we wished to interpolate. For extrapolation, the same formula is used with $\omega > 1$. An extrapolated or accelerated form of Picard-Peano iteration will be obtained, then, by putting

(1.2) $$x^0 \in R^1, \quad x^{k+1} = (1 - \omega)x^k + \omega g(x^k)$$

with some value $\omega \in R^1$. We let $\omega : \Omega \to R^1$ be a function of $k \in \Omega$ and determine ω_k in the best way we can:

$$\exists \, \xi^k \in (x, x^k) \quad \text{or} \quad (x^k, x) \ni$$

$$(x^{k+1} - x) = (x^k - x) + \omega_k(g(x^k) - g(x) - (x^k - x))$$
$$= (x^k - x) + \omega_k[g'(\xi^k) - 1](x^k - x)$$

or $$\varepsilon^{k+1} = [1 + \omega_k(g'(\xi^k) - 1)]\varepsilon^k.$$

The optimal choice of ω_k would be obtained by putting the factor multiplying ε^k equal to zero, but ξ^k is not known in general. Since the fixed point x is not in general known, our only possible choice is to put

$$[1 + \omega_k(g'(x^k) - 1)] = 0.$$

This gives

$$\omega_k = \frac{1}{1 - g'(x^k)},$$

if $g'(x^k) \neq 1$, and combining this with (1.1) and (1.2), we obtain

$$x^{k+1} = x^k - \frac{f(x^k)}{f'(x^k)}$$

as an iteration to a root of $f(x)$. This is known as the Newton method, and Picard iteration accelerated in the best way we can (though not perhaps in an optimal sense) gives us this method; it is usually obtained from successive linearizations as we will see. In this book, therefore, the Newton method, where it can be applied, is given considerable preference computationally to Picard iteration; but Picard iteration, it will be seen, has very general theoretical value in analysis of computational procedures.

Having made a brief excursion to investigate the possibilities for iterative methods, we now return to a more serious consideration of their mathematical content.

3. PRINCIPLE OF BISECTIONS

Theorem

$$(f : [a,b] \to R^1 \land f \in C[a,b])$$

$$\land \ (\exists \ x^0, x^1 \in [a,b] \ni f(x^0) < 0 \land f(x^1) > 0)$$

$$\land \left(x^{n+1} = \frac{x^i + x^j}{2} \right) \quad where \quad i = \max \ \{k \mid (k \in \Omega_n) \land f(x^k) > 0\},$$

$$j = \max \ \{k \mid (k \in \Omega_n) \land f(x^k) < 0\}$$

$$\Rightarrow \exists \ x \in [a,b] \ni f(x) = 0 \land \{x^n\} \to x.$$

Note: Computationally, one terminates when $|x^n - x^m| < \tau$, where τ is some preset tolerance. The method has the advantage of universality (for continuous functions) and is extremely reliable. It is, however, painfully slow, especially if extended to higher dimension. It should be regarded as providing a method to fall back upon (for continuous functions) if all others fail.

The proof is an *exercise*. One may expect to use the intermediate value theorem and convergence of Cauchy sequences of real numbers.

4. PICARD–PEANO ITERATION

Proposition

$$(g : E^1 \to E^1 \land g \in C^1(E^1) \land \exists \ K < 1 \ni |g'(x)| \leq K \ \forall \ x \in E^1)$$

$$\land \ (\exists \ x \in E^1 \ni x = g(x)) \land (x^0 \in E^1, \quad x^{n+1} = g(x^n) \forall \ n \in \Omega) \Rightarrow \{x^n\} \to x.$$

Proof

$$|\varepsilon^n| = |x^n - x| = |g(x^{n-1}) - g(x)| = |g'(\xi^{n-1})| \ |x^{n-1} - x|$$
$$= |g'(\xi^{n-1})| \ |\varepsilon^{n-1}| \quad where \quad \xi^n \in (x^n, x) \quad or \quad \xi^n \in (x, x^n)$$

$$\Rightarrow |\varepsilon^n| = \left(\prod_{i=1}^{n} |g(\xi^i)| \right) |\varepsilon^0| \Rightarrow \lim_{n \to \infty} |\varepsilon^n| = 0$$

$$\Rightarrow \lim_{n \to \infty} (x^n - x) = 0 \Rightarrow \lim_{n \to \infty} x^n = x. \quad \blacksquare$$

Note: If we weaken the condition on $g \ni |g'(x)| < 1$ (rather than $\leq K < 1$), the error is reduced at every iteration. This does not necessarily provide convergence but is computationally a very important property. The proposition, as it is given above, is to some extent phony, since one rarely confronts a function with all the properties required. Mathematicians often proceed by first constructing propositions of this type and then tailoring them to more realistic demands. This is our intent here as will be seen in the next theorem.

Theorem

$$(g: [a,b] \to [a,b] \wedge \exists\, K < 1 \ni \forall\, x_1, x_2 \in [a,b],$$

$$x_1 \neq x_2, \quad |g(x_1) - g(x_2)| \leq K|x_1 - x_2|) \wedge (x^0 \in [a,b] \wedge x^{n+1} = g(x^n))$$
$$\Rightarrow (\exists\, x \in [a,b] \ni x = g(x)) \wedge (\{x^n\} \to x) \wedge (|x^n - x| < K^n(b - a))$$

Note: This last is an error bound. Try to find a better one before proceeding to Corollary 2. If g has the assumed properties, it is said to be contractive.

Proof

$$\forall\, \varepsilon > 0 \ \exists\, N \in \Omega \ni n, m > N$$

$$\Rightarrow |x^n - x^m| = |g(x^{n-1}) - g(x^{m-1})| \leq K|x^{n-1} - x^{m-1}|$$
$$\leq K^2|x^{n-2} - x^{m-2}| \leq \cdots \leq K^m|x^{n-m} - x^0|$$
$$\leq K^m(b - a) < \varepsilon.$$

$\therefore \exists\, x \ni \{x^n\} \to x.$ But $\forall\, x_1, x_2 \varepsilon[a,b] \wedge \forall\, \varepsilon > 0 \ \exists\, \delta = \varepsilon/K \ni |x_1 - x_2| < \delta \Rightarrow |g(x_1) - g(x_2)| < K\delta = K\varepsilon/K = \varepsilon$, so that $g \in C[a,b]$. $\therefore \lim_{n \to \infty} x^{n+1} = \lim_{n \to \infty} g(x^n) \Rightarrow x = g(\lim_{n \to \infty} x^n) = g(x).$ $\blacksquare$

Corollary 1 (Uniqueness)

$$(x_1, x_2 \in [a,b]) \wedge (x_1 = g(x_1)) \wedge (x_2 = g(x_2)) \Rightarrow x_1 = x_2$$

Proof

$$x_1 \neq x_2 \Rightarrow |x_1 - x_2| = |g(x_1) - g(x_2)| \leq K|x_1 - x_2| < |x_1 - x_2|. \quad \blacksquare$$

Examples.[4]

(1) $$g(x) = x^2, [a,b] = [0, \tfrac{1}{2} - 0.001], x^0 = \tfrac{1}{4}$$

$$\{x^n\} = \tfrac{1}{4}, \tfrac{1}{16}, \tfrac{1}{256}, \cdots \to 0$$

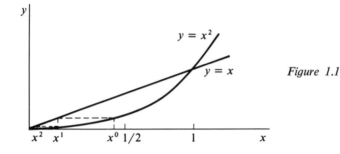

Figure 1.1

Theory applies.

(2) $$g(x) = x^2, [a,b] = [\tfrac{1}{2}, 1], x^0 = \tfrac{3}{4}$$

$$g([a,b]) \not\subseteq [a,b], x^0 = \tfrac{3}{4}, x^1 = \tfrac{9}{16}, x^2 = \tfrac{81}{256} \in [0, \tfrac{1}{2} - 0.001]$$

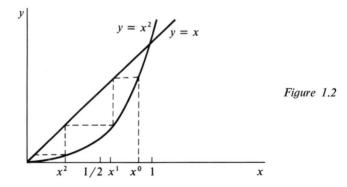

Figure 1.2

Theory does not apply, but series converges because, if x^2 is identified as x^0, example (1)'s conditions apply.

---

[4] $x^2 = x \cdot x$. x^2 is the second sequence element value in a sequence $\{x^n\}$.

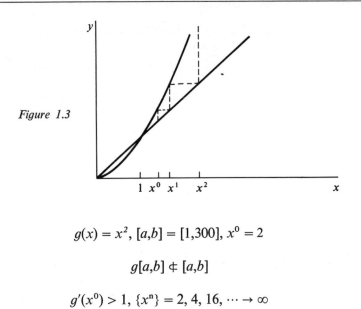

Figure 1.3

(3) $$g(x) = x^2, \ [a,b] = [1,300], \ x^0 = 2$$

$$g[a,b] \not\subset [a,b]$$

$$g'(x^0) > 1, \ \{x^n\} = 2, 4, 16, \cdots \to \infty$$

Theory does not apply. Series does not converge. Note that the fixed point $x = 1$ of the function x^2 cannot be reached by Picard iteration of the function x^2, but it can be reached by Picard iteration of

$$x - \frac{x^2 - x}{2x - 1}.$$

This becomes the Newton method for $f(x) = x^2 - x$.

Corollary 2

After n iterations are performed, a bound for the error is given by

$$|x^n - x| \le \frac{K^n}{1 - K} |x^1 - x^0|.$$

Proof

(i) $$|x^2 - x^1| = |g(x^1) - g(x^0)| \le K|x^1 - x^0|$$

$$|x^3 - x^2| = |g(x^2) - g(x^1)| \le K|x^2 - x^1| \le K^2|x^1 - x^0|.$$

By induction on n

$$|x^{n+1} - x^n| \le K^n|x^1 - x^0|.$$

(ii)
$$|x^{n+2} - x^n| \leq |x^{n+2} - x^{n+1}| + |x^{n+1} - x^n|$$
$$\leq K^{n+1}|x^1 - x^0| + K^n|x^1 - x^0|$$

$$|x^{n+3} - x^n| \leq |x^{n+3} - x^{n+2}| + |x^{n+2} - x^n|$$
$$\leq K^{n+2}|x^1 - x^0| + (K^{n+1} + K^n)|x^1 - x^0|$$
$$= (1 + K + K^2)K^n|x^1 - x^0|.$$

By induction on p

$$|x^{n+p} - x^n| < (1 + K + K^2 + \cdots + K^{p-1})K^n|x^1 - x^0|$$
$$= \frac{1 - K^p}{1 - K} K^n|x^1 - x^0|.$$

(iii)
$$\lim_{p \to \infty} |x^{n+p} - x^n| = |x^n - x| \leq \frac{K^n}{1 - K}|x^1 - x^0|. \quad \blacksquare$$

If one considers now any set A and a non-negative real-valued function called a 'metric' on pairs from A, which is symmetric, transitive, and satisfies the triangle inequality (so that the metric can replace the concept of distance in A), all the above may be repeated where absolute value of a difference is now regarded as a special case of a metric 'distance.' If the space is complete (i.e., sequences in A that are Cauchy in the sense of the metric converge in the sense of the metric), Picard iteration converges to a fixed point for any function on A into A contractive in the sense of the metric. This simple theory has great power and usefulness when used in its full generality. We feel free to refer to it without developing it, since it is available in a number of both elementary and erudite sources, but we do not really ever use it here. The error bound corollary above can be used to prove convergence when the metric space is not bounded.

5. NEWTON'S METHOD

As Successive Solutions of Linearizations

We seek a root of f; that is, we seek a solution of $f(x) = 0$.

$$\circ f \in C^2[a,b] \wedge \exists x \in [a,b] \ni f(x) = 0.$$

$$\forall x^n \in [a,b] \ \exists \ \xi^n \in (x, x^n) \vee \xi^n \in (x^n, x) \ni$$

$$0 = f(x) = f(x^n) + f'(x^n)(x - x^n) + (f''(\xi^n)/2)(x - x^n)^2.$$

If x^n is a 'good guess' of the root x, then $(f''(\xi^n)/2)(x - x^n)^2$ can be expected to be small relative to $f'(x^n)(x - x^n)$. Note that $f \in C^2[a,b] \Rightarrow f''$ bounded on $[a,b]$, so that the 'better' x^n is a guess of x, the 'better' this statement becomes. Therefore, approximately,

$$0 \cong f(x^n) + f'(x^n)(x - x^n).$$

Solving

$$x \cong x^n - \frac{f(x^n)}{f'(x^n)},$$

which we can expect to be closer to the root than x^n if, indeed, x^n is a good guess of the root; so we put

$$x^{n+1} = x^n - \frac{f(x^n)}{f'(x^n)}$$

and *expect* that $\{x^n\} \to x \ni f(x) = 0$, provided an x^0 is chosen so that it is a 'good guess' of the root.

This kind of linearization technique represents the classical way of thinking for an applied mathematician. It is not adequate by modern standards, but remains a major technique for generating useful algorithms.

A bit more precisely, consider the Newton algorithm,

(1.3) $$x^{n+1} = x^n - \frac{f(x^n)}{f'(x^n)}.$$

$\exists\, \xi^n \in (x,x^n) \vee \xi^n \in (x^n,x) \ni f(x^n) = f(x) + f'(\xi^n)(x^n - x)$, so we have

$$(x^{n+1} - x) = (x^n - x) - \frac{f'(\xi^n)}{f'(x^n)}(x^n - x)$$

and $$\varepsilon^{n+1} = \left[1 - \frac{f'(\xi^n)}{f'(x^n)}\right]\varepsilon^n.$$

If $0 < f'(\xi^n)/f'(x^n) < 2$, we get convergence (or at least a strictly reducing error). Thus it can be seen that, if x^n is close to x (so that ξ^n is close to x), and if f'' is small on (x^n,x), then the rate of convergence will be very fast. In fact,

$$\exists\, \eta_n \ni f'(\xi^n) = f'(x^n) + f''(\eta^n)(\xi^n - x^n),$$

so that

$$\varepsilon^{n+1} = \frac{-1}{f'(x^n)} f''(\eta^n)(\xi^n - x^n)\varepsilon^n$$

and

$$|\varepsilon^{n+1}| \le \frac{|f''(\eta^n)||\varepsilon^n|}{|f'(x^n)|} |\varepsilon^n| \le M|\varepsilon^n|^2$$

if $M = M_1/N$, where $|f''(x)| < M_1 \wedge |f'(x)| > N > 0 \, \forall \, x \in [a,b]$. From the first inequality, one expects convergence if x^0 is $\ni$ the initial error times the curvature in $[a,b]$ is small relative to the slope; from the second, provided all iterates are in $[a,b]$, $|\varepsilon^{n+1}|$ is bounded by a proportion of $|\varepsilon^n|^2$, so that the convergence is very rapid. It may be noted that, since it has been assumed that $f \in C^2[a,b]$, we have, automatically, that $\exists \, M_1 \ni |f''(x)| < M_1 \, \forall \, x \in [a,b]$. Also, in order even that (1.3) defines a sequence, some condition implying that $f'(x^k) \ne 0 \, \forall \, k \in \Omega$ must be imposed so that the condition $\exists \, N > 0 \ni |f'(x)| > N \, \forall \, x \in [a,b]$ is not a severe one to add in order to obtain convergence for the sequence defined by (1.3).

As Picard Iteration or as a Series dominated by the Newton Series for a Quadratic Function

It was shown above that the Newton method for finding a root of f can be regarded as a best acceleration of Picard iteration for finding a fixed point for g where $x - g(x) = f(x)$. It can also be regarded as Picard iteration of another mapping; thus

$$x^{n+1} = x^n - \frac{f(x^n)}{f'(x^n)}$$

is Picard iteration of the mapping

$$G(x) = x - \frac{f(x)}{f'(x)}.$$

In particular,

$$(f(x) = x^2 - a) \Rightarrow \left(x^{n+1} = x^n - \frac{(x^n)^2 - a}{2x^n} = \frac{1}{2}\left(x^n + \frac{a}{x^n} \right) \right),$$

and this gives a useful and popular method of computing square roots; more importantly, it gives a special case where convergence and error bounds for the Newton method can be treated rigorously by ignoring the above rough considerations and considering conditions for contraction of the mapping $\frac{1}{2}(x + a/x)$, and applying our theorem and Corollary 2 for contractive maps. In turn, iteration of the function given by $\frac{1}{2}(x + a/x)$ provides a series that can be used as a majorant series, thus generating conditions on functions f such that the Newton method for f converges.

EXERCISE

Find a closed interval on which the mapping with values $\frac{1}{2}(x + a/x)$ is contractive, and from this state a theorem on convergence of the Newton method for square roots.

If for a given function f the Newton algorithm defines a sequence $\{x^n\}$, it will be called the Newton sequence for f. If $\{x^n\}$ is written in the form

$$\left\{ x^0 + \sum_{i=1}^{n} (x^i - x^{i-1}) \right\},$$

it will be called the Newton series for f.

EXERCISE

Find conditions on a function f, so that the Newton sequence for f is defined and converges by finding conditions on f, so that the Newton series for f is dominated by the Newton series for square root.

In general, the theorem developed in the exercise above will give convergence of the Newton method for a function that has a root in a small interval about $\sqrt{a}$. As was evident in our theorems on contractive maps, we can only expect in nonlinear problems to treat of roots in some finite interval, especially if uniqueness is involved as it is here, but this is too restrictive in this case, for the interval is of very short length. It would therefore suit us to consider domination by the Newton series for a function that can be written as a quadratic form with distinct real linear factors, in order to provide a larger interval in which the roots can occur. The following theorem has apparently been obtained in this fashion.

Theorem (Kantorowich)

  Let $x^0 \in E^1 \ni$

(1) $\exists\ \delta_0 > 0 \ni f \in C^2[(x^0 - \delta_0, x^0 + \delta_0)] \wedge \exists\ K \ni |f''(x)| \leq K$
     $\forall\ x \in (x^0 - \delta_0, x^0 + \delta_0)$

(2) $\exists \beta_0, \eta_0 \ni |1/f'(x^0)| \le \beta_0 \wedge |f(x^0)/f'(x^0)| \le \eta_0$

and (3) $h_0 =: \beta_0\eta_0 K < \frac{1}{2} \wedge (1/h_0)(1 - \sqrt{1 - 2h_0})\eta_0 < \delta_0.$

Then x^n defined by

$$x^{n+1} = x^n - \frac{f(x^n)}{f'(x^n)}$$

exists $\forall n \in \Omega$ and $\{x^n\} \to x^* \in (x^0 - \delta_0, x^0 + \delta_0) \ni f(x^*) = 0.$ x^* is unique in every closed interval

$[x^0 - r, x^0 + r] \subset (x^0 - \delta_0, x^0 + \delta_0)$ with $r < (1/h_0)(1 + \sqrt{1 - 2h_0})\eta_0.$

An error bound is given by

$$|x^* - x^n| \le 2^{-(n-1)}(2h_0)^{2^n - 1}\eta_0.$$

EXERCISE

Prove existence of a root by induction.

EXERCISE[5]

Prove uniqueness by contradiction; i.e., prove

$$f(\tilde{x}) = 0 \Rightarrow \lim_{n \to \infty} x^n = \tilde{x}.$$

Note on the Kantorowich Theorem: An example of f is now shown which demonstrates that no stronger claim than the above can be made for existence and uniqueness. In this generality, then, no better theorem can be given. Let $f(x) = (\frac{1}{2})x^2 - x + h, \wedge x^0 = 0.$ We have

$$f'(x^0) = -1 \wedge f''(x^0) = 1.$$

If we let $\beta_0 = K = 1$, $\eta_0 = h_0 = h$ (given), the conditions of the theorem are satisfied. The roots of f are

$$1 \pm \sqrt{1 - 2h}$$

if $h \le \frac{1}{2}$. The smaller root

$$x^* = (1 - \sqrt{1 - 2h}) = \frac{1}{h_0}(1 - \sqrt{1 - 2h_0})\eta_0 < \delta_0.$$

---

[5] Optional.

The other root is

$$\frac{1}{h_0}(1 + \sqrt{1 - 2h_0})\eta_0$$

and is just excluded from the region where uniqueness is claimed.

Presumably, Kantorowich [1][2] obtained his theorem by comparison with the Newton series for $(\frac{1}{2})x^2 - x + h$, much as suggested in the exercise for comparison with the Newton series for $x^2 - a$. The 'full' Kantorowich theorem is here specialized from one on convergence of a Newton method on a real Banach space presented in [1] and [2].

We repeat for emphasis that the student should notice that, although a strong case has been built for the computational superiority of the Newton method to Picard iteration, the latter plays an indispensable role in analysis of computational procedures.

6. AVOIDANCE OF SUBTRACTIONS, SQUARE ROOT OF A COMPLEX NUMBER

Complex Root Routines

Newton Method. The Newton method is very effective if a complex arithmetic routine is available.

EXERCISE

See if it is possible to adapt the contraction analysis of the first exercise to prove convergence of the Newton method for square roots when x is complex. Of course, the contraction theory itself must be reexamined where $|x_1 - x_2|$ means modulus of the complex number $(x_1 - x_2)$.

Reduction to Polar Form. Here, there is too much computing involved. The method uses two long subroutines for trigonometric functions and inverse trigonometric functions; we have

$$\sqrt{z} = \sqrt{x + iy} = \rho^{1/2}[\cos\theta + i\sin\theta]^{1/2} = \rho^{1/2}e^{i\theta/2}$$
$$= \rho^{1/2}\cos\frac{\theta}{2} + i\left(\rho^{1/2}\sin\frac{\theta}{2}\right),$$

where

$$\rho = \sqrt{x^2 + y^2} \wedge \theta = \arcsin\left(\frac{y}{\rho}\right).$$

Algebraic. (wlog $\mathbf{0}(x \geq 0) \wedge (y \geq 0)$).

$$(a + ib = \sqrt{z} = \sqrt{x + iy}) \Rightarrow (a^2 - b^2 = x) \wedge (2ab = y)$$

$$\Rightarrow 2b\sqrt{x + b^2} = y \Rightarrow 4b^4 + 4xb^2 - y^2 = 0 \Rightarrow b^2 = -\tfrac{1}{2}x \pm \tfrac{1}{2}\sqrt{x^2 + y^2}.$$

Since b is real,

(1.4) $$b^2 = -\tfrac{1}{2}x + \tfrac{1}{2}\sqrt{x^2 + y^2} \wedge b = \sqrt{-\tfrac{1}{2}x + \tfrac{1}{2}\sqrt{x^2 + y^2}}.$$

For y small (1.4) may give a serious loss of accuracy in computing b. We rationalize the numerator:

$$2b^2 = (-x + \sqrt{x^2 + y^2})\frac{(-x - \sqrt{x^2 + y^2})}{(-x - \sqrt{x^2 + y^2})} = \frac{y^2}{x + \sqrt{x^2 + y^2}}$$

(1.5) $$\Rightarrow b = \frac{y}{\sqrt{2}\sqrt{x + \sqrt{x^2 + y^2}}} = \frac{y}{\sqrt{2x[1 + \sqrt{1 + (y/x)^2}]}}.$$

We now list some examples taken from an actual engineering computation where accuracy of b was very important. We show b computed from the polar form, from (1.4), and from (1.5).

m	x	y	$b = \sqrt{\sqrt{x^2 + y^2}} \sin \theta/2$ $\theta = \arcsin x/\sqrt{x^2 + y^2}$
1	32.60753453	0.06658981373	0.005830671896
2	32.64748807	0.03329395575	0.002913469402
3	32.66081028	0	0
4	0.9503303150	0.003798284583	0.001948136399
5	0.9480641746	0.001892185764	0.0009716608200
6	0.9473103760	0	0

$m = 1$	(1.4)	(1.5)
1	0.005830523133	0.005830671804
2	0.0029134760460	0.002913469392
3	0	0
4	0.001948127306	0.001948136334
5	0.000971648844	0.0009716608193
6	0	0

Presumably, if we now proposed the admonition, 'Thou shalt not subtract (large numbers whose difference is small),' we might be caught up in a maelstrom of protest over our lack of seriousness. We therefore propose a more sober version as advice to the young computor: 'Learn arithmetic well—learn how to add, multiply, and divide and *how not to subtract* (if you can avoid it).' Of course, you cannot always avoid it, but you can often overcome its effects by iteration as we will see.

7. DEFINITION OF RATE OF CONVERGENCE

Let $g : [a,b] \to [a,b]$ satisfy a Lipschitz condition on $[a,b]$. Let $A = \{K \,|\, (|g(x_1) - g(x_2)| \le K |x_1 - x_2|) \;\forall\; x_1, x_2 \in [a,b]\}$.

Definition

$\alpha = \mathrm{glb}\; A$ will be called the contraction modulus.

EXERCISE

Show that, if g' exists on $[a,b]$, then

$$|g'(x)| \le \alpha \;\forall\, x \in [a,b].$$

We have $(x \in [a,b] \ni x = g(x)) \wedge (x^0 \in [a,b] \wedge x^{n+1} = g(x^n)$ is defined$)$ $\Rightarrow |\varepsilon^{n+1}| = |x^{n+1} - x| = |g(x^n) - g(x)| \le \alpha |\varepsilon^n|$. Thus it is seen that α deserves the name 'factor of reduction,' since it provides a proportion of the error at the nth iteration, which is a bound for the error at the $(n + 1)$th iteration.

If we give meaning to the phrase 'rate of convergence,' it should be a real number that is the functional value of some function r

$$r(\alpha) \begin{cases} = \infty & \text{for} & \alpha = 0 \\ = 0 & \text{for} & \alpha = 1 \\ < 0 & \text{for} & \alpha > 1. \end{cases}$$

It would also be convenient to choose some 'smooth' function with these properties. We, therefore, take the following definition.

Definition

If g is a contraction with modulus α, then the 'rate of convergence' of Picard iteration is $-\ln \alpha = \ln(1/\alpha)$. This will be used in a similar but broader context later.

REFERENCES

[1] L. V. Kantorowich, 'On Newton's method for functional equations,' *Dokl. Akad. Nauk. SSSR*, **59** (1948), 1237–1240.

[2] H. A. Antosievicz, 'Numerical analysis and functional analysis,' in *A Survey of Numerical Analysis*, McGraw-Hill, New York, 1962, pp. 485–517.

CHAPTER 2

DISCRETIZATIONS OF THE DIRICHLET PROBLEM FOR THE LAPLACE EQUATION

1. REGULAR SOLUTIONS, UNIQUENESS

Let E^n be the set of n-tuples of real numbers $x = (x_1, \cdots, x_n)$, where $\forall\, x,\ y \in E^n$, $x + y = (x_1 + y_2, \cdots, x_n + y_n)$, $\forall\, x \in E^n$ and $\forall\, \alpha \in R^1$, $\alpha x = (\alpha x_1, \alpha x_2, \cdots, \alpha x_n)$, and a metric (distance function) is defined by

$$\rho(x,y) = \left(\sum_{i=1}^{n} (x_i - y_i)^2 \right)^{1/2}.$$

Let A be a region (open connected set) in E^n, and let δA be the boundary (set of limit points of A not in A) of A. If S is any set of E^n, $C^m(S)$ will denote the set (class) of functions defined on S which possess continuous *partial derivatives of order m with respect to* $x_1, \cdots, x_n$.

Definition

Given $f: \delta A \to R^1$, then $u = \Phi(x)$, ($\Phi: A \cup \delta A \to R^1$) will be said to be a 'regular solution of the Dirichlet problem for the Laplace equation on A with data f' if
(i) $\Phi \in C^2(A)$
(ii) $\Delta\Phi = \sum_{i=1}^{n} \Phi_{x_i x_i}(x) = 0\ \forall\, x \in A$
(iii) $\Phi \in C^1(A \cup \delta A)$
(iv) $\Phi = f\ \forall\, x \in \delta A.$

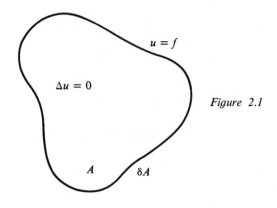

Figure 2.1

Existence of regular solutions is in general somewhat difficult, though not for some particular regions like rectangles or circles. Uniqueness is easy. To breed familiarity with the subject, we prove uniqueness of regular solutions for a rectangular region in E^2 in a way that can easily be extended to any region in E^2 in which the divergence theorem is valid, and thence to any region in which the divergence theorem is valid (a 'Green's region') in E^n.

Theorem

Let $R = \{(x_1,x_2) \mid (0 < x_1 < 1) \wedge (0 < x_2 < 1)\}$. *u is a regular solution of the Dirichlet problem on R with data zero implies* $u = 0 \ \forall \ x \in R$.

Proof

$$0 = \int_R u(u_{x_1x_1} + u_{x_2x_2})dR$$

$$= -\int_R (u_{x_1}{}^2 + u_{x_2}{}^2)dR + \int_R [(uu_{x_1})_{x_1} + (uu_{x_2})_{x_2}]dR$$

$$= -\int_R (u_{x_1}{}^2 + u_{x_2}{}^2)dR + \int_0^1\left(\int_0^1 (uu_{x_1})_{x_1}dx_1\right)dx_2 + \int_0^1\left(\int_0^1 (uu_{x_2})_{x_2}dx_2\right)dx_1$$

$$= -\int_R (u_{x_1}{}^2 + u_{x_2}{}^2)dR$$

$$\Rightarrow (u_{x_1} = 0) \wedge (u_{x_2} = 0) \ \forall \ x \in R \cup \delta R \Rightarrow u = \text{const} \ \forall \ x \in R \cup \delta R. \quad \blacksquare$$

The terms 'uu_{x_1}' and 'uu_{x_2}' vanish at $x_1 = 0,1$ and $x_2 = 0,1$, respectively, since condition (iii) for regularity provides that u_{x_1} and u_{x_2} are bounded on $R \cup \delta R$. Vanishing of the last integral above gives that u_{x_1} and u_{x_2} are zero on R, and condition (iii) gives that they are zero on all limit points of R. Thus we have, $(u = \text{const.} \; \forall \, x \in R \cup \delta R) \wedge (u = 0 \; \forall \, x \in \delta R) \Rightarrow u = 0 \; \forall \, x \in R \cup \delta R$.

Comments: Notice that the same proof gives uniqueness for the problem (Neumann), where the normal derivative of u is specified on the boundary or, for that matter, where u is specified for some points of the boundary, and its normal derivative is specified at all other points of the boundary (mixed problem). In the former case, of course, the last step cannot be completed unless u is given at one point of δR.

Again let A be a region of E^n and let δA be its topological boundary. Let $\alpha = \{a \mid a : A \cup \delta A \to E^n \wedge a_{i,x_i} \text{ bounded on } A \cup \delta A \; \forall \, i \in \Omega_n\}$, $\beta = \{b \mid b : A \cup \delta A \to E^1\}$, and let

$$\text{div} : \alpha \to \beta \ni \forall \, a \in \alpha, \; \text{div} \, a = \sum_{i=1}^{n} a_{i,x_i}.$$

If at any point $x \in \delta A$, $N(x)$ is the outer normal to A and

$$(a,N) = \sum_{i=1}^{n} a_i(x) \cdot N_i(x),$$

then the divergence theorem is written

$$\int_A \text{div} \, a \, dA = \int_{\delta A} (a,N) ds.$$

We call a region A for which this statement is true a Green's region.

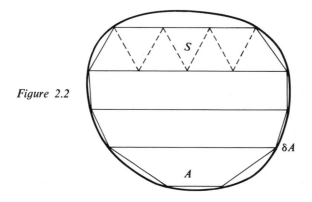

Figure 2.2

Obviously, any region in E^2 or E^3 that can be filled with (a finite number of) trapezoids or parallelepipeds is a Green's region, for in each trapezoid or parallelepiped, proof of the divergence theorem is essentially only a matter of replacing an area or volume integral by an iterated integral. In elementary books, the divergence theorem is proved for regions that can be filled by a limit of regions finitely constructed from trapezoids or parallelepipeds. More elementary regions, the 'simplest,' from which trapezoids or parallelepipeds can in turn be finitely constructed, are triangles for E^2, and tetrahedrons for E^3. The concept of such an elementary region is generalized, as embodied in the concept of a 'simplex' in algebraic topology in such a way that it carries over quite readily to E^n. *We thus have the evident sufficient condition that a region in E^n is a Green's region, that it can be filled by a finite number of simplices or a limit of simplices.* That not every region has this property is shown by the example of a region in E^2 bounded by a semicircular arc and a diameter, except that a center segment of the diameter is replaced

Figure 2.3

by a graph of sin $1/x$. Of course, an example in E^3 is quickly obtained by constructing a cylindrical surface, using the boundary above as directrix and considering the region bounded by this surface and two parallel planes. It is apparently not known whether or not such regions are Green's regions, but they fail to satisfy our simple sufficiency condition.

EXERCISE

Prove uniqueness for the Dirichlet problem for the Laplace equation for any Green's region in E^2. Use the proof above, but use the divergence theorem in step three rather than simply inverting the order of integration.

EXERCISE

Prove uniqueness of the Dirichlet problem for the Laplace equation on any Green's region in E^n. Start with

$$\int_R \left(u \sum_{i=1}^n u_{x_i x_i} \right) dR = 0$$

and use the proof of the exercise above with n replacing 2.

An obvious necessary condition for existence of a regular solution is that $f \in C(\delta A)$. It may often happen that even this condition is not satisfied, but our 'computational procedures' will be such that this fact will not be noted insofar as the calculations are concerned. In these cases, the meaning of a solution must be extended, but such considerations are more appropriately treated in a course on partial differential equations. We do find it desirable, however, to make several brief mentions of the nature of weak solutions in this volume, especially at the end of Chapter 5 and in Appendix D.

In elementary books, it is shown, using the divergence theorem, that if S^n is the surface of an n-dimensional sphere with center P, and S^n is contained in a region where u is harmonic,

$$\left(\sum_{i=1}^n u_{x_i x_i} = 0 \right),$$

then $u(P) = \dfrac{1}{\Omega_n} \displaystyle\int_{S^n} u\,dS^n$ (Gauss Mean Value Theorem),

where Ω_n is the surface area of S^n. From this a simple argument shows that, if u is a regular solution of the Dirichlet problem on A with data f, then

$$\max_{A \cup \delta A} |u| = \max_{\delta A} |f| \qquad \text{(maximum principle)}.$$

Other arguments can be used to get the same result (see R. Creighton Buck, *Advanced Calculus*, 2nd Edition, McGraw-Hill, 1965, 358–359). It will be used to give an error bound for one type of discretization and, obviously, can also be used to give uniqueness of solutions $u \in C(A \cup \delta A)$ of the Dirichlet problem for the Laplace equation.

2. A FIVE-POINT FINITE-DIFFERENCE ANALOGUE IN E^2

We consider the Dirichlet problem for the Laplace equation on a rectangular region $R \subset E^2$ with sides that can be partitioned with the same equal mesh size h. We seek to determine u at points of intersection of the mesh, by replacing derivatives in the equation $\Delta u = 0$ by finite-difference quotients, and applying the boundary conditions only at

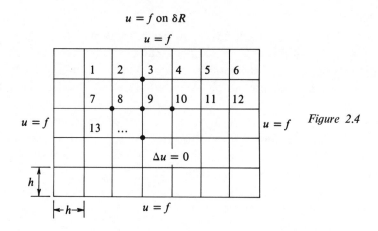

Figure 2.4

points where the mesh intersects the boundary. Let a typical set of points marked above be denoted as

$$N$$

$$W \quad\quad C \quad E$$

From the Taylor theorem, $\exists\, \xi \in [C,E] \wedge \exists\, \eta \in [W,C] \ni$

$$u_E = u_C + u_{xC}h + u_{xxC}\frac{h^2}{2!} + u_{xxxC}\frac{h^3}{3!} + u_{xxxx\xi}\frac{h^4}{4!}$$

$$u_W = u_C - u_{xC}h + u_{xxC}\frac{h^2}{2!} - u_{xxxC}\frac{h^3}{3!} + u_{xxxx\eta}\frac{h^4}{4!}$$

provided $u \in C^4\,(R \cup \delta R)$. Adding[1]

$$u_E + u_W = 2u_C + u_{xxC}h^2 + O(h^4),$$

[1] A function f is said to be of order h^n, written $O(h^n)$, if

$$\exists M \in R^1 \ni \lim_{h\to 0}\frac{f(h)}{h^n} = M.$$

since

$$\exists\, M \ni |u_{xxxx\xi}| < M, \ \wedge\ |u_{xxxx\eta}| < M \ \forall\, \xi \in [C,E] \ \wedge\ \forall\, \eta \in [W,C].$$

Thus,

$$u_{xxC} = \frac{u_W - 2u_C + u_E}{h^2} + O(h^2).$$

Similarly,

$$u_{yyC} = \frac{u_N - 2u_C + u_S}{h^2} + O(h^2),$$

so that at the point C

$$u_{xx} + u_{yy} = \frac{u_N + u_S + u_E + u_W - 4u_C}{h^2}$$

with error $O(h^2)$. It should be noted that

(i) this is the error in the differential equation, not in the solution of the boundary value problem;

(ii) in general, an irregular boundary will force the use of 'short-leg' difference analogues at points adjacent to the boundary, thereby giving much less accuracy in the differential equation replacement at those points, i.e., $O(h)$;

(iii) to get $O(h^2)$ accuracy, we had to assume a far stronger regularity condition than would have been required for uniqueness. Since it is easily shown that $\Delta u = 0$ in $A \Rightarrow u \in C^\infty(A)$, it is a question of behavior in the vicinity of δA.

Numerically, the use of the fact of $O(h^2)$ accuracy is to ensure that where the mesh size is halved, the bound for the error (in the differential equation here) will be multiplied by $\frac{1}{4}$. Of course, a mesh size h in one direction, and k in the other, will make no essential difference in the above considerations; but the finite-difference analogue of the Laplace operator will be altered.

We are now provided with a large linear system of equations by writing

(2.1) $$u_N + u_S + u_E + u_W - 4u_C = 0$$

for every point C of intersection of the mesh in R, by writing u_i for u_C, $i = 1, \cdots, n$, and by noting that if u_N, u_S, u_E, u_W is a boundary point, the value is known and should be written on the right side. It may be necessary to make h (or h and k) very small, thereby giving a very large system. Note that if we have 100 points on each side of R, we must solve a linear system of 10,000 equations in 10,000 unknowns! In higher dimensions the linear system of equations in unknowns that need to be solved greatly increases. Moreover, it is unrealistic to consider computations of error bounds to the solution of the differential equation boundary value problem from approximate solutions of this discretization. Formulas given in the literature demand availability of quantities such as a bound of the fourth derivative of the solution in order to compute the error bound. Using successive subpartitions of R until agreement is reached to the required accuracy one usually simply proceeds without really having any knowledge of how far a solution function over a given partition of R is from the solution of the boundary value problem on R for the differential equation. Agreement to some stated accuracy of computations using successive subpartitions is taken as evidence of 'convergence to that accuracy.'

The equation (2.1) can be written as

$$(2.2) \qquad u_C = \frac{u_N + u_S + u_E + u_W}{4},$$

in which form it is the finite-difference analogue of the Gauss mean value theorem. It is then tempting to try the following iteration: Let

$$u_i^{(0)} = 0, \quad i = 1, \cdots, n, \qquad \text{where} \qquad u_i^{(0)}$$

is a first approximation to the solution at intersection points of the mesh in R. 'Fixing' the boundary values, successively correct interior points by replacing them according to (2.2) by the average of neighboring points, scanning from left to right and down (as a television tube scans). Strangely enough, the iteration converges. The proof of this and improvement of the rate is a major burden of this course.

EXERCISE

Try this iteration by hand on a rectangle containing a (3 × 3) mesh. Select convenient but not entirely trivial values for the boundary data.

Note: If we program a problem as pictured, the machine, so to speak, will not know about the discontinuity on the boundary for any mesh size.

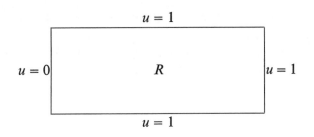

$$u = 1$$

$$u = 0 \qquad R \qquad u = 1$$

$$u = 1$$

3. "CONTINUOUS" METHODS

Least Squares Approximation Using Harmonic Polynomials

Let $\{h^k(x,y)\} = \{h^1(x,y),\cdots,h^n(x,y)\}$ be a set of harmonic polynomials; i.e., $h^k(x,y) = \mathrm{Re}(x + iy)^k$ or $\mathrm{Im}(x + iy)^k$. Let

$$u^n(x,y) = \sum_{k=1}^{n} c_k h^k(x,y)$$

and seek those c_k's, $k = 1,\cdots,n$, $\ni$

$$Q(c_1,\cdots,c_n) = \int_{\delta A} (f - u^n)^2 ds$$

is minimized, where s is arc length or any other parameter that can be used to parametrize δA. Since Q is quadratic, the desired c_k's satisfy

$$\frac{\partial Q}{\partial c_l} = 2 \int_{\delta A} \left(f - \sum_{k=1}^{n} c_k h^k\right) h^l ds = 0, \quad l = 1,\cdots,n.$$

Thus the desired c_k's are solutions of the linear system

(2.3) $$\sum_{k=1}^{n} a_{kl} c_l = b_l, \quad l = 1,\cdots,n,$$

where

$$a_{kl} = \int_{\delta A} h^k h^l ds \wedge b_l = \int_{\delta A} h^l f ds.$$

Note that (2.3) is likely to be required to be of much lower order than the system generated by the five-point finite-difference approximation for the same accuracy of solution. However, there are fewer zero coefficients, and the entire system must be recorded; i.e., there is no 'representative equation' such as (2.2). Coefficients a_{kl} and b_l, however, can be generated automatically on the machine by utilizing a machine routine for 'elementary' operations on 'elementary' functions (a freshman-sophmore calculus homework-doer routine). If quadratures (see Appendix A) are used to evaluate a_{kl} and b_l, the method becomes yet another finite-difference method.

Noting that since both u and u^n are harmonic,

$$\max_{A \cup \delta A} |u - u^n| = \max_{\delta A} |f - \sum_{k=1}^{n} c_k h^k|.$$

This is our error bound. Note that it is valid whether or not the c_k's satisfy (2.3). *We will later develop a bound for*

$$\left(\int_A (u - u^n)^2 dA \right)^{1/2}.$$

This bound will be smaller when the c_k's are determined by least squares and is far easier to compute.

Orthogonalization (Gram-Schmidt) of the approximating family will allow successively higher-order approximation without recomputation of the lower-order coefficients. This is *not recommended* for computations unless one wishes to approximate solutions to the same boundary value problem for several different given functions f since orthogonalization with respect to integration on δA is numerically equivalent to the solution of the problem.

Equivalence of the Galierkin Procedure

For the present problem, the Galierkin procedure is as follows: Given a family of approximating functions $\{h^k\}$, $k = 1, \cdots, n$, find $c_k \ni$

$$\int_{\delta A} \left(f - \sum_{k=1}^{n} c_k h^k \right) h^l \, ds = 0 \ \forall \ l = 1, \cdots, n.$$

This is, of course, one of the steps in the least squares procedure above, so that, for this problem, the Galierkin procedure is equivalent.

More generally, let L be a differential operator and let it be required to find $u \ni Lu = g$ on A and $u = f$ on δA. Let $v : A \cup \delta A \to R^1$ be $\ni v = f$ on δA. Then if $w = u - v$, we have

$$Lw = F \quad \text{on} \quad A \wedge w = 0 \quad \text{on} \quad \delta A,$$

where, in case L is linear, $F = g - Lv$. Take $\{v^k\}$ to be an approximating family $\ni \forall \, k = 1, \cdots, n, v^k = 0$ on δA. The Galierkin procedure is to determine the c_k's in

$$u^n = \sum_1^n c_k v^k$$

$$\ni \int_A (Lu^n - F)L(v^l) \quad dA = 0, \; \forall \, l = 1, \cdots, n.$$

The least squares procedure is to determine the c_k's $\ni$

$$\int_A (Lu^n - F)^2 \quad dA$$

is minimized. If L is linear, Galierkin and least squares procedures are obviously equivalent; otherwise, the Galierkin procedure is far simpler computationally.

The need to solve very large linear algebraic systems numerically in order to approximate the solution of boundary value problems has been demonstrated. So far, only the simplest examples of boundary value problems that could give the correct idea have been undertaken, and they have been presented for the purpose of motivating the study of numerical solutions of large linear systems. In Chapter 5 and after, we will return to the subject of approximations of solutions of boundary value problems and their applications since elucidation of this subject is the principal burden of our course.

CHAPTER 3

METHODS FOR SOLVING
LINEAR SYSTEMS

1. DIRECT METHODS

Classes of direct methods are as follows:

(i) Determinants—usually involves unnecessarily extensive computation;
(ii) inversion of matrices—'similar' to a solution of n linear systems;
and
(iii) systematic elimination—superior to most other methods if losses
due to subtraction are tolerable.

The most popular systematic elimination method is elimination below
the main diagonal combined with back substitution; it is called '*Gaussian
elimination.*' There are a number of variants, depending on the order in
which one divides by the diagonal coefficient or subtracts and also on
the ordering of the equations in the subtraction computations. Savings
of accuracy can be effected by the use of these variants, but usually one
would not take full advantage of these in machine computations. In
general, it would seem that the proliferation of names for these variants
is a carry-over from hand-computation days, when the differences
among them were considered important. One rather different variant
of Gaussian elimination, in which the computor eliminates above and
below the main diagonal and then solves the resulting diagonal system,
has been called '*Gauss–Jordan,*' although it is doubtful that the name is
justified.

2. LOSS OF ACCURACY IN USE OF DIRECT METHODS

In general, it will be impossible to retain all digits in a calculation involving the solution of a large linear system. One must select in advance how many significant digits he will use in a calculation. The difficulty in retaining all digits is due this time not to the occurrence of irrational numbers, but to the occurrence of rational numbers that have repeated decimal digits that do not terminate (e.g., $\frac{2}{3} = 0.666 \cdots$), and to the rapid accumulation in direct methods—say, elimination—of large numbers of digits if all are retained. We give an example of a 2×2 system, to be solved by elimination, retaining two significant digits, where it is possible to retain all significant digits for comparison. It must be borne in mind that similar examples can be given for any choice of the number of significant digits. Also, the larger the system, the more opportunity there is for losses due to subtraction which we will now find to be our largest source of error. For 2×2 systems, a serious loss can occur only if the coefficient determinant is small. This is not true for large systems (see Goldstine and Von Neumann, *AMS Bulletin*, 1947). In our example, the place of loss is easily noted, as it always will be in hand calculations.

2-Digit Calculation

$$0.21x + 0.12y = 1.0$$
$$\underline{0.090x + 0.050y = 1.0}$$

$$0.019x + 0.011y = 0.090$$
$$\underline{0.019x + 0.010y = 0.210}$$

$$\text{lost}$$
$$\downarrow$$
$$0.001y = -0.12$$

$$\boxed{y = -120}$$

$$0.010x + 0.0060y = 0.050$$
$$\underline{0.019x + 0.0060y = 0.12}$$
$$\text{lost} \qquad\qquad \text{lost}$$
$$\downarrow \qquad\qquad \downarrow$$
$$0.009x \qquad\quad = 0.07$$

$$\boxed{x = 7.8}$$

Exact Calculation

$$0.01890x + 0.01080y = 0.090$$
$$0.01890x + 0.01050y = 0.210$$

$$\boxed{y = -\frac{0.12}{0.003} = -400}$$

$$x = \frac{1 + 0.12(400)}{0.21} = \frac{49}{0.21}$$

$$\boxed{x = 233\tfrac{1}{3}}$$

This example and others we have given in connection with complex square-root routines causes us to formulate our *pathological difficulty of numerical analysis: large losses in accuracy can occur from the subtraction of terminating decimal representations of large numbers whose difference is small.*

'Large' and 'small' here are, of course, relative, and refer to the position in a decimal representation of a real number of the first nonzero digit. This difficulty is referred to as pathological, because it is an essential one, not trivially circumvented except in rare cases, since we can only compute with terminating decimals. It does not affect analysis in the real field, though it has an analogue there in differentiation of a real-valued function of a real variable.

3. RECOVERING ACCURACY: NUMERICAL ANALYSIS

Techniques

Absolute knowledge of the loss of accuracy due to subtractions occurring in the solution of linear systems by direct methods can be obtained by writing programs that monitor losses of significant digits. Cursory information is available by checking residuals. In order to recover accuracy when it is lost in the use of direct methods, we seek iterative methods that

  (i) converge;
 (ii) reduce the error at each iteration if possible or, otherwise, provide an asymptotic factor of reduction of the error that is less than one;
and
(iii) provide an error bound to the solution vector after a finite number of iterations.

The problems of providing such computational procedures, and of providing error bounds to solution of a problem from approximate solution of a discretized version of the problem, define modern numerical analysis. We have been driven to seek iterative methods in solution of one nonlinear equation by the fact that a solution may exist only as a real number that can be represented as a Cauchy sequence of rationals and not as a rational number, certainly not as a terminating decimal. For linear systems with terminating decimal coefficients, solutions will be rational; but, even if the decimal representations terminate, they will be too long to retain, and this is true in intermediate steps, so that large losses can occur from subtractions.

Jacobi Method, Diagonal Domination

We wish to solve the linear system

$$Ax = b \quad \text{where} \quad |A| \neq 0.$$

The method of *simultaneous replacements*, associated with the name of Jacobi is as follows:

Given $x_1^0, x_2^0, \cdots, x_n^0$ (for example $x_1^0 = x_2^0 = \cdots x_n^0 = 0$), let

$$x_i^{k+1} = \frac{1}{a_{ii}} \left(b_i - \sum_{\substack{j=1 \\ i \neq j}}^{n} a_{ij} x_j^k \right).$$

To examine convergence, since $\exists \, x \ni Ax = b$, put

$$x_i = \frac{1}{a_{ii}} \left(b_i - \sum_{\substack{j=1 \\ i \neq j}}^{n} a_{ij} x_j \right).$$

Subtracting, and putting $\varepsilon^k = x^k - x$,

$$\varepsilon_i^{k+1} = - \sum_{\substack{j=1 \\ i \neq j}}^{n} \frac{a_{ij}}{a_{ii}} \varepsilon_j^k,$$

$$|\varepsilon_i^{k+1}| \leq \frac{1}{|a_{ii}|} \sum_{\substack{j=1 \\ i \neq j}}^{n} |a_{ij}| \, |\varepsilon_j^k|,$$

and

$$\max_{i=1,\cdots,n} |\varepsilon_i^{k+1}| \leq \max_{i=1,\cdots n} \left\{ \frac{1}{|a_{ii}|} \sum_{\substack{j=1 \\ i \neq j}}^{n} |a_{ij}| \right\} \max_{j=1,\cdots,n} |\varepsilon_j^k|.$$

Thus, the method of simultaneous replacements converges if

$$(3.1) \qquad |a_{ii}| > \sum_{\substack{j=1 \\ i \neq j}}^{n} |a_{ij}| \; \forall \, i = 1, \cdots, n.$$

Note that the value of the initial estimate $x^{(0)}$ is irrelevant to convergence. It will be seen that this is typical of linear iterative methods for *linear systems.* Also, note that the value of the 'constant vector' b is irrelevant to convergence.

Diagonal domination such as would be required by (3.1) *for convergence has possibly never been satisfied for any problems except those devised to demonstrate it.* Moreover, it can be seen that, even if convergence is obtained, it *can be* exceedingly slow if

$$\frac{1}{|a_{ii}|} \sum_{\substack{j=1 \\ i \neq j}}^{n} |a_{ij}|$$

is close to one. *We are therefore forced to add to the problems given above as defining the field of numerical analysis, the criteria that*

(i) *iteration methods must give conditions that are 'general enough' to be useful in 'practical' cases,* and

(ii) *iteration methods must at least give rates of convergence fast enough so that they can be successfully carried to a length that yields a small enough error bound for practical use.*

Thus the subject of numerical analysis, although highly theoretical in mathematical content, is irretrievably tied to practical problems. The author is convinced that the two aspects cannot be separated, and he regrets any tendency to separate the field of numerical analysis from the general area of applied mathematics.

4. REVIEW OF LINEAR ALGEBRA

We doubt that a convergence analysis could be supplied for any of the useful linear iterative methods we want to study without utilizing mathematical tools beyond the simple triangle inequality, and this is virtually all that was utilized above in deriving the diagonal domination condition for the method of simultaneous replacements. We will find a general theory of convergence for linear iterative methods for linear systems useful, and for this, so to speak, we require more than 'our fingers to push the pencil.' As to useful mathematical theories already available to us for this purpose, there is, with some minor extensions to be made, the theory of contractive maps, but since that theory is designed for use on nonlinear problems, it cannot be expected to yield as good results as can be provided from a purely linear theory. Some of the elementary theory of analytic functions of a complex variable, according to a theorem of L. Cesari, is useful in the general linear theory, but there are also insights into the general theory of convergence of linear iterative methods for linear systems that seem to be provided only by the elementary theory of linear algebra up to the canonical forms of matrix representations of linear transformations on a finite-dimensional vector space. We now provide a quick review of this material and give some comments relevant thereto. A proof is given of the diagonal form, but not of the more general Jordan form we intend to use.

Definition

The pair $\{a,b\}$ is the set with the two elements a and b.

Definition[1]

The ordered pair (a,b) is the pair $\{a,\{a,b\}\}$.

Definition

Where A and B are sets, the Cartesian product

$$A \times B = \{(a,b) \mid a \in A \land b \in B\}.$$

Definition

R is a relation of a set A to a set B if $R \subset A \times B$.

Note: Our symbol $\subset$ is in some other places written $\subseteq$. However, if we mean to indicate that A is a *proper* subset of B, we write $A \subsetneq B$.

Definition

$f\colon A \to B$ is a function on A into B if

(i) f is a relation of A to B;
(ii) $((a,b_1) \in f \land (a,b_2) \in f) \Rightarrow b_1 = b_2$; and
(iii) $\forall a \in A \ \exists (a,b) \in f.$

A is called 'the' domain of f, B 'a' range of f.[2]

Notation: For $(a,b) \in f$, we write $b = f(a)$. $f(A) = \{f(a) \mid a \in A\}$.

---

[1] In order to understand the contents of this book, it is not necessary to understand this set-theoretic definition of an ordered pair. For our purposes, the intuitive notion may even be preferable, but we know of no other defensible way to define 'ordered pair.'

[2] Function, map, mapping, and transformation will be synonymous here. An operator is a function whose domain and range are vector spaces.

Definition

$f: A \rightarrow B$ is said to be onto B if $f(A) = B$.

Definition

$R^{-1} = \{(b,a) \,|\, (a,b) \in R\}$ is the inverse of any relation R of A to B.

Definition

A function f of A onto B is said to have an inverse if its inverse (as a relation) is a function.

Definition

A function $f: A \times A \rightarrow B$ is called a binary operation on A into B.

Definition

A function $f: A \times A \rightarrow A$ is called a closed binary operation in A.

Notation: We may write $+$, $\cdot$, $\oplus$, $\odot$, instead of f for closed binary operations (or functions $f: A \times B \rightarrow A$). Also, instead of $b = f(a,\alpha)$ or $b = +(a,\alpha)$, we may write $a + \alpha$.

Let $\mathscr{F}$ denote the field of *either* real or complex numbers. We denote the closed binary operations of addition and multiplication on $\mathscr{F}$ by $+$ and $\cdot$.

Definition

Let A be a set. Let $\oplus$ be a closed binary operation on A and let $\odot: \mathscr{F} \times A \rightarrow A$. The set $V = \langle A, \oplus, \odot, \mathscr{F} \rangle$ composed of elements A, $\oplus$, $\odot$, $\mathscr{F}$ will be said to be a vector space over $\mathscr{F}$ if

(i) $\forall\, v,w \in A,\; v \oplus w = w \oplus v$
(ii) $\forall\, v,w,z \in A,\; (v \oplus w) \oplus z = v \oplus (w \oplus z)$
(iii) $\exists\, \Phi \in A \ni \forall\, v \in A,\; v \oplus \Phi = v$
(iv) $\forall\, \alpha \in \mathscr{F} \wedge \forall\, v,w \in A,\; \alpha \odot (v \oplus w) = (\alpha \odot v) \oplus (\alpha \odot w)$
(v) $\forall\, \alpha,\beta \in \mathscr{F} \wedge \forall\, v \in A,\; (\alpha + \beta) \odot v = (\alpha \odot v) \oplus (\beta \odot v)$
(vi) $\forall\, v \in A,\; 1 \odot v = v,\; 0 \odot v = \Phi$
(vii) $(\alpha \cdot \beta) \odot v = \alpha \odot (\beta \odot v)$

Proposition

$\forall\, v \in A,\; v \oplus \Phi_1 = v,\; v \oplus \Phi_2 = v \Rightarrow \Phi_1 = \Phi_2$

Proof

(Exercise) ∎

Proposition

$$((-1) \odot v) \oplus v = \Phi \ \forall \ v \in A$$

Proof

$$(-1) \odot v \oplus v = (-1 + 1) \odot v = 0 \odot v = \Phi. \ \blacksquare$$

Conventions: We agree to indicate both $+$ and $\oplus$ by $+$, both $\cdot$ and $\odot$ by juxtaposition, and both $0 \in \mathscr{F}$ and $\Phi \in A$ by 0. The context will be depended upon to make the necessary distinctions, unless there is a possible confusion, in which case the extended symbolism will be utilized. We will speak of $v \in V = \langle A, \oplus, \odot, \mathscr{F} \rangle$ when $v \in A$ and properties (i) through (vii) are satisfied.

Definition

If V and W are vector spaces over $\mathscr{F}$, the function $L: V \to W$ will be called a linear transformation (operator), if $\forall \ v_1, v_2 \in V \ \wedge \ \forall \ \alpha, \beta \in \mathscr{F}$

$$L(\alpha v_1 + \beta v_2) = \alpha L(v_1) + \beta L(v_2).$$

Definition

Elements $v_1, \cdots, v_n \in V$, a vector space over $\mathscr{F}$, are said to be linearly independent if $\forall \ \alpha_i \in \mathscr{F}$, $i = 1, \cdots, n$,

$$\sum_{i=1}^{n} \alpha_i v_i = 0 \Rightarrow \alpha_i = 0 \ \forall \ i = 1, \cdots, n.$$

Definition

A vector space V over $\mathscr{F}$ is said to be finite dimensional if $\exists$ a set of $n(\varepsilon \Omega)$ linearly independent elements of V, and any set of $(n + 1)$ elements of V, are linearly dependent (not linearly independent). V is then said to be of dimension n, and any set of n linearly independent elements of V is said to be a basis for V.

EXERCISE

Prove that $v_1, \cdots, v_n$ is a basis for $V \Rightarrow \forall \ v \in V$,

$$\exists \ \alpha_i \in \mathscr{F} \ni v = \sum_{i=1}^{n} \alpha_i v_i.$$

Let V be an n-dimensional vector space over $\mathscr{F}$ and W an m-dimensional vector space over $\mathscr{F}$. Let $v_1, \cdots, v_n$ be a basis for V, and $w_1, \cdots, w_m$ be a basis for W. Let $L: V \to W$ be a linear transformation

$$\begin{pmatrix} v \in V \\ (v_1, \cdots, v_n) \end{pmatrix} \xrightarrow{\quad L \quad} \begin{pmatrix} w = Lv \in W \\ (w_1, \cdots, w_m) \end{pmatrix}.$$

$$\forall\, v \in V,\, \exists\, \alpha_j \in \mathscr{F} \ni \boxed{\; v = \sum_{j=1}^{n} \alpha_j v_j \;}$$

(3.2)　　　　$\wedge\, \forall\, w \in W,\, \exists\, \beta_j \in \mathscr{F} \ni \boxed{\; L(v) = w = \sum_{j=1}^{m} \beta_j w_j \;}$.

Since L is linear,

$$L(v) = \sum_{j=1}^{n} \alpha_j L(v_j).$$

But since $L(v_j) \in W \; \forall\, j = 1, \cdots, n,\, \exists\, a_{ij} \in \mathscr{F} \ni$

$$L(v_j) = \sum_{i=1}^{m} a_{ij} w_i \; \forall\, j = 1, \cdots, n.$$

(3.3)　　∴　$\boxed{\; L(v) = \sum_{j=1}^{n} \alpha_j \left(\sum_{i=1}^{m} a_{ij} w_j \right) = \sum_{i=1}^{m} \left(\sum_{j=1}^{n} a_{ij} \alpha_j \right) w_i. \;}$

Compare (3.2) and (3.3). If we now identify any vector $v \in V$ by the column matrix $\alpha = (\alpha_j)$ of its coefficients α_j (now called coordinates) with respect to the basis $v_1, \cdots, v_n$, and identify any vector $w \in W$ by the column matrix $\beta = (\beta_j)$ of its coefficients with respect to the basis $w_1, \cdots, w_n$, and let A denote the matrix (a_{ij}), it is seen that operation with L on V into W can be replaced with multiplication of α by A to get β; i.e.,

$$\beta = A\alpha.$$

Note that A is determined when it is known how the transforms of the basis elements in V can be written in terms of the basis elements of W.

Definition

A matrix $A = (a_{ij})$ represents a linear transformation $L : V \to V$ with respect to the basis $v_1, \cdots, v_n$ if

$$L(v_j) = \sum_{i=1}^{n} a_{ij}v_i \ \forall j = 1,\cdots,n.$$

Definition

Matrices A and B are said to be similar if both A and B represent the same linear transformation L on a finite-dimensional vector space V into V, with respect to some basis for V.

EXERCISE

Prove that if A is similar to B, $\exists$ a nonsingular matrix $P \ni B = PAP^{-1}$.

Note: Let Ω_n be the set of positive integers $\leq n$. An $(m \times n)$ rectangular array of $\mathscr{F}$ is a function $M: \Omega_n \times \Omega_m \to \mathscr{F}$. A set of $m \times n$ matrices is a set of $(m \times n)$ rectangular arrays, together with the usual addition and multiplication defined.

Definition

$\lambda \in \mathscr{F}$ is said to be an eigenvalue of a linear transformation L on a vector space V over $\mathscr{F}$ into V if $\exists v \in V \ni$

$$v \neq 0$$

$$\wedge \ L(v) = \lambda v.$$

Such a vector v is said to be an eigenvector of L corresponding to eigenvalue λ.

Definition

$\lambda \in \mathscr{F}$ is said to be an eigenvalue of a matrix A over $\mathscr{F}$ if A represents a linear transformation L on a vector space V over $\mathscr{F}$ into V with respect to some basis of V, and if λ is an eigenvalue of L.

Proposition

All eigenvalues λ of A are roots of $|A - \lambda I| = 0$.

Proof

With respect to an appropriate basis, we may write $Av = \lambda v$. Then $(\exists v \neq 0 \ni (A - \lambda I)v = 0) \Leftrightarrow (|A - \lambda I| = 0)$. ∎

We now give some essential facts concerning eigenvalues:

(1) The eigenvalues of a real symmetric matrix are real.

(2) If *either* A is real and symmetric *or* A is of order n and has n distinct eigenvalues, λ_i, $i = 1,\cdots,n$,

∃ a matrix $\overline{\Lambda}$ similar to A ∋

$$\overline{\Lambda} = \begin{pmatrix} \lambda_1 & & & & \text{\Large O} \\ & \lambda_2 & & & \\ & & \ddots & & \\ & & & \ddots & \\ \text{\Large O} & & & & \lambda_n \end{pmatrix} \; ;$$

i.e., ∋ $\overline{\Lambda} = (d_{ij})$, where $i \neq j \Rightarrow d_{ij} = 0 \wedge d_{ii} = \lambda_i \; \forall \; i = 1,\cdots,n$. In quoting $\overline{\Lambda}$, we will assume unless otherwise specified that $\lambda_{i+1} \geq \lambda_i \; \forall \; i = 1,\cdots,n$. A proof of the existence of a diagonal form under the conditions quoted is included at the end of this review.

(3) If A is a matrix over $\mathscr{F}$, ∃ a matrix $J = (J_{ij})$ similar to A ∋ $(J_{ii} = \lambda_i, i = 1,\cdots,n) \wedge (\lambda_{i+1} \geq \lambda_i \; \forall \; i = 1,\cdots,n) \wedge (\lambda_{i+1} = \lambda_i \Rightarrow J_{i,i+1} = 1$ or 0 (according to a rule not stated here)) $\wedge (J_{ij} = 0$ otherwise). Schematically,

$$J = \begin{pmatrix} \lambda_1 & & & & & \text{\Large O} \\ & \lambda_2 & 0 & & & \\ & & \lambda_3 & 1 & & \\ & & & \lambda_3 & 0 & \\ & & & & \ddots & \\ & & & & & \ddots \\ \text{\Large O} & & & & & \lambda_n \end{pmatrix}.$$

This is the Jordan normal form. No proof is given here because of length. It can be found in many good books on linear algebra.

EXERCISE

Show that $J - \overline{\Lambda}$ is nilpotent; i.e., show that

$$\exists \, p \in \Omega \ni (J - \overline{\Lambda})^p = 0$$

Normed Vector Spaces

Let V be a vector space over $\mathscr{F}$, the field of real or complex numbers. Let $R_+{}^1$ be the set of nonnegative real numbers, $R_+{}^1 = \{x \mid x \in R^1 \wedge x \geq 0\}$.

Definition

A function $N : V \to R_+{}^1$ is said to be a norm on V if

(i) $(N(v) = 0) \Rightarrow (v = 0)$,

(ii) $\forall \, v \in V \wedge \forall \, \alpha \in \mathscr{F}, \, N(\alpha v) = |\alpha| N(v)$,

(iii) $N(x + y) \leq N(x) + N(y) \; \forall \; x,y \in V$.

Notation: For $N(v)$ we may write $\|v\|$. The set $V = \langle A, \oplus, \odot, \mathscr{F}, N \rangle$ or $\langle A, \oplus, \odot, \mathscr{F}, \| \; \| \rangle$ will be called a normed vector space.

Comment: If $V = \langle A, +, \cdot, \mathscr{F}, \| \; \| \rangle$ is a normed linear vector space and $\rho(a,b) = \|a - b\|$, then the set $\langle A, \rho \rangle$ is a metric space   Given a metric space $\langle A, \rho \rangle$, it is not always possible to generate an equivalent normed vector space V. $\therefore$ We say a metric is more general than a norm.

Definition

Let $V = \langle A, +, \cdot, \mathscr{F}, \| \; \| \rangle$ be a finite-dimensional vector space and let $v_1, \cdots, v_n$ be a basis for V. Let

$$v = \sum_{i=1}^{n} \alpha_i v_i \in V.$$

(i) $\|v\| = \max_i |\alpha_i|$ is called the *Tchebychev norm.*

(ii) $\|v\| = \left(\sum_{i=1}^{n} \alpha_i^2 \right)^{1/2}$ is called the *Euclidean norm.*

(iii) $\|v\| = \left(\sum_{i=1}^{n} |\alpha_i|^p \right)^{1/p} \; \forall \, p \geq 1$ is the *p-norm.*

These are the usual norms utilized. They are related; e.g.,

$$\lim_{p \to \infty} \left(\sum_{i=1}^{n} \alpha_i^p \right)^{1/p} = \max_i |\alpha_i|.$$

EXERCISE

Prove the last statement.

Definition

A sequence of elements of a vector space V is a function $S : \Omega \to V$, where Ω is the set of positive integers.

Notation: Instead of writing $S(n)$ for the functional values of a sequence, we will write S_n. We write $\{S_n\}$ for S, or $S_1, S_2, \cdots$ for S. The subscripts may sometimes be understood by the order of listing; e.g., $1, \frac{1}{2}, \frac{1}{4}, \cdots \frac{1}{2}^n, \cdots = \{\frac{1}{2}^n\}$.

Definition

A sequence $\{S^n\}$ of a normed vector space V is said to converge in norm to $S \in V$ if

$$\|S^n - S\| \to 0.$$

Theorem

If a sequence S^n on a finite-dimensional vector space V converges in norm with respect to one norm, it converges with respect to any norm on V. (Without proof here.)

Comment: (1) This theorem is *no longer valid if the finite property is dropped.* For example, some Fourier series that converge in L^2 norm do not converge in supremum (T) norm. (2) The column vectors of coordinates with respect to some basis of a finite-dimensional vector space are themselves a vector space. If the Euclidean norm is utilized, such a vector space is called E^n.

Derivation of the Diagonal Form

The following is a proof of the proposition that an nth order matrix with n distinct eigenvalues has a set of n linearly independent eigenvectors.

Definition

If $x_1, x_2, \cdots, x_n$ are any n complex numbers, then the matrix

$$V = \begin{pmatrix} 1 & x_1 & x_1^2 & \cdots & x_1^{n-1} \\ 1 & x_2 & x_2^2 & \cdots & x_2^{n-1} \\ 1 & x_3 & x_3^2 & \cdots & x_3^{n-1} \\ \vdots & \vdots & \vdots & & \vdots \\ 1 & x_n & x_n^2 & \cdots & x_n^{n-1} \end{pmatrix}$$

will be called the Vandermonde matrix. By $|V|$ we denote the determinant of V.

Lemma

$$|V| = \prod_{j>i} (x_j - x_i).$$

Proof

$|V|$ is a polynomial in $x_1, x_2, \cdots, x_n$. If for any i and j, $x_i = x_j$, then V will have two identical rows, and hence $|V| = 0$. By the factor theorem of elementary algebra $|V|$ will be divisible by the factor $(x_j - x_i)$, and hence by $\prod_{j>i}(x_j - x_i)$. Therefore, we can write

$$|V| = q(x_1, x_2, \cdots, x_n) \prod_{j>i} (x_j - x_i),$$

where q is either a polynomial in the n terms x_i or a nonzero constant.
Consider the polynomial

$$(3.4) \quad \prod_{j>i} (x_j - x_i) = (x_2 - x_1)(x_3 - x_1) \cdots$$
$$(x_n - x_1)(x_3 - x_2) \cdots (x_n - x_2) \cdots (x_n - x_{n-1}).$$

The term obtained by multiplying together the first terms of each of the parentheses in (3.4) is

$$x_2 x_3{}^2 x_4{}^3 \cdots x_n{}^{n-1}.$$

This is precisely the main diagonal term in $|V|$. Both $|V|$ and (3.4) are of total degree

$$\sum_{i=1}^{n-1} i = (n-1)\left(\frac{1+(n-1)}{2}\right) = \frac{n(n-1)}{2}.$$

Therefore, q must be equal to 1.

$$\therefore \quad |V| = \prod_{j>i} (x_j - x_i). \quad \blacksquare$$

Corollary
   If $x_i \neq x_j$, $i \neq j$, then $|V| \neq 0$.

Theorem 1
   Let A be an nth order arbitrary matrix, such that A has n distinct eigenvalues. Then in the set $\{X_i\}$, X_i the eigenvector corresponding to λ_i, is linearly independent.

Proof
   Assume the contrary; i.e., there exist scalars $\alpha_i \in \mathscr{F}$, $\alpha_i \neq 0$, $\forall i = 1, \cdots, n$ such that

$$(3.5) \qquad \qquad \sum_{i=1}^{n} \alpha_i X_i = 0.$$

Since (3.5) is an n-dimensional vector, it can be operated on $(n-1)$ times by A to obtain the following:

$$A\left(\sum_{i=1}^{n} \alpha_i X_i\right) = \sum_{i=1}^{n} \alpha_i A X_i = \sum_{i=1}^{n} \alpha_i \lambda_i X_i = 0$$

$$A^2\left(\sum_{i=1}^{n} \alpha_i X_i\right) = A\left(\sum_{i=1}^{n} \alpha_i \lambda_i X_i\right) = \sum_{i=1}^{n} \alpha_i \lambda_i^2 X_i = 0, \text{ etc.}$$

Thus the following linear system is obtained:

$$\sum_{i=1}^{n} \alpha_i X_i = 0$$

(3.6)
$$\sum_{i=1}^{n} \alpha_i \lambda_i X_i = 0$$

$$\vdots$$

$$\sum_{i=1}^{n} \alpha_i \lambda_i^{n-1} X_i = 0.$$

The system (3.6) can be rewritten as

$$(\alpha_1 X_1, \alpha_2 X_2, \cdots, \alpha_n X_n) \begin{pmatrix} 1 & \lambda_1 & \lambda_1^2 & \cdots & \lambda_1^{n-1} \\ 1 & \lambda_2 & \lambda_2^2 & & \\ 1 & \lambda_3 & \lambda_3^2 & & \\ \vdots & \vdots & \vdots & & \vdots \\ 1 & \lambda_n & \lambda_n^2 & \cdots & \lambda_n^{n-1} \end{pmatrix} = 0;$$

or $CV = 0$, where C is a matrix whose columns are the vectors $\alpha_i X_i$, and where V is the Vandermonde matrix of the λ_i's. By the corollary $|V| \neq 0$ and hence V^{-1} exists.

$$\therefore \quad CVV^{-1} = C = 0, \qquad \text{the zero matrix; i.e., } \alpha_i X_i = 0 \; \forall \; i = 1, \cdots, n.$$

Since X_i cannot be a zero vector, we arrive at the contradiction that $\alpha_i \equiv 0 \; \forall \; i = 1, \cdots, n$. $\therefore$ The set $\{X_i\}$ is independent. ∎

Theorem 2

If the matrix A is of order n and if A has has n distinct eigenvalues λ_i $(i = 1, 2, \cdots, n)$, then $\exists$ a nonsingular matrix P, such that $P^{-1} A P = \bar{\Lambda}$.

Proof

The proof will be by construction. Let $P = (X_1, X_2, \cdots, X_n)$, where the ith column of P is the vector X_i corresponding to the eigenvalue λ_i.

$$\therefore AP = A(X_1, X_2, \cdots, X_n)$$

$$= (AX_1, AX_2, \cdots, AX_n)$$

$$= (\lambda_1 X_1, \lambda_2 X_2, \cdots, \lambda_n X_n)$$

$$= (X_1, X_2, \cdots, X_n) \begin{pmatrix} \lambda_1 & & & & \text{O} \\ & \lambda_2 & & & \\ & & \cdot & & \\ & & & \cdot & \\ & & & & \cdot \\ \text{O} & & & & \lambda_n \end{pmatrix}$$

$$\therefore AP = P\overline{\Lambda}.$$

Since P is composed of n linearly independent columns, P will be nonsingular, and hence P^{-1} exists.

$$\therefore P^{-1}AP = P^{-1}P\,\overline{\Lambda} = \overline{\Lambda}. \quad \blacksquare$$

4

GENERAL THEORY OF CONVERGENCE FOR LINEAR ITERATIVE METHODS FOR LINEAR SYSTEMS

1. EXAMPLES OF LINEAR ITERATIVE METHODS FOR LINEAR SYSTEMS AND THEIR MATRIX FORMS

We consider the linear system to be solved

$$Ax = b \quad \text{where} \quad (A = B + C) \wedge (|B| \neq 0).$$

Linear iterative methods are, in general, rules of inductive (or recursive) generation of sequences $\{x^k\} \ni$ the $(k + 1)$st element x^{k+1} is a linear function of the kth[1] element x^k. For a linear system, as quoted, all linear iterative methods can be written in matrix form as

$$x^0 \quad \text{given} \quad Bx^{k+1} = b - Cx^k \quad \text{or} \quad x^{k+1} = B^{-1}b - B^{-1}Cx^k,$$

although a component form will always be recommended for computation. Any specific linear iterative method for a linear system is chosen by selection of specific matrices B and C. It is assumed that when x^k is known, B has been chosen not only $\ni |B| \neq 0$, but also $\ni$ *it is feasible to compute the solution of the system*

(4.1) $$Bx^{k+1} = b - Cx^k$$

---

[1] In general, an iterative method is a rule of inductive generation of a sequence, and will be considered a computational method if the rule is a finitely generated function.

without entailing any major loss of significant digits in the process. In the iteration assigned (Chapter 2) as an exercise for computing an approximation to the five-point finite-difference discretization of the Dirichlet problem for the Laplace equation, only sums had to be taken. Though other iterations may not have quite this 'nice' a property, B should be chosen so that no excessive losses are involved in solving (4.1), such as might be expected in using elimination on the full equation $Ax = b$. When these methods converge, they are asymptotically self-correcting, so that if N-digit accuracy is to be sought in the final answer, it must be possible to compute a solution to (4.1), when x^k is given, with a loss of not more than $M - N$ digits if M-digits are to be retained in computation.

Let λ_i, $i = 1, \cdots, n$, be eigenvalues, possibly complex, of the matrix $-B^{-1}C$, and let

$$s = \max_i |\lambda_i|$$

be called the spectral norm of $-B^{-1}C$. We give here two proofs, using rather essentially different mathematical techniques, that linear iterative methods for linear systems converge if $s < 1$. Actually, this is a necessary and sufficient condition. We have

$$|A| \neq 0 \Rightarrow (\exists\, x \ni Ax = b) \wedge (Bx = b - Cx);$$

subtracting this last from (4.1),

$$\varepsilon^{k+1} = x^{k+1} - x = -B^{-1}C(x^k - x) = -B^{-1}C\varepsilon^k,$$

so that $-B^{-1}C$ is referred to as the correction matrix. Our condition for convergence is that the spectral norm of the correction matrix of the linear iterative method for the linear system be less than one.

Before giving proofs of convergence, some examples of important linear iteative methods for linear systems, for which we will specifically want to discuss convergence, will be given.

Simultaneous Replacements (Jacobi)

Computational Form.

(4.2) $$x_i^{k+1} = \frac{1}{a_{ii}}\left(b_i - \sum_{\substack{j=1 \\ i \neq j}}^{n} a_{ij}x_j^k\right) \forall\, i = 1, \cdots, n.$$

Matrix Form.
$$Dx^{k+1} = b - (L + U)x^k.$$

Here, and in succeeding examples,

$$D = (d_{ij}), \quad L = (l_{ij}), \quad \wedge \; U = (u_{ij}),$$

where

$$d_{ij}\begin{cases} = a_{ij} \; \forall \; i = j \\ = 0 \; \forall \; i \neq j, \end{cases} \qquad l_{ij}\begin{cases} = 0 \; \forall \; i \leq j \\ = a_{ij} \; \forall \; i > j \end{cases} \qquad u_{ij}\begin{cases} = 0 \; \forall \; i \geq j \\ = a_{ij} \; \forall \; i < j. \end{cases}$$

Note that $A = L + D + U$ where D, L, and U are diagonal, lower tri-angular, and upper triangular matrices of A. Simultaneous replace-ments, then, is a method where choices of B and C have been made as

$$B = D \quad \wedge \quad C = L + U.$$

Successive Replacements (Gauss–Seidel)

Computation Form.

$$(4.3) \qquad x_i^{k+1} = \frac{1}{a_{ii}}\left(b_i - \sum_{j=1}^{i-1} a_{ij}x_j^{k+1} - \sum_{j=i+1}^{n} a_{ij}x_j^k\right)$$

to be carried out successively for $i = 1,\cdots,n$. Note that a particular ordering of equations and components of x is implied.

Matrix Form.
$$(L + D)x^{k+1} = b - Ux^k.$$

This important linear iterative method for linear systems fits the above general form by choice of

$$(B = L + D) \wedge (C = U).$$

Apparently Gauss never heard of it, and Seidel recommended against its use, but these two names are associated with this method in much of the modern literature.

Accelerated Successive Replacements (Over-relaxation of D. M. Young)

Computational Form. Let $\omega \in R^1$.

$$(4.4) \qquad x_i^{k+1} = (1 - \omega)x_i^k + \frac{\omega}{a_{ii}}\left\{b_i - \sum_{j=1}^{i-1} a_{ij}x_j^{k+1} - \sum_{j=i+1}^{n} a_{ij}x_j^k\right\}.$$

Note that (4.4) reduces to (4.3) for $\omega = 1$. We expect acceleration for $\omega > 1$ and deceleration for $\omega < 1$. Analysis under certain useful conditions reveals that convergence is obtained for $0 < \omega < 2$, and that an optimum choice exists in the interval (1,2).

Matrix Form.

$$\left(L + \frac{1}{\omega}D\right)x^{k+1} = b - \left[U + \left(1 - \frac{1}{\omega}\right)D\right]x^k.$$

This form fits into the general form for linear iterative methods by choice of

$$B = \left(\frac{1}{\omega}D + L\right) \quad \wedge \quad C = U + \left(1 - \frac{1}{\omega}\right)D.$$

It will turn out that both successive replacements and its accelerated form converge if A is positive definite; i.e., $A > 0^2 \Rightarrow s(-B^{-1}C) < 1$ if $0 < \omega < 2$. Coefficient matrices that are positive definite occur quite regularly in problems of technology; all problems using least squares approximation, and almost all involving finite-difference analogues for PDE's of elliptic type (like the Laplace equation), give rise to such coefficient matrices. Therefore, the last method, which is more efficient than either (4.2) or (4.3), plays a major role in practical computation procedures.

2. TWO INDEPENDENT PROOFS OF THE SPECTRAL NORM CONDITION

Theorem

$$(\exists\, r > 1 \ni |B + \lambda C| = 0 \Rightarrow |\lambda| \geq r) \wedge (|B| \neq 0) \wedge$$
$$(x^0 \in E^n) \wedge (x^{k+1} = B^{-1}b - B^{-1}Cx^k) \Rightarrow (\{x^k\} \to x \ni (B + C)x = b).$$

EXERCISE

Prove that

$$(\exists\, r > 1 \ni |B + \lambda C| = 0 \Rightarrow |\lambda| \geq r) \Leftrightarrow (s(B^{-1}C) < 1) \Rightarrow (\exists\, x \ni (B + C)x = b).$$

The theorem may be restated.

---

[2] $(A > 0) \Leftrightarrow (x \neq 0 \Rightarrow x^T A x > 0)$.

Theorem

$$(s(B^{-1}C) < 1) \wedge (|B| \neq 0) \wedge (x^0 \in E^n) \wedge (x^{k+1} = B^{-1}b - B^{-1}Cx^k)$$
$$\Rightarrow \{x^k\} \to x \ni (B + C)x = b.$$

Proof

We use the second statement of the theorem.

$$s(B^{-1}C) < 1 \Rightarrow \exists \, x \ni x = B^{-1}b - B^{-1}Cx.$$

$$(x^{k+1} = B^{-1}b - B^{-1}Cx^k) \Rightarrow \varepsilon^{k+1} = x^{k+1} - x = -B^{-1}C\varepsilon^k$$
$$= (-B^{-1}C)^2\varepsilon^{k+1} = \cdots = (-B^{-1}C)^{k+1}\varepsilon^0.$$

We now express vectors ε^{k+1} and ε^k with respect to a basis $\ni -B^{-1}C$ is in Jordan normal form. Multiplication of this matrix by the vector ε^k in the new coordinates represents transformation to the same vector ε^{k+1} in the new coordinates. Write this matrix as

$$\overline{\Lambda} + \psi,$$

where it is noted that $\psi^n = 0$ if $B + C$ is an $n \times n$ square matrix, and that $\overline{\Lambda}$ commutes with ψ. We have, with respect to our new basis,

$$\varepsilon^{k+1} = (\overline{\Lambda} + \psi)^{k+1}\varepsilon^0$$

$$= \left(\overline{\Lambda}^{k+1} + \binom{k+1}{1}\overline{\Lambda}^k\psi + \cdots + \binom{k+1}{j}\overline{\Lambda}^{k+1-j}\psi^j + \cdots \psi^{k+1}\right)\varepsilon^0$$

where $\forall \, k > 0$ at most n terms are nonzero; i.e., $\forall \, k > n - 1$,

$$\varepsilon^{k+1} = \left(\sum_{j=0}^{n-1} \binom{k+1}{j}\overline{\Lambda}^{k+1-j} \, \psi^j\right)\varepsilon^0.$$

Each of the terms of ε^{k+1} is of the form

$$\frac{(k+1)!}{(k+1-j)!j!} \overline{\Lambda}^{k+1-j} \psi^j \varepsilon^0, \quad j = 1, \cdots, n - 1.$$

Then each element of the matrix multiplying $\psi^j\varepsilon^0$ in each term is less in modulus than $P_j(k)e^{(k+1-j)\ln s}$, $j = 1, \cdots, n - 1$, where s is the spectral norm, $s(-B^{-1}C)$, and $P_j(k)$ is a polynomial of degree j in k. Since $s < 1$ and the exponential dominates a polynomial of any order, the limit of the above expression is zero. We have

$$\lim_{k \to \infty} \varepsilon^{k+1} = 0. \quad \blacksquare$$

Note that x^0 and b are irrelevant to convergence.

Proof (L. Cesari, 1937 [2])

We use the first statement of the theorem. Let $x(\lambda)$ denote the functional values of the function $x: C^1 \to E^n$ satisfying a linear equation

(4.5) $$(B + \lambda C)x(\lambda) = b + (1 - \lambda)R,$$

where $\lambda \in C^1$, and $R \in E^n$ is to be regarded as an arbitrary vector. If we think of (4.5) as a system to be solved by determinants, we see that each component of $x(\lambda)$ is a rational function (a quotient of polynomial functions) of λ. Select $r > 1 \ni |B + \lambda C| = 0 \Rightarrow |\lambda| \geq r$. Then $\forall \lambda \ni |\lambda| < r$, each component of $x(\lambda)$ is an analytic function of λ (from an elementary theorem on analytic functions of a complex variable). Then

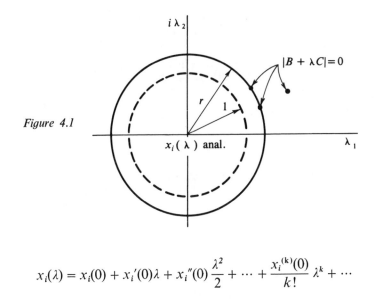

Figure 4.1

$$x_i(\lambda) = x_i(0) + x_i'(0)\lambda + x_i''(0)\frac{\lambda^2}{2} + \cdots + \frac{x_i^{(k)}(0)}{k!}\lambda^k + \cdots$$

$\forall \ i = 1, \cdots, n \ \wedge \ \forall \ \lambda \ni |\lambda| < r$, or, in vector notation,

$$x(\lambda) = x(0) + x'(0)\lambda + x''(0)\frac{\lambda^2}{2} + \cdots + x^{(k)}(0)\frac{\lambda^k}{k!} + \cdots$$

$$\forall \ \lambda \ni |\lambda| < r.$$

In particular, for $\lambda = 1$ (note that $r > 1$), we have from (4.5)

$$x(1) = x \ni (B + C)x = b,$$

and, from the above expression for $x(\lambda)$,

$$x = x(1) = x(0) + x'(0) + \frac{x''(0)}{2!} + \cdots + \frac{x^{(k)}(0)}{k!} + \cdots$$

gives us a series converging to x, the solution of our linear system. To express this series as an iteration, we consider the sequence of partial sums,

$$X^0 = x(0)$$

$$X^1 = x(0) + x'(0)$$

$$X^2 = x(0) + x'(0) + \frac{x''(0)}{2!}$$

$$\vdots$$

$$X^k = x(0) + x'(0) + \frac{x''(0)}{2} + \cdots + \frac{x^{(k)}(0)}{k!}.$$

From (4.5)

(4.6) $$Bx(0) = b + R$$

or $$X^0 = x(0) = B^{-1}b + B^{-1}R,$$

which is arbitrary, since R is arbitrary. Again from (4.5)

(4.7) $$(B + \lambda C)x'(\lambda) + Cx(\lambda) = -R$$

or

(4.8) $$Bx'(0) + Cx(0) = -R.$$

Adding (4.6) and (4.8)

(4.9) $$BX^1 + CX^0 = B(x'(0) + x(0)) + Cx(0) = b$$

or $$X^1 = B^{-1}b - B^{-1}CX^0.$$

From (4.7)

(4.10) $$(B + \lambda C)x''(\lambda) + 2Cx'(\lambda) = 0$$

or

(4.11) $$B\frac{x''(0)}{2} + Cx'(0) = 0.$$

Adding (4.9) and (4.11)

(4.12) $$BX^2 + CX^1 = b$$

or $$X^2 = B^{-1}b - B^{-1}CX^1.$$

Once again, from (4.10)

$$(B + \lambda C)x'''(\lambda) + 3Cx''(\lambda) = 0$$

or

(4.13) $$B\frac{x'''(0)}{3!} + C\frac{x''(0)}{2} = 0.$$

Adding (4.12) and (4.13)

$$BX^3 + CX^2 = b$$

or $$X^3 = B^{-1}b - B^{-1}CX^2.$$

We complete the proof by induction.

    ʊ (i) $(B + \lambda C)x^{(k)}(\lambda) + kCx^{(k-1)}(\lambda) = 0$

∧ ʊ (ii) $BX^k + CX^{k-1} = b.$

Both (i) and (ii) have been shown to be true for $k = 2$. Differentiating (i) with respect to λ, we see that (i) is true for k replaced by $(k + 1)$, so that (i) is established. Then from (i)

$$Bx^{(k)}(0) + kCx^{(k-1)}(0) = 0$$

or $$B\frac{x^{(k)}(0)}{k!} + C\frac{x^{(k-1)}(0)}{(k-1)!} = 0.$$

Adding this last to (ii)

$$BX^{k+1} + CX^k = b,$$

and the theorem is established. ∎

3. USE OF THE SPECTRAL NORM CONDITION

Definition of Rate of Convergence

Writing, as above, $\forall\, k > n - 1$,

$$\varepsilon^{k+1} = \sum_{j=0}^{n-1} \frac{(k+1)!}{(k+1-j)!\,j!}\, \overline{\Lambda}^{k+1-j} \psi^j \varepsilon^0$$

and

$$\varepsilon^{k+2} = \sum_{j=0}^{n-1} \frac{(k+2)!}{(k+2-j)!\,j!}\, \overline{\Lambda}^{k+2-j} \psi^j \varepsilon^0.$$

Therefore, $\forall\, \delta > 0 \; \exists\, K \ni \forall\, k > K$

$$\max_i |(\varepsilon^{k+2} - \overline{\Lambda}\, \varepsilon^{k+1})_i|$$

$$= \max_i \left| \left(\sum_{j=0}^{n-1} \left[\frac{(k+2)!}{(k+2-i)!\,j!} - \frac{(k+1)!}{(k+1-j)!\,j!} \right] \cdot \overline{\Lambda}^{k+2-j} \psi^j \varepsilon^0 \right)_i \right| < \delta,$$

so that for large k, the spectral norm can be regarded as the factor of reduction; i.e., it can be regarded as an asymptotic factor of reduction. As formerly for a contractive mapping (where the modulus of contraction was the factor of reduction), *we define the rate of convergence of a linear iterative method for a linear system as* $-\ln s(B^{-1}C)$. This gives us for 'rate' a 'smooth' function of s and one that is infinite for $s = 0$, zero for $s = 1$, positive for $0 \le s < 1$, and negative otherwise.

Comparison of Rates

Note that in using an iterative method for a linear system (i) a rearrangement of equations or renumbering (and reordering) of variables does not affect the solution to the system, and that (ii) such rearrangements may affect convergence markedly. The reason for (i) is the simple use of logical conjunction in describing what is meant by solution of a system. The reason for (ii) is that convergence depends on the spectral norm of the matrix $B^{-1}C$, and that both B and C can be greatly altered by any rearrangements of equations or variables.

Definition (D. Young)

A matrix A is said to have property A if, by reordering rows and columns, it can be written in the form

$$A = \begin{pmatrix} D_1 & G \\ F & D_2 \end{pmatrix},$$

where $D_1 \wedge D_2$ are diagonal and $F \wedge G$ are rectangular matrices. A linear system will be said to be in property A form if the coefficient matrix is in a form such as above.

EXERCISE

Show that the linear system obtained by the five-point finite-difference analogue for the Dirichlet problem on a rectangle for the Laplace equation is in property A form if the ordering of equations is from left to right and down skipping alternate points as shown.

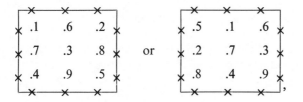

We assume *in this section and the next only* (Chapter 4, sec. 3, pp. 54–57) that we deal with linear systems in property A form. For systems in this form, let

> μ be any eigenvalue of the correction matrix for simultaneous replacements

and λ be any eigenvalue of the correction matrix for successive replacements.

Then

$$|-D^{-1}(L + U) - \mu I| = 0 \qquad \text{or} \qquad |L + U + \mu D| = 0$$

or

$$\begin{vmatrix} \mu D_1 & G \\ F & \mu D_2 \end{vmatrix} = 0$$

and

$$|-(D + L)^{-1} U - \lambda I| = 0 \qquad \text{or} \qquad |U + \lambda(D + L)| = 0$$

or
$$\begin{vmatrix} \lambda D_1 & G \\ \lambda F & \lambda D_2 \end{vmatrix} = 0.$$

From the last equation, if D_1 is of order p

$$\lambda^{p/2} \begin{vmatrix} \sqrt{\lambda} D_1 & G \\ \sqrt{\lambda} F & \lambda D_2 \end{vmatrix} = 0,$$

and if D_2 is of order q

$$\lambda^{\frac{p+q}{2}} \begin{vmatrix} \sqrt{\lambda} D_1 & G \\ F & \sqrt{\lambda} D_2 \end{vmatrix} = 0, \qquad \text{where} \qquad p + q = n.$$

Therefore, either $\lambda = 0$ or $\lambda = \mu^2$. Of course, not all $\lambda = 0$.
$\therefore s^2(-D^{-1}(L + U)) = s(-(D + L)^{-1}U)$ and *the rate of convergence of successive replacements is twice that of simultaneous replacements for any linear system in property A form.*

Rate Optimization of a Computing Parameter

For the accelerated successive replacements, letting $\lambda(\omega)$ be any eigenvalue of the correction matrix, we have

$$\left| -\left(L + \frac{1}{\omega} D\right)^{-1}\left(U + \left(1 - \frac{1}{\omega}\right)D\right) - \lambda(\omega)I \right| = 0$$

or
$$|\omega U + (\omega - 1)D + \lambda(\omega)(\omega L + D)| = 0$$

or
$$\begin{vmatrix} (\lambda(\omega) + (\omega - 1))D_1 & \omega G \\ \omega \lambda(\omega)F & (\lambda(\omega) + (\omega - 1))D_2 \end{vmatrix} = 0$$

or
$$\begin{vmatrix} \dfrac{1}{\omega}(\lambda(\omega) + (\omega - 1))D_1 & G \\ \lambda(\omega)F & \dfrac{1}{\omega}(\lambda(\omega) + (\omega - 1))D_2 \end{vmatrix} = 0$$

or
$$\begin{vmatrix} \dfrac{\lambda(\omega) + (\omega - 1)}{\omega\sqrt{\lambda(\omega)}}D_1 & G \\ F & \dfrac{\lambda(\omega) + (\omega - 1)}{\omega\sqrt{\lambda(\omega)}}D_2 \end{vmatrix} = 0.$$

From above

$$\frac{\lambda(\omega) + (\omega - 1)}{\omega \sqrt{\lambda(\omega)}} = \mu,$$

unless $\lambda(\omega) = 0$. Noting that the μ's do not depend on ω and are real, in fact, if the coefficient matrix A is symmetric, it is seen that we now have an expression for $\lambda(\omega)$ in terms of ω, so that it is possible to examine for that ω that makes $|\lambda(\omega)|$ the smallest. We will not pursue the matter further here. The Young [1] thesis and several books give the result. An optimum ω is found, not unexpectedly, to be between one and two. For the five-point finite-difference analogue of the Dirichlet problem for the Laplace equation, the optimum ω is shown to be between that for the smallest enclosing rectangle and that for the largest enclosed rectangle, while the optimum ω for any rectangle can be directly computed. The student may wish to read about these detailed matters; we are here content to have shown in a concise manner a use of the spectral norm theory in acceleration techniques. Factors of six hundred have sometimes been saved in machine time by use of the accelerated simultaneous displacements, and the method is heartily recommended where applicable.

Bounds for Spectral Norms of Matrices

An obvious possible use of the spectral norm condition for convergence of linear iterative methods for linear systems is to find an upper bound for the modulus of any eigenvalue of the correction matrix, and to find those conditions on the matrix such that this upper bound is less than one. Where λ^A is any eigenvalue of a matrix A, we have

$$|\lambda^A|_{\max} \leq n \max_{i,k=1,\cdots,n} |a_{ik}| \qquad \text{(Hirsch, [3], 1902)}$$

$$|\lambda^A|_{\max} \leq \max_{i=1,\cdots,n} \sum_{k=1}^{n} |a_{ik}| \qquad \text{(Wittmeyer, [4], 1936)}$$

This method of analysis of convergence (i.e., using bounds for spectral norms of the correction matrix) can be quite involved because of the difficulty in getting conditions on the elements of the correction matrix down to usable conditions on elements of the coefficient matrix and because of the difficulty of getting 'practical' conditions from such bounds. In spite of these difficulties, the method has been quite successfully used in the literature (see, e.g., L. Cesari, 1935, 1937), so we present a proof of the Wittmeyer bound, noting that the Hirsch bound is a trivial consequence thereof. As an example of the use of the Wittmeyer bound for convergence analysis, where the resulting conditions are of no practical import, we recommend the following exercise.

EXERCISE

Prove the diagonal domination condition for convergence of the simultaneous replacements method, using the spectral norm condition on the correction matrix and the Wittmeyer bound.

It may be more practical in actual applications to apply the Wittmeyer bound to some matrix similar to the correction matrix, rather than to the correction matrix itself, in order to obtain more practical conditions for convergence. The problem then becomes to find a nonsingular matrix P such that the Wittmeyer bound applied to PAP^{-1} gives a practical condition for convergence.

Lemma

$$||x| - |y|| \leq |x - y|.$$

Proof

$$|x| = |x - y + y| \leq |x - y| + |y| \Rightarrow |x| - |y| \leq |x - y|$$

$$|y| = |y - x + x| \leq |y - x| + |x| \Rightarrow |y| - |x| \leq |x - y|. \quad \blacksquare$$

Theorem

If A is a complex matrix, then

$$\min_{i=1,\cdots,n} |\lambda_i^A| \geq \min_{(i=1,2,\cdots,n)} \left(|a_{ii}| - \sum_{\substack{k=1 \\ k \neq i}}^{n} |a_{ik}| \right),$$

and

$$\max_{i-1,\cdots,n} |\lambda_i^A| \leq \max_{i=1,\cdots,n} \sum_{k=1}^{n} |a_{ik}|.$$

Proof

Let λ be any eigenvalue of A. Then the linear system $(\lambda I - A)x = 0$; i.e.,

$$(\lambda - a_{ii})x_i - \sum_{\substack{k=1 \\ k \neq i}}^{n} a_{ik}x_k = 0, \quad i = 1,2,\cdots,n,$$

has nontrivial solutions. Let i be

$$\ni |x_i| = \max_{j=1,\cdots,n} |x_j|.$$

Then

$$|\lambda - a_{ii}|\,|x_i| = \left| \sum_{\substack{k=1 \\ k \neq i}}^{n} a_{ik}x_k \right| \leq \sum_{\substack{k=1 \\ k \neq i}}^{n} |a_{ik}|\,|x_k| \leq |x_i| \sum_{\substack{k=1 \\ k \neq i}}^{n} |a_{ik}|.$$

Hence

$$|\lambda - a_{ii}| \leq \sum_{\substack{k=1 \\ k \neq i}}^{n} |a_{ik}|.$$

From the lemma

$$|a_{ii}| - |\lambda| \leq |\lambda - a_{ii}| \leq \sum_{\substack{k=1 \\ k \neq i}}^{n} |a_{ik}|$$

and

$$|\lambda| \geq |a_{ii}| - \sum_{\substack{k=1 \\ k \neq i}}^{n} |a_{ik}| \geq \min_{i=1,\cdots,n} \left(|a_{ii}| - \sum_{\substack{k=1 \\ k \neq i}}^{n} |a_{ik}| \right),$$

which is the first contention.
Also from the lemma

$$|\lambda| - |a_{ii}| \leq |\lambda - a_{ii}| \leq \sum_{\substack{k=1 \\ k \neq i}}^{n} |a_{ik}|,$$

and we have

$$|\lambda| \leq |a_{ii}| + \sum_{\substack{k=1 \\ k \neq i}}^{n} |a_{ik}| = \sum_{k=1}^{n} |a_{ik}| \leq \max_{i=1,\cdots,n} \sum_{k=1}^{n} |a_{ik}|.$$

Convergence of Successive Replacements for Symmetric Positive Definite Systems

The transpose of a matrix $A = (a_{ij})$ is the matrix (a_{ji}) and is denoted A^T. A matrix A is said to be positive definite if for any nonzero vector x (column matrix), $x^T A x = (x, Ax) > 0$; we may write for 'A positive definite,' simply $A > 0$

EXERCISE

Show that for a real symmetric matrix A,

$$((z \in C^1) \wedge (z \neq 0) \Rightarrow (\bar{z}^T A z > 0)) \Leftrightarrow ((x \in R^1) \wedge (x \neq 0) \Rightarrow x^T A x > 0).$$

EXERCISE

The second order, n-dimensional (linear) partial differential equation $Lu = a^{ij}(x)u_{x_ix_j} + b^i(x)u_{x_i} + c(x)u = h(x)$, where $x \in R \subset E^n$, is said to be of elliptic type in R if $a^{ij}(x)\lambda_i\lambda_j \geq 0$ for all real λ_i, $\lambda_j \wedge \forall x \in R$ and $a^{ij}(x)\lambda_i\lambda_j = 0 \Rightarrow \lambda_i = 0 \forall i = 1,\cdots,n \wedge \forall x \in R$. Prove that the natural extension to E^n of the five-point finite-difference analogue (given in Chapter 3 for $n = 2$) for any second-order, n-dimensional (linear) partial differential equation $Lu = h(x)$ that is elliptic in R and for which $b_i(x) = 0$ gives on any mesh over R a linear system of equations whose coefficient matrix is positive definite. (Note that the Laplace equation is of elliptic type.)

It will be shown later that all least squares discretizations of linear boundary value problems, for which there exist unique solutions, yield linear systems with positive definite coefficient matrix if the approximating family is linearly independent. Thus, although it may not be quite true that 'almost all' large linear systems one needs to solve in practical situations are positive definite, it still is usually true that one can choose an approximation method for linear boundary value problems to get positive-definite systems to be solved.

We demonstrate, using the spectral norm theory, that the method of successive replacements converges for linear systems with positive definite coefficient matrix. An exercise will show that the accelerated form then converges for $0 < \omega < 2$, and that one can expect that, for some $\omega \ni 1 < \omega < 2$, a greatly increased rate is obtained. Recalling that the correction matrix for successive replacements is $-(L + D)^{-1}U$, our theorem is as follows.

Theorem

$$(A = (a_{ij})) \wedge (a_{ij} \in R^1 \wedge a_{ij} = a_{ji} \forall i,j = 1,\cdots,n)$$

$$\wedge (A > 0) \Rightarrow s(-(L + D)^{-1}U) < 1.$$

Remarks: According to the discussion above, accelerated successive replacements is an 'almost uniformly good' method to have available for solution of linear systems. In fact, most modern computing laboratories consider a routine for Gaussian elimination and one for accelerated successive replacements a basic pair of routines for linear problems. The proof of our theorem is essentially that given by Edgar Reich [5] in 1949. The theorem given there provides a necessary and sufficient condition for convergence.

Proof

$\forall$ eigenvalue $\lambda \in C^1$ of $(L + D)^{-1}U$, $\exists z \neq 0 \ni$

(4.14) $(L + D)^{-1}Uz = \lambda z.$ $\therefore Uz = \lambda(L + D)z$

(4.15) $\wedge Az = (L + D + U)z = (L + D)z + Uz = (1 + \lambda)(L + D)z.$

$\therefore (A\bar{z} = (1 + \lambda)(L + D)\bar{z}) \wedge (\bar{z}^T A = (1 + \lambda)\bar{z}^T(U + D)).$

$\therefore \bar{z}^T Az = (1 + \lambda)\bar{z}^T Uz + (1 + \lambda)\bar{z}^T Dz$

(4.16) $(4.14) = (1 + \lambda)\lambda\bar{z}^T(L + D)z + (1 + \lambda)\bar{z}^T Dz.$

$(4.15) \Rightarrow (\bar{z}^T Az = (1 + \lambda)\bar{z}^T(L + D)z)$

$$\Rightarrow \frac{(1 + \lambda)\lambda}{1 + \lambda} \bar{z}^T Az = (1 + \lambda)\lambda\bar{z}^T(L + D)z.$$

$\therefore (4.16) \Rightarrow \bar{z}^T Az = \dfrac{(1 + \lambda)\lambda}{1 + \lambda} \bar{z}^T Az + (1 + \lambda)\bar{z}^T Dz$

$$\Rightarrow \left[\left(1 - \frac{(1 + \lambda)\lambda}{1 + \lambda}\right)\bar{z}^T Az\right] = (1 + \lambda)\bar{z}^T Dz$$

(4.17) $\Rightarrow (1 - |\lambda|^2)\bar{z}^T Az = |1 + \lambda|^2\bar{z}^T Dz.$

By hypothesis, A is positive-definite. From this, one easily sees that $a_{ii} > 0 \; \forall \; i = 1, \cdots, n$, by letting x be a vector with all zero components except one, at position i, which is the unit of the real numbers, and by noting then that $a_{ii} = x^T Ax > 0$. Thus,

$$(\bar{z}^T Az > 0) \wedge (\bar{z}^T Dz > 0) \; \forall \; z \neq 0.$$

Then from (4.17)

$$1 - |\lambda|^2 \geq 0,$$

and the equality holds only if $|1 + \lambda| = 0$; i.e., if $1 + \lambda = 0$. However, in this case, from (4.15)

$$\bar{z}^T Az = 0,$$

which contradicts the hypothesis that A is positive-definite. Thus

$$1 - |\lambda|^2 > 0 \qquad \text{or} \qquad |\lambda| < 1. \quad \blacksquare$$

One may wonder, for the sake of completeness, if a similar theorem can be proved for simultaneous replacements. A counterexample is given:

Let $A = \begin{pmatrix} 3 & 2 & 1 \\ 2 & 3 & 2 \\ 1 & 2 & 3 \end{pmatrix}$, $x = \begin{pmatrix} x_1 \\ x_2 \\ x_3 \end{pmatrix}$, $b = \begin{pmatrix} 6 \\ 7 \\ 6 \end{pmatrix}$. $x = \begin{pmatrix} 1 \\ 1 \\ 1 \end{pmatrix}$ is the (unique)

solution. A is positive-definite, since $\forall z \in R^n$

$$z^T A z = (z_1 \quad z_2 \quad z_3) \begin{pmatrix} 3 & 2 & 1 \\ 2 & 3 & 2 \\ 1 & 2 & 3 \end{pmatrix} \begin{pmatrix} z_1 \\ z_2 \\ z_3 \end{pmatrix}$$

$$= 3z_1{}^2 + 3z_2{}^2 + 3z_3{}^2 + 4z_1 z_2 + 4z_2 z_3 + 2z_1 z_3$$

$$\geq 2z_1{}^2 + 3z_2{}^2 + 2z_3{}^2 + 4z_1 z_2 + 4z_2 z_3 + 2z_1 z_3$$

$$= (z_1 + z_2 + z_3)^2 + (z_1 + z_2)^2 + (z_2 + z_3)^2.$$

Since $|-D^{-1}(L+U) - \lambda I| = 0 \Rightarrow |D^{-1}(L+U) + \lambda I| = \begin{vmatrix} \lambda & \frac{2}{3} & \frac{1}{3} \\ \frac{2}{3} & \lambda & \frac{2}{3} \\ \frac{1}{2} & \frac{2}{3} & \lambda \end{vmatrix} = 0,$

we have

$$0.7 < \lambda_1 < 0.8$$
$$0.3 < \lambda_2 < 0.4$$
$$-1.2 < \lambda_3 < -1.1,$$

as can be verified by noting the change of sign in the determinant at end points of these intervals. Thus

$$s(-D^{-1}(L+U)) > 1.$$

EXERCISE

Adapt the Reich proof for the case of accelerated successive replacements with $0 < \omega < 2$.

Any serious computor will be able to devise an effective empirical procedure for determining an efficient, if not optimal, value of $\omega \ni 1 < \omega < 2$. One usually knows as a guide that the optimal ω will be closer to one for smaller systems and closer to two for larger ones. In the case of approximations of solutions of boundary value problems, experiments on ω can be carried out first for low-order approximations (either large mesh sizes or small approximating families), so that small linear systems and short computation times are involved in finding a good value of ω. This kind of procedure will become essential, anyway, when we move to considerations of nonlinear problems. Of course, if property A is available, literature exists in which it is explained how to find an upper and lower bound for the optimal value of ω. To fill the indicated theoretical gap, we suggest the following research exercise.

RESEARCH EXERCISE

For the general case, A positive definite, find a practical (a priori)[3] way to determine good upper and lower bounds of the acceleration parameter ω for successive replacements used on a system $Ax = b$.

Linear Iterative Methods for Linear Systems that Are Unconditionally Convergent

The unrelenting search by mathematicians, encouraged by the 'angry' demands of computing laboratories and engineering colleagues, for iterative methods that converge, regardless of what the linear system is like—that is, for unconditional convergence theorems— finds an unexpected realization in the case of linear iterative methods for linear systems. If A is nonsingular, then $A^T A$ is positive definite, because

$$x^T(A^T A)x = (Ax)^T(Ax) = \sum_{i=1}^{n}(Ax)_i^2 > 0 \ \forall \ x \neq 0,$$

and either successive replacements, or its accelerated form, converges for the system

$$A^T Ax = A^T b,$$

to the solution of $Ax = b$, if only $|A| \neq 0$. While this gives a practical procedure for systems of moderate size, it may not be practical where either the system size is excessively large or, as is more often the case, where one does not choose to write down the entire system.

In the early 1930s, Cimmino, an Italian mathematician, suggested the following very simple iterative scheme that has been virtually forgotten since. Given x^0 any element of E^n, let x^k be an element of the sequence $\{x^k\}$ to be generated. Considering each equation of the linear system to be a hyperplane in E^n, find the mirror image of x^k with respect to each hyperplane—*one at a time, and in any order, or simultaneously*—and

---

[3] Before carrying out the computation.

simply average all mirror images of x^k together with x^k to get x^{k+1}. A very simple geometric argument shows that this method converges to the solution of the linear system if a unique solution exists, regardless of the nature of the system; in fact, this method will converge to the centroid of the volume enclosed by the hyperplanes if no solution exists (m equations in n unknowns, $m > n$), or to one of the solutions in a linear manifold of solutions if more than one exists! If this all seems too good to be true it must be said that, usually for large systems, the method is intolerably slow and, anyway, quite impractical. Note, however, that it supplies a 'free steering' theorem in Ostrowski's sense in that convergence is obtained regardless of the ordering of the equations, regardless of which variable is corrected using which equation, or even whether such an ordering is maintained from one iteration to the next. Some situations may arise where other criteria of practicality will have to be abandoned for these advantages.

EXERCISE

Using a simple geometrical argument, prove convergence of the Cimmino mirror-images averaging method.

In spite of a geometric statement of the method, and the obvious advantage of a geometric argument for convergence, it is evident that x^{k+1} is given as a linear function of x^k and, thus, that the method should come under our general theory of convergence of linear iterative methods for linear systems. We can test the power of this theory by seeing if this method can be analyzed in terms of the spectral norm theory. In component form, the iteration can be written

$$(4.18) \qquad x_j^{k} = x_j^{k-1} - \frac{2}{n+1} \sum_{i=1}^{n} \frac{\sum_{p=1}^{n} a_{ij}a_{ip}x_p^{k-1} - b_i}{\sum_{p=1}^{n} a_{ip}^2}.$$

EXERCISE (OPTIONAL)

Show that (4.18) is one expression for the geometrical description of Cimmino.

RESEARCH EXERCISE

(1) Try to accelerate the mirror-images averaging method.
(2) Find an iterative method for nonlinear systems that reduces to mirror-images averaging when the system to be solved is linear.

Before applying the spectral norm theory, we give a development of (4.18) independently of geometrical descriptions. Both developments are due to L. Cesari.

Given $Ax = b$, $|A| \neq 0$, let

$$\|a_i\|^2 = \sum_{j=1}^{n} a_{ij}^2.$$

Let $G = (g_{ij})$, where $g_{ii} = 1/\|a_i\| \wedge g_{ij} = 0 \ \forall \ i \neq j$. Then

(4.19) $Ax = b \Rightarrow A^T G^T G A x = A^T G^2 A x = A^T G^2 b$

or $0 = -\dfrac{2}{n+1} A^T G^2 A x + \dfrac{2}{n+1} A^T G^2 b$

or

(4.20) $x = \left(I - \dfrac{2}{n+1} A^T G^2 A\right) x + \dfrac{2}{n+1} A^T G^2 b.$

Since the fixed point of (4.20) is the solution of (4.19), consider the iteration

(4.21) $x^k = \left(I - \dfrac{2}{n+1} A^T G^2 A\right) x^{k-1} + \dfrac{2}{n+2} A^T G^2 b,$

which will converge if $s(I - \frac{2}{n+1} A^T G^2 A) < 1$. Note that $A^T G^2 A = A^T G^T G A = (GA)^T GA$ is positive definite, since GA is nonsingular. Then λ_i an eigenvalue of $A^T G^2 A$ implies $\lambda_i > 0$ (real). Let v_i be any eigenvalue of $I - [2/(n+1)]A^T G^2 A$. Then

$$\left| v_i I - \left(I - \dfrac{2}{n+1} A^T G^2 A\right)\right| = 0$$

or $$\left| (v_i - 1)I + \dfrac{2}{n+1} A^T G^2 A \right| = 0$$

or $$\left| \dfrac{n+1}{2}(1 - v_i)I - A^T G^2 A \right| = 0$$

$\Rightarrow$ $\dfrac{n+1}{2}(1 - v_i) = \lambda_i$ or $v_i = 1 - \dfrac{2\lambda_i}{n+1}.$

$$\max_i |v_i| < 1 \Leftrightarrow -1 < 1 - \frac{2\lambda_i}{n+1} < 1 \Leftrightarrow 0 < \lambda_i < n+1. \quad \therefore \ \lambda_i < n+1 \Rightarrow$$

the iteration converges. Note that

$$\left(\sum_{i=1}^{n} \lambda_i = Tr(A^T G^2 A) \right) \wedge (\lambda_i > 0).$$

$\therefore \ \max \lambda_i < Tr(A^T G^2 A) = Tr(G^2 A^T A).$ Now $(G^2 A^T A)_{ij} =$

$$\sum_{k=1}^{n} \frac{a_{ki} a_{kj}}{\|a_k\|^2}. \quad \therefore \ Tr(A^T G^2 A) = \sum_{i=1}^{n} (A^T G^2 A)_{ii} = \sum_{i=1}^{n} \sum_{k=1}^{n} \frac{a_{ki}^2}{\|a_k\|^2}$$

$$= \sum_{k=1}^{n} \frac{1}{\|a_k\|^2} \sum_{i=1}^{n} a_{ki}^2 = \sum_{i=1}^{n} \frac{\|a_k\|^2}{\|a_k\|^2} = n.$$

$\therefore \ \max \lambda_i < Tr(A^T G^2 A) = n < n+1$ and (4.21) converges.

Another linear iterative method that converges unconditionally is the method of steepest descent or one of its many variations. We consider an iteration to approximate the root of $Ax = b$, $|A| \neq 0$, $A > 0$.

Let $\qquad\qquad Q(x) = Q(x_1, \cdots, x_n) = x^T(Ax - b).$

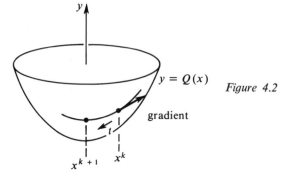

Figure 4.2

The n-dimensional surface $y = Q(x)$, being quadratic in $x_1, \cdots, x_n$, has one minimum only, and that minimum is the root. Given x^0, let x^k be any member of the iterative sequence. To form x^{k+1}, write the equation of the projection of the gradient of the surface $y = Q(x)$ at x^k with parameter t positive in the negative direction of the gradient $x_i = x_i^k - (\partial Q/\partial x_i)(x^k) \cdot t \ \forall \ i = 1, \cdots, n$. Then its 'shadow' on the surface $Q(x(t))$ $= Q(x_1^k - (\partial Q/\partial x_1)(x^k) \cdot t, \cdots, x_n^k - (\partial Q/\partial x_n)(x^k) \cdot t)$ is a function of t for which the $t = t^k$ at minimum is easily computed. Then $x^{k+1} = x^k - t^k$ grad $Q(x^k)$. Since the gradient vector has the direction of steepest ascent, the negative direction on the gradient, as taken, gives us a steepest descent from each point x^k.

EXERCISE

Find the formulas to be used in computation for the steepest descent method. Put them in matrix form and prove convergence, using the spectral norm condition.

The surface

$$Q = (Ax - b)^T(Ax - b)$$

is more difficult to utilize than the one given above, since it yields a nonlinear iterative method. However, the surface must be utilized for nonlinear systems. That is, in general, if

$$f_i(x_1, \cdots, x_n) = 0,$$

we consider the surface

$$Q = \sum_{i=1}^{n} f_i^2$$

and try to minimize it. We may here obtain only a relative minimum that is unrelated to a root. The march down the gradient should probably be made a fixed distance (rather than to the minimum), testing after each iteration if the value of Q has been reduced, and backing up to march halfway if it has not. Of course, the functions f_i should have derivatives.

Another geometric view of the steepest descent or gradient method is revealing. Functions $Q(x) = C$, in the linear case, represent 'concentric'

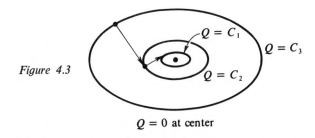

Figure 4.3

$Q = 0$ at center

ellipsoidal surfaces. In iterating, we move in discrete steps normal to the local contour and 'spiral' into the solution surface (point) $Q = 0$. Another method, that of conjugate gradients, involves taking advantage of the fact that the contours of Q are ellipsoidal surfaces, so that we move directly at the root on the so-called conjugate gradients, instead of on normals. We recommend study of the conjugate gradient method elsewhere, since it will not be further discussed here. It is, theoretically, an n-step method (for systems of order n), and it would appear to belong in a class of direct methods, except where errors due to subtractions require iteration.

Remarks: Any linear iterative method for linear systems

$$x^{k+1} = -B^{-1}Cx^k + B^{-1}b$$

can be thought of as Picard iteration of a linear mapping

$$-B^{-1}Cx + B^{-1}b$$

that has as a fixed point the root of the linear system

$$(B + C)x = Ax = b$$

to be solved. Without mentioning eigenvalues, we obviously could get conditions sufficient for convergence by simply requiring that the contraction condition be satisfied on the mapping $-B^{-1}Cx + B^{-1}b$; i.e., that for some norm on E^n, $\exists\, K < 1 \ni \forall\, x, y \in E^n$,

$$\|(-B^{-1}C)(x - y)\| = \|(-B^{-1}C)x - (-B^{-1}C)y\| \le K\|x - y\|$$

or $$\forall\, z \in E^n$$

$$\|(-B^{-1}C)z\| \le K\|z\|.$$

We learn in functional analysis to call the infimum of all K that satisfy such a relation the norm of the matrix $-B^{-1}C$ (and quickly show that

$$\|-B^{-1}C\| = \inf_{\|x\| < 1} \|-B^{-1}Cx\|).$$

Thus the contraction condition, which is sufficient for convergence, is simply

$$\|-B^{-1}C\| < 1$$

in any norm. Obviously, $s(-B^{-1}C)$ is a norm if $-B^{-1}C$ has a diagonal form; otherwise, the techniques of our proofs of the spectral norm condition for convergence show that *the spectral norm behaves as though it were a norm with respect to convergence questions.* It is not a norm on the set of linear transformations on a finite-dimensional vector space, as $n = 2$ examples easily show. It is, rather, a generalization of a norm, and it is sometimes called the 'spectral radius,' rather than spectral norm, to avoid confusion. The theoretical value in linear theory clearly demonstrated above for the spectral norm condition (as contrasted with norm conditions) is probably due to the fact that $s(-B^{-1}C) < 1$ is both a necessary and sufficient condition for convergence.

As as example of the use of a matrix norm condition, if

(4.22)
$$\max_i \sum_{j=1}^{n} |(-B^{-1}C)_{ij}| = K < 1,$$

then

$$\max_i \sum_{j=1}^{n} |(-B^{-1}C)_{ij}z_j| \le K \max_j |z_j|$$

or

$$\|(-B^{-1}C)\|_T < 1,$$

where $\| \ \|_T$ is the maximum or Tschebychev norm. If $B = D \wedge C = (L + U)$, (4.22) again gives us the diagonal domination condition. Other norms give other conditions on the coefficient matrix, although any of these conditions, according to a convergence theorem quoted in our review of linear algebra, imply convergence in all norms. This is not surprising in view of the fact that computation procedures on finite-dimensional spaces do not utilize a norm or imply the utilization of one. Also, any of these conditions is implied by the condition that $s(-B^{-1}C) < 1$.

Use of the theory of contractive maps would, of course, allow computation of error bounds in the norm to be utilized. Also, error bounds could be computed by using a remainder expression for the power series in the Cesari proof of the spectral norm condition, and probably could be obtained in many other ways. We know of no comparative study of error bounds for linear iterative methods, and we rely on having developed the maturity of the student to the point where he can obtain such formulas for himself.

We tend to take here the attitude that large *linear* systems will usually appear as discretizations of boundary value problems, and to emphasize ways of obtaining error bounds to solutions of boundary value problems from good approximations of discretizations, rather than ways of obtaining error bounds to solutions of discretizations.

Finally, it should be noted that the most important use of the spectral norm condition or, for that matter, of the theory of contractive maps, may well be judged to be not in the analysis of convergence of iterative methods as such, but in the analysis of stability of marching schema, to which it is adapted in Chapters 7, 8, 9, and 11.

4. METHODS POSSIBLY SUITABLE FOR ANALOGUE EQUIPMENT

Where $(A \subset R^1) \wedge (x: A \to E^n) \wedge (f: A \times E^n \to E^n)$, the system of differential equations

$$\frac{dx}{dt} = f(t,x)$$

is said to be asymptotically stable on $N \subset E^n$ if $\forall\ x^0 \in N \ni$ a unique solution $x: [0,\infty] \to E^n \ni x(0) = x^0$ and $\lim_{t \to \infty} x(t)$ exists, and $\forall$ two solutions $x = x(t),\ y = y(t) \ni x(0),\ y(0) \in N$,

$$\lim_{t \to \infty} (x(t) - y(t)) = 0.$$

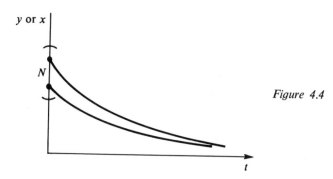

Figure 4.4

Convergence of iterative methods for algebraic systems and asymptotic stability of systems of differential equations are similar enough to be almost, though not quite, identified. The latter provide a very interesting possibility for approximating solutions to boundary value problems of partial differential equations *with error bound*, by integrating initial value problems for systems of ordinary differential equations on analogue computers. The asymptotic values of the solutions correspond, of course, to limits of iterative sequences. Naturally, one must insure that he integrates systems that are asymptotically stable, just as he must insure convergence of an iterative method. Machine errors, almost impossible to assess for analogue equipment, are of no consequence if problems are undertaken in which methods on boundary value problems, like that of least squares, are used where, whatever the source of computational answers, an error bound to the solution of the boundary value problem can be computed. Then, of course, if this bound is adequate, the amount or nature of computational losses will not concern us. We take the attitude here that the basic operation of an analogue computer is integration of an initial value problem for an ordinary differential equation (just as addition is for a digital computer) and that, up to a point limited by availability of multipliers and function generators, any method utilizing integration of initial value problems for systems of ODE's is directly suited to analogue equipment.[4] Our least squares discretization yields systems of moderate size to be solved. As far as we know, no other method suggested for analogue equipment gives a legitimate check point for the error.

Let
$$x^k = -B^{-1}Cx^{k-1} + B^{-1}b$$

be a linear iterative method for approximating solution of the linear system

$$(B + C)x = Ax = b, \quad |A| \neq 0.$$

We consider asymptotic stability of the system

$$(4.23) \quad \left(\frac{x^k - x^{k-1}}{1} \cong\right) \frac{dx}{dt} = -(I + B^{-1}C)x + B^{-1}b = Mx + B^{-1}b.$$

---

[4] Actually the analogue equipment, by means of a feedback mechanism, performs a 'continuous iteration' of the equivalent (Volterra type) integral equation for an initial value problem of ordinary differential equations. Its basic operation is formation of a (definite) integral. In modern electronic analogue computing machines, amplifiers are provided in various circuits with resistors and capacitors to give output voltages proportional to sums, quotients, or indefinite integrals of input voltages, where the variable of integration is identified with time. Thus the basic unit may be said to be the amplifier.

If the system is asymptotically stable, it can be shown that $\lim_{t \to \infty} dx/dt$ exists and must, therefore, vanish. From (4.23),

$$0 = -(I + B^{-1}C) \lim_{t \to \infty} x(t) + B^{-1}b$$

or

$$A(\lim_{t \to \infty} x(t)) = (B + C)(\lim_{t \to \infty} x(t)) = b,$$

so that the asymptotic value of the vector x is the solution of our system. Let $x(t)$ and $y(t)$ be any solutions of (4.23), let $(x(0) = x^0) \wedge (y(0) = y^0)$, and let $z = x - y$. Then

(4.24) $\left(\dfrac{dz}{dt} = Mz\right) \wedge (z(0) = x^0 - y^0 = z^0).$

Asymptotic stability on E^n demands that $\forall z^0 \in E^n$, $\lim_{t \to \infty} z(t) = 0$.

It can be shown that the two series

$$\sum_{i=0}^{\infty} \frac{M^i t^i}{i!}$$

and

$$\sum_{i=1}^{\infty} \frac{M^i t^{i-1}}{(i-1)!}$$

converge in matrix norm (as discussed above) $\forall t \in R^1$, and that

$$\lim_{h \to 0} \left\| \frac{1}{h} \left(\sum_{i=0}^{\infty} \frac{M^i(t+h)^i}{i!} - \sum_{i=0}^{\infty} \frac{M^i t^i}{i!} \right) - \sum_{i=1}^{\infty} \frac{M^i t^{i-1}}{(i-1)!} \right\| = 0.$$

We therefore define

$$e^M = \sum_{i=0}^{\infty} \frac{M^i}{i!} = I + M + \frac{M^2}{2} + \cdots + \frac{M^n}{n!} + \cdots,$$

and write

$$\frac{d}{dt} e^{Mt} = Me^{Mt}.$$

In these terms, the solution of (4.24) is

$$z = e^{MT} \cdot z^0.$$

Where P is any nonsingular matrix, we transform coordinates (basis) for representation of z by writing

$$Z = Pz = Pe^{Mt}z^0 = Pe^{Mt}(P^{-1}P)z^0 = (Pe^{Mt}P^{-1})Pz^0$$

or

$$Z = e^{(PMP^{-1})t}Z^0.$$

EXERCISE

Prove that $Pe^{Mt}P^{-1} = e^{(PMP^{-1})t}$.

We choose $P \ni PMP^{-1} = \overline{\Lambda} + \psi$ is in Jordan normal form (in the notation of our previous section). Then

$$Z = e^{(\overline{\Lambda} + \psi)t}Z^0,$$

and (4.23) will be asymptotically stable if

$$0 = \lim_{t \to \infty} e^{(\overline{\Lambda} + \psi)t} = I + (\overline{\Lambda} + \psi)t + \frac{(\overline{\Lambda} + \psi)^2}{2}t^2$$

$$+ \frac{(\overline{\Lambda} + \psi)^3}{3!}t^3 + \frac{(\overline{\Lambda} + \psi)^4}{4!}t^4 + \cdots$$

$$= I + (\overline{\Lambda} + \psi)t + \tfrac{1}{2}(\overline{\Lambda}^2 + 2\overline{\Lambda}\psi + \psi^2)t^2$$

$$+ \tfrac{1}{3}!(\overline{\Lambda}^3 + 3\overline{\Lambda}^2\psi + 3\overline{\Lambda}\psi^2 + \psi^3)t^3$$

$$+ \tfrac{1}{4}!(\overline{\Lambda}^4 + 4\overline{\Lambda}^3\psi + 6\overline{\Lambda}^2\psi^2 + 4\overline{\Lambda}\psi^3 + \psi^4)t^4 + \cdots$$

$$= \left(I + \overline{\Lambda}t + \frac{\overline{\Lambda}^2t^2}{2!} + \frac{\overline{\Lambda}^3t^3}{3!} + \cdots\right)$$

$$+ \psi t\left(I + \overline{\Lambda}t + \frac{\overline{\Lambda}^2t^2}{2!} + \frac{\overline{\Lambda}^3t^3}{3!} + \cdots\right)$$

$$+ \frac{\psi^2t^2}{2}\left(I + \overline{\Lambda}t + \frac{\overline{\Lambda}^2t^2}{2} + \cdots\right) + \cdots$$

$$= e^{\overline{\Lambda}t}\left(I + \psi t + \frac{(\psi t)^2}{2!} + \cdots + \frac{(\psi t)^{n-1}}{(n-1)!}\right) = e^{\overline{\Lambda}t}P_{n-1}(\psi t),$$

since $\psi^n = 0$. Then (4.23) will be asymptotically stable if $\forall v_i$, an eigenvalue of $M = -(I + B^{-1}C)$, $\text{Re } v_i < 0$, $\forall i = 1, \cdots, n$. This replaces the spectral norm condition. Note that if λ_i is any eigenvalue of $-B^{-1}C$, since

$$|-(I + B^{-1}C) - vI| = 0 \Rightarrow |-B^{-1}C - (v + 1)I| = 0,$$

we have

$$\lambda_i = 1 + v_i.$$

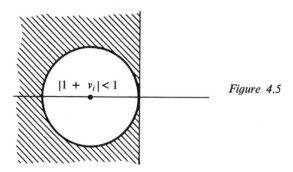

$$|1 + v_i| < 1$$

Figure 4.5

Now $|1 + v_i| < 1 \Rightarrow \operatorname{Re} v_i < 0$, although $\operatorname{Re} v_i < 0 \not\Rightarrow |1 + v_i| < 1$. Therefore, although some analogue versions of linear iterative methods for linear systems may work where the iterative method does not converge, an analogue version (4.23) of a convergent linear iterative method for linear systems is always asymptotically stable. In particular, we have proved the following theorem.

Theorem

The analogue version of accelerated successive replacements is asymptotically stable for any linear system with positive definite coefficient matrix.

Since we are not interested in operating analogue equipment unchecked, we insist on getting error bounds. Thus our least squares procedure is indicated, and then the only cases of interest are where the coefficient matrix is positive-definite.

The differential system

$$(4.25) \qquad \frac{dx}{dt} = -(I + B^{-1}C)x + B^{-1}b,$$

for which we seek asymptotic solutions, may be written

$$(4.26) \qquad B\frac{dx}{dt} = -Ax + b,$$

but neither form is, in general, directly suitable for computations. In each case of B, we must, as with the iterative methods, put the equations in a suitable computational form. In the case of successive replacements,

$$(L + D)\frac{dx}{dt} = -Ax + b$$

or
$$D\frac{dx}{dt} = -L\frac{dx}{dt} - Ax + b$$

or
$$a_{ii}\frac{dx_i}{dt} = -\sum_{j=1}^{i-1} a_{ij}\frac{dx_j}{dt} - \sum_{j=1}^{n} a_{ij}x_j + b_i$$

or
$$\frac{dx_i}{dt} = \frac{1}{a_{ii}}\left\{b_i - \sum_{j=1}^{n} a_{ij}x_j - \sum_{j=1}^{i-1} a_{ij}\frac{dx_j}{dt}\right\} \qquad (\forall\, i = 1,\cdots,n)$$

or
$$\frac{dx_1}{dt} = \frac{1}{a_{11}}\left\{b_1 - \sum_{j=1}^{n} a_{1j}x_j\right\}$$

$$\frac{dx_2}{dt} = \frac{1}{a_{22}}\left\{b_2 - \sum_{j=1}^{n} a_{2j}x_j - a_{21}\frac{dx_1}{dt}\right\}$$

$$\frac{dx_3}{dt} = \frac{1}{a_{33}}\left\{b_3 - \sum_{j=1}^{n} a_{3j}x_j - a_{31}\frac{dx_1}{dt} - a_{32}\frac{dx_2}{dt}\right\},$$

$$\vdots$$

which gives the system to be used in computational form where the ith equation is to be used as a function generator for $(dx_j/dt), j > i$.

In the case of accelerated successive replacements, we have from (4.26), since $B = L + (1/\omega)D$, that the differential system is

$$\frac{dx_i}{dt} = \frac{\omega}{a_{ii}}\left\{b_i - \sum_{j=1}^{n} a_{ij}x_j - \sum_{j=1}^{i-1} a_{ij}\frac{dx_j}{dt}\right\}$$

$\forall\, i = 1,\cdots,n$. If the scaling difficulty we encounter in actually carrying out our analogue calculations (see the end of this section) can be circumvented, then it is conceivable that we could use analogue equipment to determine an optimum acceleration parameter ω. The value so obtained could then be used in a more accurate digital computation, without having to make possibly expensive experiments on the digital

computer. Apparently, a new generation of large-scale equipment will
be built with features that allow for control of essentially analogue
processes from digital computations. Of course, some machines will
provide for ready communication between analogue and digital equipment. If we then wish to approximate the solution of a boundary value
problem using, say, the least squares technique, we could program[5]
the digital machine to form the required linear system (with positive
definite coefficient matrix), which would then be fed to the analogue
equipment where the operator would determine the optimum acceleration parameter ω by turning a dial and watching a display scope to
adjust the slope of the solution vector versus time. This value of ω
could then be read back into the digital computer (along with the
analogue solution to be used as initial values), and the iteration could
be completed efficiently and accurately on the digital computer.

The one-way implication of convergence for linear iterative methods
versus asymptotic stability for corresponding analogues allows also
for the possibility that our analogue of the simultaneous replacements
method for linear systems with a positive definite coefficient matrix is
asymptotically stable. To demonstrate that this is indeed the case,
we must show that the real parts of the eigenvalues of $-(B^{-1}C + I)$ are
all negative where $B = D$ and $C = L + U$; i.e., that the real parts of the
eigenvalues of $-D^{-1}(L + U)$ are less than one. A simple adaptation
of the Reich proof suffices. Earlier (Chapter 4, sec. 3) an example was
given to show that the corresponding iterative method will not always
converge.

Theorem

$(A = (a_{ij})) \wedge (a_{ij} \in R^1 \wedge a_{ij} = a_{ji} \; \forall \; i, j = 1, \cdots, n) \wedge (A > 0) \Rightarrow \forall \; eigen-$
value μ of $-D^{-1}(L + U)$, $\operatorname{Re} \mu < 1$.

Proof

$(L + U)z = -\mu Dz \Rightarrow Az = (L + U)z + Dz = (1 - \mu)Dz \Rightarrow A\bar{z} = (1 - \bar{\mu})D\bar{z}$

$\Rightarrow \bar{z}^T A = (1 - \bar{\mu})\bar{z}^T D \Rightarrow \bar{z}^T Az = (1 - \bar{\mu})\bar{z}^T Dz$. But

$$\bar{z}^T Az = (1 - \mu)\bar{z}^T Dz,$$

so, adding,

$$\bar{z}^T Az = (1 - \operatorname{Re} \mu)\bar{z}^T Dz,$$

---

[5] For a description of how this can be done, see the discussion of advisable procedures
in Chapter 5.

and the comment that then

$$1 - \operatorname{Re} \mu > 0$$

completes the proof. ∎

If one wishes to utilize separate information that μ is real, the first line of the proof suffices.

A test case of the methods was mounted on the EAI TR10, a very small analogue computer. Size limitations forced the use of a very small system, so the (3×3) subsystem of the (5×5) least square system for approximation of torsion of a rectangular beam, which will be developed in Chapter 5, was used. The method works well, showing that both the analogue of successive replacements and that of simultaneous replacements go asymptotically to the same values that are close to the digital solution, while the analogue of simultaneous replacements approaches these values a little more slowly.[6] However, it disappoints us to report that scaling problems would have prevented the use of any larger subsystems, had larger equipment been available. In analogue computers, if either the coefficients or solutions vary widely in magnitude, this problem cannot be adequately handled. Of course, equipment could be designed to overcome this difficulty. However, analogue equipment, in general, suffers in comparison to the digital equipment because it is not so accurate, nor does it provide for a 'floating point,' or range extension feature, as does the digital equipment; and it requires, essentially, a separate arithmetical unit for each arithmetical operation. This means, for example, that four separate multipliers are required to form x^4. Integrals are formed with ease on the analogue computer (as compared to the formation of a quadrature [see Appendix A] on a digital computer), but the fixed decimal-point character of the equipment is a fault that is not easily circumvented.

Our system was

$$1.00x_1 - 0.80x_2 + 0.18x_3 = 0.33$$
$$-.80x_1 + 3.00x_2 - 0.70x_3 = -0.72$$
$$1.78x_1 - 6.99x_2 + 2.40x_3 = 1.71$$

where x_1, x_2, x_3 are related to c_0, c_1, c_2 of Chapter 5 by the equations

$$x_1 = c_0, \quad x_2 = c_1, \quad x_3 = 10c_2.$$

---

[6] Of course, analogue methods for this type of problem are virtually instantaneous. Rate is only of passing interest, unless we are interested in constructing from these methods other iterative methods.

The analogue solution was

$$x_1 = 0.18, \quad x_2 = -0.19, \quad x_3 = 0.02,$$

as compared to the digital solution,

$$x_1 = 0.18, \quad x_2 = -0.18, \quad x_3 = 0.06.$$

When c_2 was scaled by a factor of 100 (so that $x_4 = 100c_2$), coefficients of the system were too small and the analogue solution,

$$x_1 = 0.18, \quad x_2 = -0.19, \quad x_4 = 0.09,$$

was off by a large factor in the last variable. The level of accuracy quoted in all cases was obtained by successively adjusting the (arbitrary) initial values until they were equal to the asymptotic values and then reading the initial values on a vernier supplied on the equipment. No accurate readout equipment was available, and readings directly from the display scope would not have been adequate.

The proof given of the last theorem, and the analogue computations indicated, were carried out by an assistant, Mr. Robert Wine.

REFERENCES

[1] D. Young, 'Iterative methods for solving partial differential equations of elliptic type,' *Trans. Am. Math. Soc.*, **76** (1954), 92–111.
[2] L. Cesari, 'Sulla risoluzione dei sisteme di equazioni lineari per approssimazioni successive,' *Atti Accad. Nazl. Lincei, Rend., Classe Sci. Fis. Mat. Nat.*, **25, 6a** (1937), 422–428.
[3] A. Hirsch, *Acta Math.*, **25** (1902), 367–370.
[4] H. Wittmeyer, *Z. Angew. Math. Mech.*, **16** (1936), 287–300.
[5] Edgar Reich, 'On the convergence of the classical iterative method of solving linear simultaneous equations,' *Ann. Math. Statist.*, **20** (1949), 448–451.

CHAPTER 5

USE OF METHODS OF CHAPTER 4 ON THE DIRICHLET AND OTHER PROBLEMS

1. DISCUSSION OF ADVISABLE PROCEDURES

Some comments relative to computational techniques are relevant if we wish to approximate solutions to large linear algebraic systems, in order to obtain approximate solutions of discretizations of boundary value problems. When finite-difference discretizations are to be used on Dirichlet-type problems for equations of elliptic type, a major advantage arises in not having to record the entire system of equations. Since such discretizations usually give rise to excessively large systems when the mesh is refined, this is fortunate. As mentioned above, a finite-difference analogue of the Dirichlet problem for a second-order equation of elliptic type usually yields a linear system with a positive definite coefficient matrix. Suppose then that we consider using successive replacements, or its accelerated form, on such a system. There will be in the discretization a representative equation for each point, and the iteration scheme will also provide such a representative equation. Registers reserved for values at points must somehow contain information as to whether the value at a point is to be left alone as a boundary point, corrected as an ordinary point, or corrected by some special technique, such as that required for short-leg computations near a curved boundary. Thus one, or at most two, computational formulas regarded as 'correction formulas' have to be programmed. This is a major advantage of finite-difference discretizations. If, as sometimes will arise, a linear combination of the function and its normal derivative

(5.1) $$\alpha u + \beta u_n = f$$

is to be specified at the boundary, rather than just u, then a finite-difference analogue of (5.1) is used to 'correct' boundary points.

Of course, extension to higher dimensions of finite-difference methods for this type of problem is difficult or impossible, and computational error bounds are virtually unavailable.

If 'continuous' methods are to be used, systems of relatively small order (30 or 40 vs. 1,000 or 10,000) give high accuracy approximation, but the entire system must be recorded and is hardly likely to contain as many zero coefficients as the finite-difference discretizations contain. However, if a machine routine for differentiation and integration of sophomore functions (polynomials, exponentials, sines, cosines, Bessel functions, etc.), along with a routine for algebraic combining and simplifying [3], is used within the framework of the program, recording the system causes no difficulty other than the rather extensive difficulty of programming such a routine.[1] The approximating family may be read into the machine on cards (in symbols for the functions, not real number functional values) together with cards describing the boundary, the boundary function (data), and the differential equation. Very often, it has been found, adequate accuracy can be obtained by using direct methods for solving the linear system. We recommend that such a program be built so that the linear system is solved by direct methods, and these, possibly inaccurate results, are automatically used as initial iterates in an efficient iterative scheme. This assures good accuracy and avoids unnecessary iteration, albeit at the expense of considerable programming. The order in which cards for the approximating family are read into the machine will control the order of subtractions under-taken in solving the linear system by direct methods, and therefore can effect accuracy appreciably, or control the rate of convergence if the solution is to be approximated by iteration.[2]

---

[1] It is expected that such routines will soon become part of the standard computation laboratory library.

[2] For a case in which reading the deck in backwards caused a linear system that could not be solved accurately by utilizing Gaussian elimination to be replaced by a system for which the same method gave high accuracy, see [3]. We could suggest a new probability game. Shuffle the deck, solve the linear system produced by elimination only, and be paid by other players in an amount inversely proportional to the error bound with which the solution of the boundary value problem is approximated. To iterate, or to increase the approximating family, would then be considered cheating. We take our work too seriously to be subject to such chance accuracy, and we therefore recommend having iteration available.

The standard practice of iterating until

$$\|x^k - x^{k-1}\| < \tau$$

(i.e., until successive iterates differ in some norm by an amount less than a prescribed tolerance τ) can be used here only with some risk. The vector $x^k - x^{k-1}$ is the difference of error vectors $\varepsilon^k - \varepsilon^{k-1}$, which may be small, though neither ε^k nor ε^{k-1} is small. For iterative methods, like successive replacements where only the asymptotic factor of reduction is less than one, such a criterion can be invoked only after a large number of iterations have been completed. One may be satisfied to use this standard criterion for stopping an iteration and depend on the over-all error bound to solution of the boundary value problem to decide whether one has provided enough iterations. However, in order to avoid uncertainties as to whether to try for high-order approximation of the boundary value problem, or for accuracy in solutions of the linear system, it would be wise to have an error bound[3] formula for the linear iterative method, programmed to be used at the conclusion of each iteration in testing, if

$$\|x^k - x\| < \tau,$$

for possible termination.

If the least squares procedure is used, the coefficient matrix will always be positive definite, as will be shown, so that successive replacements, or its accelerated form, may be used for iteration. The type of the differential equation is then irrelevant insofar as the computational procedure is concerned, but, it must be added, certainly not irrelevant in existence, uniqueness, and error bound considerations, nor in choice of an approximating family. It will develop that availability of a universal computational procedure, even one possibly adaptable to analogue computers, is quite remarkable and rather unique in numerical methods of partial differential equations. Here, one might even use the analogue equipment (which is extremely fast, but for which accuracy is likely to be limited to about .1 percent) to obtain solutions for initial iterates on the digital computer if the above-mentioned scaling problems can be resolved. This comment is particularly applicable to those analogue and digital machines that are designed to communicate readily. Each machine does what it is designed to do best. The digital machine generates the linear systems, solves them by iteration to high accuracy,

---

[3] For discussion of ways of getting these, see the end of Chapter 4, Sec. 3.

using parameters determined by the analogue machine, and then uses this high-accuracy answer to compute an error bound.[4]

All difficulties are then thrown back upon the analysis and the error bound questions delineated above, to which a great deal of thought must be given. The mathematical problems in computational procedure for linear work have here been more or less completely resolved, in the sense that we have one proper method to fall back upon, provided an appropriate approximating family can be found. It will be seen, however, that computational procedures for nonlinear problems still present a considerable area for mathematical activity. Thus, advances in computational procedures for linear problems, and the mathematical treatment of such procedures, can be expected to be made by the introduction of entirely new procedures, not by the continued development of those presented here. In this spirit we propose the following exercise.

RESEARCH EXERCISES

Find a convergent iteration for linear boundary value problems that can be carried out by the above function algebraic (nonnumeric) routine, thus avoiding intermediate discretizations and double convergence problems.

We have already avoided one of the 'double convergence problems' altogether by quoting error bounds of the solutions of differential equation boundary value problems, and depending upon the choice of approximating families for these problems for which satisfactory bounds can be computed; in functional analysis terms, we have avoided questions of completeness, which are among the most difficult questions in modern analysis. In the case of the L^2-norm needed here, only a few of the desired completeness theorems are known.

2. ERROR BOUNDS FOR BOUNDARY VALUE PROBLEMS FOR ELLIPTIC-PARABOLIC TYPE

If possible, any general routine, such as envisioned above, should incorporate an auxiliary routine to compute those quantities essential in getting bounds for the error in approximating solutions of the boundary value problem. What those quantities are to be is evident below.

Consider a region $A \subset E^n$ with boundary Σ. Let[5]

$$Lu = a^{ij}(x)u_{x_i x_j} + b^i(x)u_{x_i} + c(x)u$$

---

[4] The search for appropriate initial values using analogue equipment should become an important feature in use of our nonlinear techniques.

[5] Summation over repeated indices is from 1 to n.

be a linear second-order, partial differential operator defined $\forall\, x = (x_1,\cdots,x_n) \in A$, where

$B = (a^{ij}(x))$ is positive semidefinite $\forall\, x \in A \cup \Sigma$; i.e.,

$(\lambda \in R^n) \wedge (\lambda \neq 0) \Rightarrow \lambda^T B(x)\lambda \geq 0 \,\forall\, x \in A \cup \Sigma,$

$a^{ij}(x) \in C^2(A \cup \Sigma),$

$b^i(x) \in C^1(A \cup \Sigma),$

and $(c(x) \in C(A \cup \Sigma)) \wedge (c(x) < 0)\,\forall\, x \in A \cup \Sigma.$

Where n_i, n_j are direction cosines of the inner normal to points of the boundary Σ, let

$\Sigma^3 = \{x \mid (x \in \Sigma) \wedge a^{ij}(x)n_i n_j \neq 0\}$

$\Sigma^2 = \{x \mid (x \in \Sigma - \Sigma^3) \wedge b(x) = (b^i(x) - a_{x_j}{}^{ij}(x))n_i < 0\}$

$\wedge$ $\Sigma^1 = \{x \mid (x \in \Sigma - \Sigma^3) \wedge b(x) = (b^i(x) - a_{x_j}{}^{ij}(x))n_i \geq 0\}.$

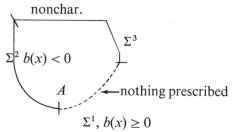

Of course, A should be such that the normal is defined except on a set of measure 0, and also such that the divergence theorem is valid. We say then that A is a Green's region.[6] We consider the boundary value problem

(5.2) $Lu = g(x)\,\forall\, x \in A$

$u = f(x)\,\forall\, x \in \Sigma^2 \cup \Sigma^3.$

---

[6] A sufficient condition that A be a Green's region is that it can be filled with a finite number of simplices or a limit of simplices. Necessary conditions seem not to be known. See Chapter 3.

The very general problem, as stated, includes the Dirichlet problem for a modified Laplace equation ($u_{xx} + u_{yy} - u = 0$), the slab problem for a modified heat equation ($u_{xx} - u_t - u = 0$), and many more, including problems for equations that are of neither elliptic nor parabolic[7] type. The equation $Lu = g$ is said to be of elliptic-parabolic type. The Σ^3 boundary is called noncharacteristic, and the function $b(x)$ discriminates between those characteristic portions of the boundary where data must be specified or should not be specified.

EXERCISE

Show that the Dirichlet problem for the equation

$$\sum_{i=1}^{n} u_{x_i x_i} - u = 0$$

in n-dimensions is included above.

EXERCISE

The slab problem is $u \in C^2(A)$, $u \in C^1(A \cup \Sigma)$, $u_{xx} - u_t = 0$ in $A = \{(x,t)|0 < x < 1, 0 < t < T\}$, $u(x,0) = f(x)$, $u(0,t) = g_1(t)$, $u(l,t) = g_2(t)$. Show that this problem, with $u_{xx} - u_t - u$ replacing $u_{xx} - u_t$, is included above.

Let any member of the class

$$C_L = \{u \mid (u \in C^1(A \cup \Sigma)) \wedge (u \in C^2(A)) \wedge Lu \text{ bounded in } A)\}$$

be called a regular function. A function $u \in C_L \ni (5.2)$ is satisfied will be called a regular solution of our boundary value problem.

In a remarkably general work [1], including problems where the conormal derivative, $a^{ij}u_{x_i}n_j$,[8] of u can be specified instead of u on arbitrary parts of Σ^3, and where uniqueness of regular solutions and the existence of solutions in a certain weak sense are established, Professor Gaetano Fichera of the University of Rome proved the following two theorems.

---

[7] Such that there exists one and only one family of curves in A with $a^{ij}n_i n_j = 0$ on these curves.

[8] This can be made to include the case where normal derivatives are specified. The conormal derivatives are natural boundary conditions, in the sense that they arise from variational (see [5]) problems using the Hamilton principle of mathematical physics, where constraints are removed at the boundary.

Theorem

$\forall\, u \in C_L \ni Lu(x) = 0 \;\forall\, x \in A,$

$$\max_{A \cup \Sigma} |u| = \max_{\overline{\Sigma}^2 \cup \overline{\Sigma}^3} |u|.$$

Theorem

$\forall\, u \in C_L \ni u(x) = 0 \;\forall\, x \in \Sigma^2 \cup \Sigma^3,$

$$\max_{A \cup \Sigma} |u| \le \operatorname*{lub}_{A} \frac{Lu}{c}.$$

Note here that we have required $c < 0$ in our formulation of L. Proofs of these theorems can be read in reference [1]. They would ordinarily be studied in a second-semester graduate course in partial differential equations.

We now phrase, more generally than before, the least square's computational procedure, and we show how to use the above theorems to compute error bounds for this large class of problems of elliptic-parabolic type. Let $\{v^k\}$ be an approximating family $\ni Lv^k$ is bounded in $A \;\forall\, k \in \Omega_n$. Then

$$u^n = \sum_{k=1}^{n} c_k v_k$$

will be considered an approximate solution to our boundary value problem if the c_k's are so determined that the quadratic form

$$\mu_n(c_1,\cdots,c_n) = \int_A (Lu^n - g)^2 \, dA + \int_{\Sigma^2 \,\cup\, \Sigma^3} (u^n - f)^2 \, ds$$

is minimized; i.e., if the c_k's are the solutions of

$$\sum_{k=1}^{n} a_{hk} c_k = b_h, \quad h = 1,\cdots,n,$$

where

$$a_{hk} = \int_A (Lv^h)(Lv^k) \, dA + \int_{\Sigma^2 \,\cup\, \Sigma^3} v^h v^k ds$$

$$b_h = \int_{\Sigma^2 \cup \Sigma^3} f v^h \, ds + \int_A g L v^h \, dA.$$

We desire to obtain a bound for $|u - u^n|$, and we have neither that $L(u - u^n) = 0$ in A nor that $(u - u^n) = 0$ on $\Sigma^2 \cup \Sigma^3$, as required by the Fichera theorems. To remedy this, $\forall\, v \in C_L$, let $v_1 \in C_L$ be such that

$$Lv_1 = 0 \quad \text{in} \quad A$$

$\wedge$

$$v_1 = v \quad \text{on} \quad \Sigma^2 \cup \Sigma^3.$$

(We thus assume no more about the existence of a regular solution than is required in assuming that a regular solution u of our original boundary value problem exists.) Then, letting $v_2 = v - v_1$, we have

$$Lv_2 = L(v - v_1) = Lv \quad \text{in} \quad A$$

$$v_2 = 0 \quad \text{on} \quad \Sigma^2 \cup \Sigma^3,$$

and from the theorems, $\forall\, v \in C_L$,

$$\max_{A \cup \Sigma} |v| = \max_{A \cup \Sigma} |v_1 + v_2| \leq \max_{A \cup \Sigma} |v_1| + \max_{A \cup \Sigma} |v_2| \leq \max_{\bar{\Sigma}^2 \cup \bar{\Sigma}^3} |v_1| + \operatorname*{lub}_{A} \left| \frac{Lv_2}{c} \right|$$

$$= \max_{\bar{\Sigma}^2 \cup \bar{\Sigma}^3} |v| + \operatorname*{lub}_{A} \left| \frac{Lv}{c} \right|.$$

Thus the Fichera theorems can be restated,

Corollary

$$\forall\, v \in C_L \qquad \max_{A \cup \Sigma} |v| \leq \max_{\bar{\Sigma}^2 \cup \bar{\Sigma}^3} |v| + \operatorname*{lub}_{A} \left| \frac{Lv}{c} \right|,$$

and applied to $v = u - u^n$ to get the error bound formula,

$$\max_{A \cup \Sigma} |u - u^n| \leq \max_{\bar{\Sigma}^2 \cup \bar{\Sigma}^3} |f - u^n| + \operatorname*{lub}_{A} \frac{g - Lu^n}{c}$$

This elementary procedure of obtaining an error bound in 'boundary and volume parts,' so to speak, is a basic general technique in numerical analysis for linear problems. Note that this bound is valid in any dimension, and for all problems stated, with no points in the region A, where Lu is hyperbolic.[9]

While it is thoroughly remarkable that an error bound expression of this generality can be obtained, the computational value is doubtful,

---

[9] i.e., where $a^{ij}n_i n_j = 0$ has two real nontrivial solutions.

since the least upper bound and maximum required for the known functions can be difficult to compute, and one may be driven to assessment by computation of Lu^n and u^n over a fine mesh, a move that is indefensible on logical ground. If u^n is to be computed by least squares, we do not expect error bounds in maximum norm to be as good as those in L^2 norm, which will be shown to be computationally as well as theoretically, sound.

In both [1] and [2], Fichera develops methods of finding a number $H \in R^1 \ni$

$$(5.3) \qquad \int_A (u - u^n)^2 dA \leq H \left\{ \int_A (Lu^n - g)^2 dA + \int_{\Sigma^3 \cup \Sigma^3} (u^n - f)^2 ds \right\}$$
$$= H \mu_n(c_1, \cdots c_n,)$$

for problems of elliptic-parabolic type, so that the following simple lemma is of great computational importance.

Lemma

$$\mu_n = \int_{\Sigma^2 \cup \Sigma^3} f^2 ds + \int_A g^2 dA - \sum_{h=1}^{n} c_h b_h$$

Proof

$$\sum_{h=1}^{n} c_h b_h = \sum_{h=1}^{n} c_h \sum_{k=1}^{n} a_{hk} c_k = \sum_{h=1}^{n} \sum_{k=1}^{n} a_{hk} c_h c_k$$

$$= \sum_{h=1}^{n} \sum_{k=1}^{n} \left(\int_A Lv^h Lv^k dA + \int_{\Sigma^2 \cup \Sigma^3} v^h v^k ds \right) c_h c_k$$

$$= \int_A \left(\sum_{h=1}^{n} \sum_{k=1}^{n} c_h c_k Lv^h Lv^k \right) dA + \int_{\Sigma^2 \cup \Sigma^3} \left(\sum_{h=1}^{n} \sum_{k=1}^{n} c_h c_k v^h v^k \right) ds$$

$$= \int_A \left(\sum_{h=1}^{n} c_h Lv^h \right)^2 dA + \int_{\Sigma^2 \cup \Sigma^3} \left(\sum_{h=1}^{n} c_h v^h \right)^2 ds$$

$$= \int_A \left[L \left(\sum_{h=1}^{n} c_h v^h \right) - g \right]^2 dA + \int_{\Sigma^2 \cup \Sigma^3} \left(\sum_{h=1}^{n} c_h v^h - f \right)^2 ds - \int_A g^2 dA$$

$$\quad - \int_{\Sigma^2 \cup \Sigma^3} f^2 dA + 2 \int_A \sum_{k=1}^{n} c_k g Lv^k dA + 2 \int_{\Sigma^2 \cup \Sigma^3} \sum_{k=1}^{n} c_k f v^k ds$$

$$= \mu_n - \int_A g^2 dA - \int_{\Sigma^2 \cup \Sigma^3} f^2 ds + 2 \sum_{k=1}^{n} c_k b_k. \quad \blacksquare$$

The quantities

$$\sum_{h=1}^{n} c_h b_h, \quad \int f^2 ds, \quad \int g^2 dA$$

are those referred to above as necessary for arriving at an error bound. Certainly, while the problem of solving the linear system is still on the machine, the inner product of the solution vector c and the vector b can conveniently be taken. However, to recommend use of

$$\sum_{h=1}^{n} c_h b_h$$

in computing an error bound would be to fall into the classical pitfall of numerical analysis of not realizing that a correct formula of analysis may be improper computationally. Since the $c_h, h = 1, \cdots, n$, are approximate solutions only of the linear system, *it cannot be correctly said that*

$$\sum_{k=1}^{n} a_{hk} c_k = b_h.$$

If, in the proof above, we delete the expression before the first equality, we obtain

$$\mu_n = \int_{\Sigma^2 \cup \Sigma^3} f^2 \, ds + \int_A g^2 \, dA - \sum_{h=1}^{n} c_h (b_h - r_h)$$

where $r = (a_{hk})c - b,$

so that the formula of the lemma appears as a special case, to be used when the values of the residuals r_h have been checked to be zero to the number of significant digits to be quoted. The formula in the lemma may also be used when an error bound for solution of the discretized problem has been used in the computation, and when c_h is known to the number of digits to be quoted. Whichever of these choices is to be taken, care must be used to monitor the loss of significant digits in all 'sums' that enter into the error bound computation, so that no more digits are quoted for such a bound than are valid. Almost any losses other than total loss can be tolerated in computation of μ_n, since one would rarely wish to quote more than one nonzero digit in an error bound. In fact, loss of significant digits in the last subtraction made in forming μ_n as above is actively sought.

We have assured that a_{hk}, b_h are exact. This is because they have been evaluated by direct use of the fundamental theorem of calculus, not by a finite sum (quadrature, see Appendix A) replacing the integral. The general program discussed should monitor any loss of significant digits in subtracting values of the anti-derivative at upper and lower limits, so that it is known to what accuracy coefficients can be considered known, and so that other calculations may be carried forth to this accuracy. In case this accuracy is insufficient, or one wants to prescribe the accuracy in advance, the routine can be made to go to higher precision arithmetic when these losses occur in evaluating a coefficient.

Some computationally minded students will be irritated by the fact that we consider (5.3) (or its square root) to be an error bound, since it does not bound the error of the numbers quoted. It supplies a bound in norm of the error of a function approximating the solution of a boundary value problem, rather than supplies a bound of the functional values of such a function. This is more consistent with modern views, although it must be admitted that a Gibbs phenomenon can develop, so that when high-order accuracy is obtained in L^2 norm, large errors are found at some points, especially boundary points.[10] Corners are boundary points in two senses in our minimization of μ_n. In [3], a modification of our computation procedure, which we call 'boundary extension,' is developed to overcome this difficulty by sacrificing a little accuracy in L^2 norm for large gains in accuracy in maximum norm. It has been astutely stated that 'before one makes a computation he should consider in what sense (norm) the error is to be considered.' One could add, recalling our standard that practical requirements must guide criteria in numerical analysis, that the sense of the error should be determined by the nature of the technological problem to be considered. In fact, the view might be taken that a major part of the formulation of a modern technological problem should be a decision concerning in what sense errors of approximation are to be taken. Although this is an entirely admirable standard, it has almost certainly never been met. If this standard, then, were to be adopted, it would seem that we must await enunciation of a principle for determining the sense of the error as basic to physics as the Hamilton principle is to determining

---

[10] In other terms, least squares is not a uniform approximation technique. L^2 does not provide the uniform topology.

the mathematical model. And had we such a principle at our disposal, the question would then arise, Can we evaluate error bounds in this sense? Here, we take the attitude that just as we can really accept as mathematical models for events only those models (not all those given by Hamilton's principle!) we can handle well mathematically, so also we can accept only a sense of error that can be well handled mathematically. At this time, this virtually restricts us to consideration of error bounds in L^2 norm.

3. PROOF THAT LEAST SQUARES GIVES A LINEAR SYSTEM WITH POSITIVE DEFINITE COEFFICIENT MATRIX

The following is to be regarded as corollary to the theorem that the method of successive replacements converges for linear systems with positive definite coefficient matrix.

Corollary

If in the least squares technique given in Chapter 5, Sec. 2, the families $\{v^k\}$, $k \in \Omega_n$, are linearly independent, then $A = (a_{hk})$ is positive-definite.

Proof

From the proof of the lemma in Chapter 5, Sec. 2

$$c^T A c = \sum_{h=1}^{n} c_h \left(\sum_{k=1}^{n} a_{hk} c_k \right)$$

$$= \int_A \left(\sum_{h=1}^{n} c_h L v^h \right)^2 dA + \int_{\Sigma^2 \cup \Sigma^3} \left(\sum_{h=1}^{n} c_h v^h \right)^2 ds$$

$\therefore c^T A c = 0 \Rightarrow (L u^n = 0 \quad \text{in} \quad A) \wedge (u^n = 0 \quad \text{in} \quad \Sigma^2 \cup \Sigma^3) \Rightarrow u^n = 0 \quad \text{in}$

$A \cup \Sigma^2 \cup \Sigma^3 \Rightarrow c = 0.$ ∎

4. NUMERICAL EXAMPLES

Torsion of a Rectangular Beam

It is shown in elasticity that the torsion of a beam is the solution of the Dirichlet problem for the Laplace equation on a cross-section where $u = x^2 + y^2$ on the boundary. On the two-unit square, $A = \{(x,y)|\ |x| < 1 \wedge |y| < 1\}$, values on the boundaries are $1 + x^2$ and $1 + y^2$. Below, we approximate the solution of the Dirichlet problem for the Laplace equation for boundary values $u(\pm 1,y) = y^2$, $u(x,\pm 1) = x^2$, and think to add a unit to this in order to approximate torsion.

The method of least squares is used where the approximating family is the first five harmonic polynomials having appropriate symmetry properties. Although we have emphasized machine computation here throughout, the method is elucidated by giving the details of a hand computation. Iteration was found to be quite unnecessary in solving the linear system, so long as the order of elimination was carefully chosen to avoid losses of significant digits. Maximum and L^2 error bounds are compared for several orders of approximation. In [3], the same problem is solved using the first thirty monomials that (not harmonic) have the required symmetry properties, in order to demonstrate that it is possible to choose an adequate approximating family without a very complete knowledge of the problem. On the other hand, the same boundary value problem, but for the equation $u_{xx} - u_{yy} = 0$, does not have a unique solution and use of the computational procedure demonstrated in [3] that almost any solution could be obtained by appropriate choice of the approximating family.

We wish to emphasize strongly that test of a numerical method on the Laplace equation, especially for a Dirichlet problem on a square, is not at all adequate. *We include this problem not as a numerical test but as the simplest nontrivial numerical example that is useful for training purposes.* However, it must be stated that a rectangle has been popularly used to test finite-difference methods on the Dirichlet problem for the Laplace equation.

In [3], the method is put to severe test on much more difficult problems—some problems of elliptic-parabolic type that cannot be categorized as purely elliptic or purely parabolic. The method is used on a problem where the solution is C^∞ in a two-unit square region A and yet vanishes on the unit circle interior to A and takes on the values on the boundary of the square, as given for the problem stated above. Monomial approximating families are still utilized to demonstrate how far one may ignore the character of the problem in the choice of approximating families. Also in [3], error bounds are provided for a problem where exact solutions are known in order to provide an over-all mathematical and numerical check.

In using a computational procedure that minimizes the L^2 norm of the error in boundary values and in the differential equation, we may get large maximum errors. Corners are particularly susceptible; this is the well-known tail-off effect in least squares—a Gibbs phenomenon, as it were. In [3], as we have said, this is circumvented by artificially extending the boundary for the fit, thus sacrificing a little L^2 accuracy for a large gain in maximum error bound.

In [3], it will be noted, proper evaluation of

$$\max_{\overline{\Sigma}^2 \cup \overline{\Sigma}^3} |f - u^n| \quad \text{and} \quad \operatorname*{lub}_A \left| \frac{Lu^n}{c} \right|$$

was too tedious to carry out, even with a large-scale computer in hand, so these quantities were estimated from assessment on a fine grid. This casts doubt, of course, on the maximum error bounds quoted, but emphasizes the importance of the L^2 error bounds, which, as has been shown, can easily be computed. Since the computation given below is hand-done, it is even assumed that the maximum of $|x^2 - u^n|$ occurs at the corner. This is preferable to evaluating $(x^2 - u^n)$ over a fine mesh. It is hoped that serious students will want to see whether the maximum error bound is really as quoted. Of course, the L^2 error bounds are properly computed; in [2], a value $H = 1$ for the Laplace equation is explicitly quoted, and this is used here. Since the residual vector r was zero to eight digits, it was proper, in computing L^2 error bounds, to use the first form quoted for μ_n in Chapter 5, Sec. 2, p. 87.

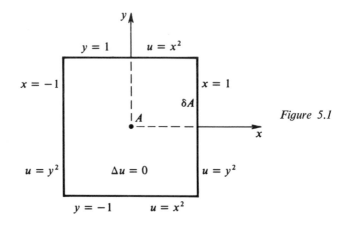

Figure 5.1

Problem: Approximate $u \ni \Delta u = 0$ in A

$$\wedge (u(x, \pm 1) = x^2) \wedge u(\pm 1, y) = y^2$$

$$\wedge (u \in c^2(A)) \wedge (u \in c^1(A \cup \delta A)).$$

We use the least squares technique, adopting harmonic polynomials as approximating functions, and take only those polynomials that are invariant when x is replaced by $-x$, y is replaced by $-y$, and x is replaced by y.

It can be seen that these arise as

$$\mathrm{Re}\,(x + iy)^{4n}, \quad n = 0,1,\cdots .$$

Thus we put

$$p_0 = \mathrm{Re}\,(x + iy)^0$$
$$p_1 = \mathrm{Re}\,(x + iy)^4$$
$$p_2 = \mathrm{Re}\,(x + iy)^8$$
$$p_3 = \mathrm{Re}\,(x + iy)^{12}$$
$$p_4 = \mathrm{Re}\,(x + iy)^{16}$$

and consider u^n an approximation to u when

$$u^n = \sum_{k=1}^{n} c_k p_k$$

and the c_k's have been determined, so that $\int_0^1 \left(\sum_{k=1}^{n} c_k p_k(1,y) - y^2 \right)^2 dy$ is minimized; i.e., when c_k satisfies $a_{hk} c_k = b_h$ with

$$a_{hk} = \int_0^1 p_h(1,y) p_k(1, y)\,dy$$

$$b_h = \int_0^1 y^2 p_h(1,y)\,dy.$$

Generation of p_k.[11] Binomial coefficients here are conveniently calculated from the Pascal triangle,

---

[11] We are interested in illustrating general procedures and refrain here from taking advantage of any simplifications in evaluation of the integral expressions for a_{hk} and b_h that arise from considerations special to the problem. Properties that hinge on the theory of analytic functions of a complex variable are particularly to be avoided for general illustration, since these properties do not extend to problems in E^n for $n > 2$.

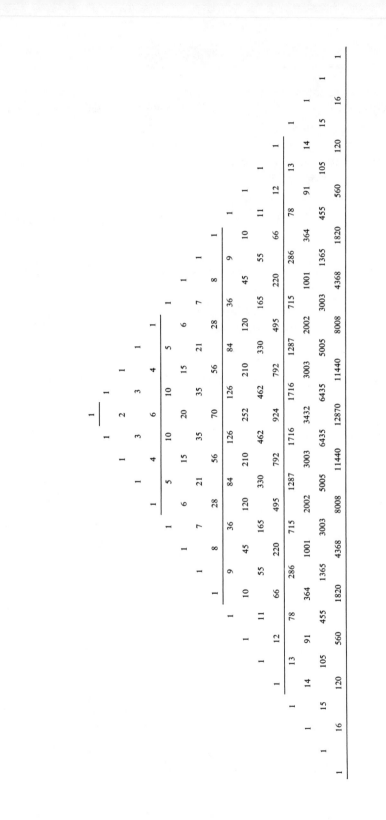

We have

$$p_0 = 1$$
$$p_1 = x^4 - 6x^2y^2 + y^4$$
$$p_2 = x^8 - 28x^6y^2 + 70x^4y^4 - 28x^2y^6 + y^8$$
$$p_3 = x^{12} - 66x^{10}y^2 + 495x^8y^4 - 924x^6y^6 + 495x^4y^8 - 66x^2y^{10} + y^{12}$$
$$p_4 = x^{16} - 120x^{14}y^2 + 1820x^{12}y^4 - 8008x^{10}y^6 + 12870x^8y^8 - 8008x^6y^{10}$$
$$+ 1820x^4y^{12} - 120x^2y^{14} + y^{16}.$$

Now

$$a_{00} = \int_0^1 1 \cdot 1 \, dy = 1$$

$$a_{01} = \int_0^1 (1 - 6y^2 + y^4) \, dy = 1 - 2 + \tfrac{1}{5} = -0.8000000000$$

$$a_{02} = \int_0^1 (1 - 28y^2 + 70y^4 - 28y^6 + y^8) \, dy = 1 - \frac{28}{3} + \frac{70}{5} - \frac{28}{7} + \frac{1}{9}$$
$$= 1.777777778$$

$$a_{03} = \int_0^1 (1 - 66y^2 + 495y^4 - 924y^6 + 495y^8 - 66y^{10} + y^{12}) \, dy$$
$$= 1 - 22 + \frac{495}{5} - \frac{924}{7} + \frac{495}{9} - 6 + \frac{1}{13} = -4.92307692$$

$$a_{04} = \int_0^1 (1 - 120y^2 + 1820y^4 - 8008y^6 + 12870y^8 - 8008y^{10} + 1820y^{12}$$
$$- 120y^{14} + y^{16}) \, dy$$
$$= 1 - 40 + \frac{1820}{5} - \frac{8008}{7} + \frac{12870}{9} - \frac{8008}{11} + \frac{1820}{13} - \frac{120}{15} + \frac{1}{17}$$
$$= 15.058823529$$

$$a_{11} = \int_0^1 (1 - 6y^2 + y^4)(1 - 6y^2 + y^4) \, dy$$
$$= \int_0^1 (1 - 6y^2 + y^4 - 6y^2 + 36y^4 - 6y^6 + y^4 - 6y^6 + y^8) \, dy$$
$$= \int_0^1 (1 - 12y^2 + 38y^4 - 12y^6 + y^8) \, dy$$
$$= 1 - 4 + \frac{38}{5} - \frac{12}{7} + \frac{1}{9} = 2.996825397$$

$$a_{12} = \int_0^1 (1 - 6y^2 + y^4)(1 - 28y^2 + 70y^4 - 28y^6 + y^8) \, dy$$
$$= \int_0^1 (1 - 28y^2 + 70y^4 - 28y^6 + y^8 - 6y^2 + 168y^4 - 420y^6 + 168y^8$$
$$- 6y^{10} + y^4 - 28y^6 + 70y^8 - 28y^{10} + y^{12}) \, dy$$
$$= \int_0^1 (1 - 34y^2 + 239y^4 - 476y^6 + 239y^8 - 34y^{10} + y^{12}) \, dy$$

$$= 1 - \frac{34}{3} + \frac{239}{5} - \frac{476}{7} + \frac{239}{9} - \frac{34}{11} + \frac{1}{13}$$

$$= -6.99176379$$

$$a_{13} = \int_0^1 (1 - 6y^2 + y^4)(1 - 66y^2 + 495y^4 - 924y^6 + 495y^8$$
$$- 66y^{10} + y^{12})\, dy$$

$$= \int_0^1 (1 - 72y^2 + 892y^4 - 3960y^6 + 6534y^8 - 3960y^{10}$$
$$+ 892y^{12} - 72y^{14} + y^{16})dy$$

$$= 1 - \frac{72}{3} + \frac{892}{5} - \frac{3960}{7} + \frac{6534}{9} - \frac{3960}{11} + \frac{892}{13} - \frac{72}{15} + \frac{1}{17}$$

$$= 19.5599224$$

$$a_{14} = \int_0^1 (1 - 6y^2 + y^4)(1 - 120y^2 + 1820y^4 - 8008y^6 + 12870y^8$$
$$- 8008y^{10} + 1820y^{12} - 120y^{14} + y^{16})dy$$

$$= \int_0^1 (1 - 126y^2 + 2541y^4 - 19048y^6 + 62738y^8 - 93236y^{10}$$
$$+ 62738y^{12} - 19048y^{14} + 2541y^{12} - 126y^{18} + y^{20})dy$$

$$= 1 - 42 + \frac{2541}{5} - \frac{19048}{7} + \frac{62738}{9} - \frac{93236}{11} + \frac{62738}{13}$$

$$- \frac{19048}{15} + \frac{2541}{17} - \frac{126}{19} + \frac{1}{21} = -60.0340066$$

$$a_{22} = \int_0^1 (1 - 28y^2 + 70y^4 - 28y^6 + y^8)(1 - 28y^2 + 70y^4 - 28y^6 + y^8)dy$$

$$= \int_0^1 (1 - 56y^2 + 924y^4 - 3976y^6 + 6470y^8 - 3976y^{10} + 924y^{12}$$
$$- 56y^{14} + y^{16})dy$$

$$= 1 - \frac{56}{3} + \frac{924}{5} - \frac{3976}{7} + \frac{6470}{9} - \frac{3976}{11} + \frac{924}{13} - \frac{56}{15} + \frac{1}{17}$$

$$= 23.9700901$$

$$a_{23} = \int_0^1 (1 - 28y^2 + 70y^4 - 28y^6 + y^8)(1 - 66y^2 + 495y^4 - 924y^6$$
$$+ 495y^8 - 66y^{10} + y^{12})dy$$

$$= \int_0^1 (1 - 94y^2 + 2413y^4 - 19432y^6 + 62866y^8 - 92532y^{10}$$
$$+ 62866y^{12} - 19432y^{14} + 2413y^{16} - 94y^{18} + y^{20})dy$$

$$= 1 - \frac{94}{3} + \frac{2413}{5} - \frac{19432}{17} + \frac{62866}{9} - \frac{92532}{11} + \frac{62866}{13}$$

$$- \frac{19432}{15} + \frac{2413}{17} - \frac{94}{19} + \frac{1}{21}$$

$$= -73.2013079$$

$$a_{24} = \int_0^1 (1 - 28y^2 + 70y^4 - 28y^6 + y^8)(1 - 120y^2 + 1820y^4 - 8008y^6$$
$$+ 12870y^8 - 8008y^{10} + 1820y^{12} - 120y^{14} + y^{16})dy$$
$$= \int_0^1 (1 - 148y^2 + 5250y^4 - 67396y^6 + 367855y^8 - 980008y^{10}$$
$$+ 1352988y^{12} - 980008y^{14} + 367855y^{16} - 67396y^{18}$$
$$+ 5250y^{20} - 148y^{22} + y^{24})dy$$
$$= 1 - \frac{148}{3} + \frac{5250}{5} - \frac{67396}{7} + \frac{367855}{9} - \frac{980008}{11} + \frac{1352988}{13}$$
$$- \frac{980008}{15} + \frac{367855}{17} - \frac{67396}{19} + \frac{5250}{21} - \frac{148}{23} + \frac{1}{25}$$
$$= (000)231.918148$$

$$a_{33} = \int_0^1 (1 - 66y^2 + 495y^4 - 924y^6 + 495y^8 - 66y^{10} + y^{12})$$
$$(1 - 66y^2 + 495y^4 - 924y^6 + 495y^8 - 66y^{10} + y^{12})dy$$
$$= \int_0^1 (1 - 132y^2 + 5346y^4 - 67188y^6 + 367983y^8 - 980232y^{10}$$
$$+ 1352540y^{12} - 980232y^{14} + 367983y^{16} - 67188y^{18}$$
$$+ 5346y^{20} - 132y^{22} + y^{24})dy$$
$$= 1 - 44 + \frac{5346}{5} - \frac{67188}{7} + \frac{367983}{9} - \frac{980232}{11} + \frac{1352540}{13}$$
$$- \frac{980232}{15} + \frac{367983}{17} - \frac{67188}{19} + \frac{5346}{21} - \frac{132}{23} + \frac{1}{25}$$
$$= +254.373341$$

$$a_{34} = \int_0^1 (1 - 66y^2 + 495y^4 - 924y^6 + 495y^8 - 66y^{10} + y^{12})(1 - 120y^2$$
$$+ 1820y^4 - 8008y^6 + 12870y^8 - 8008y^{10} + 1820y^{12} - 120y^{14}$$
$$+ y^{16})dy$$
$$= \int_0^1 (1 - 186y^2 + 10235y^4 - 188452y^6 + 1553673y^8 - 6562534y^{10}$$
$$+ 15209211y^{12} - 20060280y^{14} + 15209211y^{16} - 6562534y^{18}$$
$$+ 1553673y^{20} - 188452y^{22} + 10235y^{24} - 186y^{26} + y^{28})dy$$
$$= 1 - 62 + \frac{10235}{5} - \frac{188452}{7} + \frac{1553673}{9} - \frac{6562534}{11} + \frac{15209211}{13}$$
$$- \frac{20060280}{15} + \frac{15209211}{17} - \frac{6562534}{19} + \frac{1553673}{21} - \frac{188452}{23}$$
$$+ \frac{10235}{25} - \frac{186}{27} + \frac{1}{29}$$
$$= -855.72005$$

$$a_{44} = \int_0^1 (1 - 120y^2 + 1820y^4 - 8008y^6 + 12870y^8 - 8008y^{10}$$
$$+ 1820y^{12} - 120y^{14} + y^{16})^2 dy$$
$$= \int_0^1 (1 - 240y^2 + 18040y^4 - 452816y^6 + 5260060y^8 - 32253936y^{10}$$
$$+ 112900424y^{12} - 235712080y^{14} + 300546630y^{16}$$
$$- 235712080y^{18} + 112900424y^{20} - 32253936^{22} + 5260060y^{24}$$
$$- 452816y^{26} + 18040y^{28} - 240y^{30} + y^{32})dy$$
$$= 1 - \frac{240}{3} + \frac{18040}{5} - \frac{452816}{7} + \frac{5260060}{9} - \frac{32253936}{11} + \frac{112900424}{13}$$
$$- \frac{235712080}{15} + \frac{300546630}{17} - \frac{235712080}{19} + \frac{112900424}{21}$$
$$- \frac{32253936}{23} + \frac{5260060}{25} - \frac{452816}{27} + \frac{18040}{29} - \frac{240}{31} + \frac{1}{33}$$
$$= 3051.4444$$

$$b_0 = \frac{1}{3} = 0.333333333$$

$$b_1 = \frac{1}{3} - \frac{6}{5} + \frac{1}{7} = -0.723809524$$

$$b_2 = \frac{1}{3} - \frac{28}{5} + \frac{70}{7} - \frac{28}{9} + \frac{1}{11} = 1.713131313$$

$$b_3 = \frac{1}{3} - \frac{66}{5} + \frac{495}{7} - \frac{924}{9} + \frac{495}{11} - \frac{66}{13} + \frac{1}{15} = -4.8293040$$

$$b_4 = \frac{1}{3} - \frac{120}{5} + \frac{1820}{7} - \frac{8008}{9} + \frac{12870}{11} - \frac{8008}{13} + \frac{1820}{15} - \frac{120}{17} + \frac{1}{19}$$
$$= 14.882696$$

Our system, then, is

$1.000000000c_0 - 0.8000000000c_1 + 1.777777778c_2 - 4.923076923c_3 + 15.05882353c_4 = 0.3333333333$
$-0.800000000c_0 + 2.996825397c_1 - 6.991763792c_2 + 19.55992243c_3 - 60.03400658c_4 = -0.7238095238$
$1.777777778c_0 - 6.991763792c_1 + 23.97009004c_2 - 73.20130795c_3 + 231.9181486c_4 = 1.713131313$
$-4.923076923c_0 + 19.55992243c_1 - 73.20130795c_2 + 254.3733424c_3 - 855.7200398c_4 = -4.829304029$
$15.05882353c_0 - 60.03400658c_1 + 231.9181486c_2 - 855.7200398c_3 + 3051.444046c_4 = 14.88269693.$

Dividing by leading coefficients, and eliminating below the diagonal on successively smaller subsystems, we have

$c_0 - 0.8000000000c_1 + 1.777777778c_2 - 4.923076932c_3 + 15.05882353c_4 = 0.3333333333$
$-c_0 + 3.746031746c_1 - 8.739704740c_2 + 24.44990303c_3 - 75.04250822c_4 = -0.9047619047$
$c_0 - 3.932867132c_1 + 13.48317564c_2 - 41.17573571c_3 + 130.4539585c_4 = 0.9636363636$
$-c_0 + 3.973109243c_1 - 14.86901567c_2 + 51.66958517c_3 - 173.8181330c_4 = -0.9809523809$
$c_0 - 3.986633249c_1 + 15.40081455c_2 - 56.82515889c_3 + 202.6349561c_4 = 0.9883040929,$

and

$$c_0 - 0.8000000000c_1 + 1.777777778c_2 - 4.923076923c_3 + 15.05882353c_4 = 0.3333333333$$
$$2.946031746c_1 - 6.961926962c_2 + 19.52682611c_3 - 59.98368469c_4 = -0.5714285714$$
$$-0.186835386c_1 + 4.74347090c_2 - 16.72583268c_3 + 55.41145028c_4 = 0.0588744589$$
$$0.040242111c_1 - 1.38584003c_2 + 10.49384946c_3 - 43.3641745c_4 = -0.0173160173$$
$$-0.013524006c_1 + 0.53179888c_2 - 5.15557372c_3 + 28.8168231c_4 = 0.0073517120,$$

and

$$c_0 - 0.8000000000c_1 + 1.777777778c_2 - 4.923076923c_3 + 15.05882353c_4 = 0.3333333333$$
$$c_1 - 2.363154087c_2 + 6.628179121c_3 - 20.36084124c_4 = -0.1939655172$$
$$-c_1 + 25.38850376c_2 - 89.52176050c_3 + 296.5789910c_4 = 0.3151140699$$
$$c_1 - 34.43375580c_2 + 260.7678672c_3 - 1077.582001c_4 = -0.4302959479$$
$$-c_1 + 39.32258533c_2 - 381.2164620c_3 + 2130.790469c_4 = 0.5436046094,$$

and

$$c_0 - 0.8000000000c_1 + 1.777777778c_2 - 4.923076923c_3 + 15.05882353c_4 = 0.3333333333$$
$$c_1 - 2.363154087c_2 + 6.628179121c_3 - 20.36084124c_4 = -0.1939655172$$
$$23.02534967c_2 - 82.89358138c_3 + 276.2181498c_4 = 0.1211485527$$
$$-9.04525204c_2 + 171.2461067c_3 - 781.003010c_4 = -0.1151818780$$
$$4.88882953c_2 - 120.4485948c_3 + 1053.208468c_4 = 0.1133086615,$$

and

$$c_2 - 3.600100870c_3 + 11.99626297c_4 = 0.005261529333$$
$$-c_2 + 18.93215423c_3 - 86.34397433c_4 = -0.01273396003$$
$$c_2 - 24.63751171c_3 + 215.4316205c_4 = 0.02317705307,$$

and

$$15.33205336c_3 - 74.34771136c_4 = -0.00747243070$$
$$-5.70535748c_3 + 129.0876462c_4 = 0.01044309304,$$

and

$$c_3 - 4.849168576c_4 = -0.0004873731211$$
$$-c_3 + 22.62568938c_4 = 0.001830401175,$$

$$17.77652080c_4 = 0.001343028054.$$

Our system in Gaussian 'echelon form' is then

$$c_0 - 0.8000000000c_1 + 1.777777778c_2 - 4.923076923c_3 + 15.05882353c_4 = 0.3333333333$$
$$c_1 - 2.363154087c_2 + 6.628179121c_3 - 20.36084124c_4 = -0.1939655172$$
$$c_2 - 3.600100870c_3 + 11.99626297c_4 = 0.005261529333$$
$$c_3 - 4.849168576c_4 = -0.0004873731211$$
$$c_4 = 0.00007555066984.$$

Back substitution yields for the (5×5) case,

$$c_4 = 0.00007555066984$$
$$c_3 = -0.0004873731211 + 0.0003663579341$$

or $\quad c_3 = -0.0001210151870$
$$c_2 = 0.005261529333 - 0.000906325703 - 0.000435666880$$

or $c_2 = 0.003919536750$

$c_1 = -0.1939655172 + 0.0015382752 + 0.0008021103$
$+ 0.0092624693$

or $c_1 = -0.1823626624$

$c_0 = 0.3333333333 - 0.0011377042 - 0.0005957671 - 0.0069680653$
$- 0.1458901299$

or $c_0 = 0.1787416668,$

and

$$\sum_{h=0}^{4} c_h b_h = +0.0595805556$$
$$+0.1319958318$$
$$+0.0067146811$$
$$+0.0005844191$$
$$+0.0011243977$$
$$= +0.1999998853$$

Back substitution yields for the (3×3) case,

$$c_2 = 0.00526152934$$
$$c_1 = -0.19396552 + 0.01243380$$

or $c_1 = -0.18153172$

or $c_0 = 0.33333333 - 0.00935383 - 0.14522537$

or $c_0 = 0.17875413,$

and $\sum_{h=0}^{2} c_h b_h = 0.059584710 + 0.13139439 + 0.009013691 = 0.199992791$

Back substitution yields for the (2×2) case

$$c_1 = -0.19396552$$
$$c_0 = 0.33333333 - 0.15517242$$

or $c_0 = 0.1786091$

and $\sum_{h=0}^{1} c_h b_h = 0.14039409 + 0.059386970 = 0.199781061$

We have repeatedly emphasized that maximum error bounds are usually difficult to compute. Computing them is so cumbersome with our present hand-computation method that we have resorted to evaluation of $|1 - u^n(1,1)|$ as an estimate of

$$\max_{0 \leq x \leq 1} |x^2 - u^n(x,1)|.$$

On a machine, one might undertake to find all roots of the function $2x - u_x{}''(x,1)$ by the methods of Chapter 1, and evaluate $|x^2 - u''(x,1)|$ at all these stationary points and at $(1,1)$, to find $\max_{0 \le x \le 1} |x^2 - u''(x,1)|$.

Here, we have computed the following:

$$p_0(1, 1) = 1$$

$$u^1(1,1) = \sum_{k=0}^{1} c_k \, p_k(1,1) \qquad p_1(1,1) = -4$$

$$= +0.17816091 \qquad p_2(1,1) = 16$$

$$\underline{+0.77586208} \qquad p_3(1,1) = -64$$

$$= \quad 0.95402299 \qquad p_4(1,1) = 256$$

$$\max_A |u - u^1| \le \max_{0 \le x \le 1} |x^2 - u^1(x,1)| \overset{?}{=} |1 - 0.954| = 0.046$$

$$u^2(1,1) = \sum_{k=0}^{2} c_k p_k(1,1) = +0.17875413$$

$$+0.72612688$$

$$\underline{+0.08418447}$$

$$= \quad 0.98906548$$

$$\max_A |u - u^2| \le \max_{0 \le x \le 1} |x^2 - u^2(x,1)| \overset{?}{=} |1.00 - 0.989| = 0.011$$

$$\cong 20\% \quad \text{of} \quad \max_A |u - u^1|$$

$$u^4(1,1) = \sum_{k=0}^{4} c_k p_k(1,1) = +0.17874166$$

$$+0.72945065$$

$$+0.06271259$$

$$+0.00774497$$

$$\underline{+0.01934097}$$

$$= +0.99799084$$

$$\max_A |u - u^4| \le \max_{0 \le x \le 1} |x^2 - u^4(x,1)| \overset{?}{=} |1.000 - 0.998| = 0.002$$

$$\cong 4\% \quad \text{of} \quad \max_A |u - u^1| \cong 18.2\% \quad \text{of} \quad \max_A |u - u^2|.$$

L^2 error bounds squared are given as follows where $H = 1$:

$2 \times 2:$ $\int_A \int (u - u^1)^2 dA \leq 8\left(\int_0^1 (x^2)^2 dx\right) - \sum c_h b_h = 8(\frac{1}{5} - 0.19978)$

$$= 8(0.00022) = 0.00176$$

$3 \times 3:$ $\int_A \int (u - u^2)^2 dA \leq 8(\frac{1}{5} - 0.199993) = 8(0.000007) = 0.000056$

$5 \times 5:$ $\int_A \int (u - u^4)^2 dA \leq 8(\frac{1}{5} - 0.19999989) = 8(0.00000011)$

$$= 0.00000088.$$

One must take the square root of the above numbers for comparison with maximum error bound.

5. A NOTE ON RALEIGH-RITZ METHODS

By variational methods it is easily shown that if $u \in C_L$

$$\int_A \left(\sum_{i=1}^n u_{x_i}^2\right) dA \leq \int_A \left(\sum_{i=1}^n \varphi_{x_i}^2\right) dA$$

$\forall \varphi \in C^1(A \cup \Sigma) \ni \varphi = f$ on Σ, then u is a solution of the Dirichlet problem [5],

$$\Delta u = 0 \quad \text{in} \quad A, \quad u = f \quad \text{on} \quad \Sigma$$

This is called the Dirichlet principle, and many boundary value problems can be expressed, as here, as the 'Euler equation' for minimization of some quadratic form. Consideration of the minimization, or even of existence of a minimum of such a form, without attention to the associated partial differential equation is usually referred to as a 'direct method,' in deference to a feeling that minimization of such an integral is physically more fundamental than the equating of forces. This is because of the generality that the Hamilton's principle has been found to have in physics.

Taking an approximating family $\{v^k\} \ni v^k \in C_L \ \forall \ k = 0,1,\cdots,N, \ \wedge \ v^0 = f$ on Σ, $v^k = 0$ on $\Sigma \ \forall \ k = 1,\cdots,N$, we write

$$u^N = v^0 + \sum_{k=1}^N c_k v^k$$

and determine c_k, $k = 1,\cdots,N, \ni$

$$Q_N(c_1,\cdots,c_N) = \int_A \sum_{i=1}^n (u_{x_i}^N)^2 \ dA$$

is minimized. We find again that we require the root of a linear system with positive definite coefficient matrix, so that our best iteration method, accelerated successive replacements, is still available. It can be easily shown, in fact, that from any approximation of the solution of the linear system, the associated value of Q_N can be computed as we computed μ_n above. Then from the Dirichlet principle,

$$Q = \int_A \left(\sum_{i=1}^n u_{x_i}^2 \right) dA \leq Q_N$$

so that we can compute an upper bound for the functional Q from any approximation of the solution of the relevant linear system. A lower bound can be obtained in like manner from Sir William Thomson's (or Lord Kelvin's) principle [6].

If the value of some quadratic functional Q of the solution of a boundary value problem is itself of interest for applications, then a variational principle involving Q should be used, if possible, for computational procedures; however, methods using such functionals usually fail to yield computable error bounds for the solution of the boundary value problem, except when the least squares procedure, formulated earlier, is employed.

Since variational methods have, by way of Hamilton's principle, played a primary role in the mathematical formulation of physics, it will often happen that the minimum value of such a functional will be the quantity of interest to a physical investigator. In our numerical example of Chapter 5, sec. 4, the Dirichlet integral Q over the two-unit square is called the torsional rigidity, where u is the torsion, and it is the torsional rigidity of the cross-section, not the torsion, that is the quantity usually required in the design of beams. If we had presented this example for any purpose other than a pedagogical one, we would have preferred to compute an upper bound for the torsional rigidity, rather than to compute an approximate torsion and to compute error bounds for that.

EXERCISE

Using $N = 3$, compute an upper bound for the torsional rigidity on a two-unit square.

Among other quantities of importance in physics that can be expressed as minima of quadratic functions over a region A are eigenvalues of certain linear partial differential equations over the region A. This 'application' of the above techniques was first undertaken by Lord Raleigh, and two years later by W. Ritz. Many excellent treatments *in extenso* of this subject are available, so that it is not essential (or really feasible) to give coverage here. In fact, many courses in engineering and mathematical physics dwell heavily on this topic. We wish only to make the distinctions italicized above, and to offer the relevant numerical comments. Since eigenvalues are usually expressed as minima of quadratic forms, it is easier to give analytic specification to upper bounds rather than to lower bounds, which, in general, are far more difficult to compute. The best-known method for computing lower bounds is that of A. Weinstein [7].

6. ERROR BOUNDS FOR WEAK SOLUTIONS

Where R is a region in E^n, we say for $F: R \to R^1 \land \beta \in R^1$, that $F \in C^{(\beta)}(R)$ if F satisfies the following Hölder (or order β Lipschitz) relation[12] in Euclidean norm $\| \ \|: \forall \ x,y \in R, \ \exists \ K > 0 \ni |F(x) - F(y)| < K\|x - y\|^\beta$. With reference to the boundary value problems of Fichera for second-order partial differential equations of elliptic-parabolic type, as given in Chapter 5, Sec. 2, the following conditions and notations are addended:

$$\exists \ D \supset \bar{A} \ni a^{ij} \in C^{(2+\alpha)}(D), \ b^i \in C^{(1+\alpha)}(D), \ c \in C^{(\alpha)}(D), \ 0 < \alpha < 1$$

$$\Sigma^0 = \{x \mid (x \in \Sigma - \Sigma^3) \land (b(x) = (b^i(x) - a_{x_j}{}^{ij}(x))n_i = 0)\}$$

$$\Sigma^{(1)} = \Sigma^1 - \Sigma^0, \ \Gamma = \overline{(\Sigma^0 \cup \Sigma^2)} - (\Sigma^0 \cup \Sigma^2)$$

$$L^*u = (a^{ij}u)_{x_i x_j} - (b^i u)_{x_i} + cu$$

$$\frac{\partial}{\partial \gamma} = a^{ij} \cos (n,x_j) \frac{\partial}{\partial x_i} \qquad \text{Conormal derivative}$$

Under these conditions, we indicate (without proof or detailed explanation) how it is possible to consider solutions of these problems in a weaker sense than has so far been expounded, and how one may now consider computing error bounds for weak solutions of a large class of boundary value problems. To this limited purpose only, we suggest that the student who has not studied Lebesgue measure interpret 'f measurable' as 'f integrable' and 'a set of measure zero' simply as a set over which the functional values of the integrand have no effect on the value of the integral.[13]

---

[12] Or for $N = \{x \mid (x \in \Omega) \land (x < \beta)\}$, $m = \max N$, $F \in C^{(m)}(R)$, and all directional derivatives of F of order m satisfy a Hölder condition of order $\alpha = \beta - m$.

[13] For example, the values of data functions at corners of a square do not affect the value of a boundary integral.

As expounded in [4], then,

Definition

A function u, which is bounded and measurable in A, will be called a generalized (weak) solution of the boundary value problem of Chapter 5, Sec. 2, if $(v \in C^2(A)) \wedge (v(x) = 0 \; \forall \; x \in \Sigma^{(1)} \cup \Sigma^3) \Rightarrow \int_A uL^*vdA = \int_A vgdA - \int_{\Sigma^3} \partial v/\partial \gamma \; ds + \int_{\Sigma^2} bfvds.$

As to motivation for such a definition, we only note[14] that it is possible than $u \notin C^2(A)$, and yet the defining integral identity is satisfied for every appropriate 'test' function, and also that from a Green's identity for L, derived out of the divergence theorem, it becomes evident that if u is a weak solution, and $u \in C_L$ (see Chapter 5, Sec. 2), then u satisfies the differential equation and the boundary value problem in the classical sense.

Modern theories of partial differential equations give existence of solutions for large classes of boundary value problems in some weak or generalized sense as above. This, as noted, is what is given by Fichera [1] for his boundary value problems for second-order equations of elliptic-parabolic type. However, the formulas for computing error bounds in the Fichera theory as given in Chapter 5, Sec. 2 (or [1]), and, as far as we know, in any other general theory of boundary value problems, are valid only when it is known that a regular solution exists. Then only error bounds to regular solutions are computed. In general, the question of existence of a regular solution is extremely difficult. This fact—perhaps ten to fifteen years ago—caused the several theories of generalized solutions to be initiated. It still causes a great deal of work of a special technical character whose nature is to find which ones of the known weak solutions of a class of boundary value problems can be proven to be regular. One speaks of 'regularizing' solutions, but the process is difficult, likely to be special, and cannot be lightly undertaken.

All this leaves the field of computing in a somewhat tenuous state. Error bounds can be stated either when it is known that solutions are regular or stated conditional to the later establishment of regularity. Recently, the O. A. Oleinik paper [4] alleviated this situation for a large class of problems. A formula for maximum error bounds for weak solutions is shown in the following theorem quoted (without proof) from Oleinik's paper.

---

[14] But see Appendix D.

Theorem

$(\exists\ c_0 \in R^1 \ni c \leq c_0 < 0) \wedge (g \text{ bndd on } A) \wedge (g \text{ measurable on } A) \wedge$
$(f \text{ bndd on } \Sigma^2 \cup \Sigma^3) \wedge (f \text{ measurable on } \Sigma^2 \cup \Sigma^3) \wedge (\Gamma \text{ has measure}$
$zero) \Rightarrow \exists$ *a generalized (weak) solution of the boundary value problem*
of Chapter 5, Sec. 2. $\ni$

$$|u| \leq \max \left\{ \sup_A \left| \frac{g}{c_0} \right|, \ \sup_{\Sigma^2 \cup \Sigma^3} f \right\}.$$

It should be carefully noted that Oleinik claims here only that a weak solution exists with this property—not that all weak solutions have this property. *Another theorem provides uniqueness of weak solutions.*
The point here is that if

$$W^n = \sum_{k=1}^{n} c_k v^k,$$

computed, say, by our least squares procedure, is considered an approximation to a generalized solution W of a boundary value problem $LW = g$ in A, $W = f$ in $\Sigma^2 \cup \Sigma^3$, then we have

$$L(W - W^n) = g - LW^n \quad \text{in} \quad A, \quad \wedge \ W - W^n = f - W^n \quad \text{in} \quad \Sigma^2 \cup \Sigma^3,$$

so that, putting $u = W - W^n$, the theorem yields

$$|W - W^n| \leq \max \left\{ \sup_A \left| \frac{g - LW^n}{c_0} \right|, \ \sup_{\Sigma^2 \cup \Sigma^3} (f - W^n) \right\}.$$

Mrs. Oleinik's method is a singular perturbation technique. She considers for $\varepsilon > 0$, a Dirichlet problem for the operator

$$Lu = (1 + \varepsilon)a^{ij}u_{x_i x_j} + b^i u_{x_i} + cu,$$

which is of elliptic type, and for which the classical theory gives a maximum principle. Moreover, she considers a boundary value problem for a sequence of data functions f_n, g_n, which are such that regular solutions exist when $\varepsilon = 0$. A very difficult argument follows, requiring a thorough knowledge of the Fichera results for regular solutions, which gives the stated result in the limit.

For the reasons of computability and computational efficiencies made apparent in Chapter 5, Sec. 2, we would like to have the Oleinik error bound result available in L^2 as well as T norm. It seems reasonable to believe that the methods of Oleinik can be adapted to this purpose, since the Fichera theory gives L^2 error bounds for regular solutions. In fact, Fichera obtains maximum error bounds in a secondary manner by letting $p \to \infty$ in his L^p bounds. We therefore propose a research exercise.

RESEARCH EXERCISE

Find formulas for L^2 error bounds for weak solutions of boundary value problems, bearing in mind the value of adapting error bound formulas to a form that is computable in the sense developed in Chapter 5, Sec. 2 for L^2 error bounds of regular solutions.

REFERENCES

[1] Gaetano Fichera, 'On a unified theory of boundary value problems for elliptic-parabolic equations of second order,' in *Boundary Problems in Differential Equations*, R. E. Langer, ed., University of Wisconsin Press, Madison, Wisc., 1960.

[2] Gaetano Fichera, 'Formule di maggiorazione connesse ad una classe di transformazioni lineari,' *Ann. Mat. Pure Appl.*, *Serie* IV, **Torno XXXIII,** (1954).

[3] H. M. Lieberstein, 'A continuous method in numerical analysis applied to examples from a new class of boundary value problems,' Univ. Roma, *1st Naz. Alta Mat. Rend. Mat. Appl.*, **19** (1960), 347–378.

[4] O. A. Oleinik, 'A problem of Fichera,' *Soviet Math.*, **5**, (1964) 1129–1133. (Translation of *Doklady*, *Acad. Sci. USSR*, **157**).

[5] H. Sagan, *Boundary and Eigenvalue Problems in Mathematical Physics*, John Wiley & Sons, Inc., New York, 1963.

[6] G. Polya and G. Szego, *Isoperimetric Inequalities in Mathematical Physics*, Princeton University Press, Princeton, N.J., 1951.

[7] S. M. Gould, *Variational Methods for Eigenvalue Problems*, University of Toronto Press, Toronto, 1957.

CHAPTER 6

ITERATIVE METHODS FOR NONLINEAR ALGEBRAIC SYSTEMS

The analyses of iterative methods for nonlinear algebraic systems can be quite difficult and they often involve sophisticated mathematical techniques that are beyond the scope of this volume. Therefore, we offer only some more or less rough considerations to guide computational procedures to be used.

1. PICARD-PEANO ITERATION

We pointed out earlier that the theory of contractive maps could be applied on a complete metric space. Let $g : A \to E^n$, $A \subset E^n$; then

$$x \in E^n \ni x = g(x)$$

is a root of the system of equations

$$x_i - g_i(x_1, \cdots, x_n) = 0, \quad i = 1, \cdots, n,$$

which can be 'reached' by the Picard-Peano iteration

$$x^0 \quad \text{given} \quad x^{k+1} = g(x^k)$$

if g is contractive in a neighborhood containing x^0. A general theory of contractive maps has been applied in some detail to approximation of solutions of polynomial systems by B. Marcus [1], and this analysis has been extended by him [2] to approximation of solutions of infinite polynomial systems by iteration of finite subsystems. It will be recalled that application of the Galerkin procedure for approximation of solutions of boundary value problems, equivalent to least squares for linear differential equations, gave infinite systems of nonlinear algebraic equations to be solved for nonlinear differential equations. It seems reasonable to hope that some choices of differential equation and approximating family can be made so that contractive polynomial systems are involved.

The full power of a theory of Picard iteration, however, does not lie in its direct application to a function g whose fixed point is sought. It will be recalled that Newton iteration for a function of one real variable f could be viewed as Picard iteration of the function $x - f(x)$, accelerated in a 'best' way, or simply as Picard iteration of the function $x - f(x)/f'(x)$. Linear iterative methods for linear systems $Ax = (B + C)x = b$ could be viewed as Picard iteration of the function $-B^{-1}Cx + B^{-1}b$ for some choice of $-B^{-1}C$. In general, we seek a mapping that has a fixed point in common with the function for which a fixed point is sought, but for which Picard iteration is more efficient. To illustrate this point, we develop a theory of such Picard iterations for a function of one real variable and leave the question open as to how these particular methods can be extended to functions on finite dimensional spaces or function spaces. Unless care is exercised 'to make Picard iteration efficient' it can be quite slow and inefficient.

For a function g of one real variable, suppose we are dissatisfied with the restriction $|g'(x)| < 1$ (or by the infimum of Lipschitz coefficients being less than one). We may like to perform the iteration $x^k = g(x^{k+1})$, since we could then hope to get convergence for $|g'(x)| > 1$, but this iteration would usually be impossible to perform. Following our development for analogue methods for linear systems, note that

$$x^{k+1} = g(x^k) \Rightarrow x^{k+1} - x^k = -x^k + g(x^k)$$

and that, approximately,

$$\frac{dx}{dt} = -x + g(x).$$

An asymptotic solution of this equation for $t \to \infty$ will give a fixed point of g. If we look for an asymptotic solution for $t \to -\infty$ and then revert back to our iteration form, we should accomplish to some extent our desired 'iteration in the reverse direction.' We have, replacing t by $-t$,

$$x^{k+1} - x^k \cong \frac{dx}{dt} = x - g(x) = x^k - g(x^k)$$

or

(6.1) $$x^{k+1} = 2x^k - g(x^k).$$

Note that the function defined by $2x - g(x) = x + (x - g(x))$ has a fixed point wherever g does. We examine the iteration (6.1). We have

$$|(2x - g(x))'| < 1 \Leftrightarrow -1 < 2 - g'(x) < 1 \Leftrightarrow 1 < g'(x) < 3,$$

so that the interval of values of g', for which the iteration converges, has been 'flipped over' from $(-1,1)$ to $(1,3)$ by adoption of (6.1) over iteration of g. The form of (6.1) suggests the form

(6.2) $$x^{k+1} = x^k + F(x^k - g(x^k)),$$

where $F(0) = 0$. We have

$$|(x + F(x - g(x)))'| < 1 \Leftrightarrow -1 < 1 + F'(x - g(x)) \cdot (1 - g'(x)) < 1$$

$$\Leftrightarrow -2 < (1 - g'(x)) \cdot F'(x - g(x)) < 0$$

$$\Leftrightarrow 1 < g'(x) < 1 + \frac{2}{F'(x - g(x))}$$

if $F' \geq 0$. This suggests that if we wish to find a fixed point of a function g whose derivative is greater than one, we use a function F in (6.2) $\ni F(0) = 0$, $F' \geq 0$ and $F'(0) = \varepsilon^2 \in R_+{}^1$. Then our iteration will converge in a neighborhood of the fixed point, if we choose an appropriate value of ε. Thus if we put $F(t) = \frac{1}{3}[(t + \varepsilon)^3 - \varepsilon^3]$, such an iteration is

(6.3) $$x^{k+1} = x^k + \frac{1}{3}[(x^k - g(x^k) + \varepsilon)^3 - \varepsilon^3],$$

for which in a neighborhood N of the fixed point the factor of reduction is

$$\operatorname*{lub}_{N} |1 + (x - g(x) + \varepsilon)^2(1 - g'(x))|.$$

This is evidently contractive in the neighborhood of the fixed point given by

$$(x - g(x) + \varepsilon)^2(1 - g'(x)) > -2$$

or

$$g'(x) < 1 + 2\frac{1}{(x - g(x) + \varepsilon)^2},$$

which can be made as large as we desire in a neighborhood of the fixed point. It should be noted that no computational complications are involved in using (6.3), since only powers are introduced; in particular, the complication of division by a derivative, as occurs in the Newton method, does not occur.

To find a fixed point for a function g whose derivative is less than -1, we propose iteration, using a function F in (6.2) $\ni F(0) = 0$, $F'(0) = -\varepsilon^2$, and $F' \leq 0$, so that convergence is obtained for

$$1 - \frac{2}{|F'(x - g(x))|} = 1 + \frac{2}{F'(x - g(x))} < g'(x) < 1.$$

Of course, we use $F(t) = \frac{1}{3}[-(t + \varepsilon)^3 + \varepsilon^3]$. Then (6.2) becomes

$$x^{k+1} = x^k + \frac{1}{3}[-(x^k - g(x^k) + \varepsilon)^3 + \varepsilon^3],$$

and convergence is obtained in a neighborhood of the fixed point given by

$$g'(x) > 1 - 2\frac{1}{(x - g(x) + \varepsilon)^2}.$$

We now have iterations for cases where $g'(x) > 1$ and $g'(x) < -1$. Note then that the function

$$G(x)\begin{cases} = x + \frac{1}{3}[(x - g(x) + \varepsilon)^3 - \varepsilon^3] \; \forall \; x \ni g'(x) > 1 \\ = x + \frac{1}{3}[-(x - g(x) + \varepsilon)^3 + \varepsilon^3] \; \forall \; x \ni g'(x) < -1 \end{cases}$$

is contractive in a neighborhood of the fixed point for g. Therefore, if $|g'(x)| > 1$, iteration of G

(6.4) $$x^{k+1} = G(x^k)$$

should provide a fixed point for g, thus giving our desired 'inverse direction of iteration.' Of course, in computational practice, we program the two formulas of (6.4) and test for the sign of $g'(x^k)$ before deciding which of the formulas will be used to compute x^{k+1}.

2. NEWTON METHOD

The Newton method for algebraic systems consists in successive linearizations of the functions

$$f_i(x_1,\cdots,x_n) = 0, \quad i = 1,\cdots,n,$$

of the system whose root is sought, and of solutions of the resulting linear systems. Thus, if x^0 is given, we solve the linear system

$$f_i(x_1^k,\cdots,x_n^k) + \sum_{j=1}^{n} f_{i,j}(x_1^k,\cdots,x_n^k) \cdot (x_j^{k+1} - x_j^k) = 0, \quad i = 1,\cdots,n$$

in order to compute x^{k+1} from x^k (provided, of course, $f_{i,j} = (\partial f_i/\partial x_j)$ exists $\forall\, i,j = 1,\cdots,n$). As far as pure analysis is concerned, this is a definite and important method. However, its specification as a computational procedure is incomplete until the method of solving the linear systems is specified. Many older textbooks assume that one would use determinants, but, at least for large systems, it would be absurd to do so. One might wish to use elimination, but with any direct method one faces the very real possibility that, as the root of the nonlinear system is approached, it becomes less and less feasible to solve the linear system accurately by direct methods because of the loss of accuracy in subtractions. Indeed, our own experiences indicate that this will usually be the case.

If the nonlinear algebraic system arose out of finite-difference replacement of a Dirichlet problem for a nonlinear elliptic partial differential equation,

$$a^{ij}(x,u,u_{x_1},\cdots,u_{x_n})u_{x_i x_j} = h(x,u,u_{x_1},\cdots,u_{x_n}),$$

where $a^{ij}\lambda_i\lambda_j > 0, \quad x = (x_1,\cdots,x_n),$

one who is trained in iterative methods for linear systems would surely expect that the best method for solving the linearized systems would be accelerated successive replacements. In fact, one of our major interests in presenting linear theory has been to develop such insights into methods for nonlinear systems. However, it should be noted that the student is now piling one iteration on the other and is admonished, besides, not to forget a third convergence question of the solution of difference analogues to solution of the boundary value problem for the differential equation. We are driven then, for accuracy, to make a step that costs a great deal of computing time and efficiency of programming and that takes us in a direction we would like to avoid for theoretical purposes. Because of this dual difficulty—loss of accuracy in solving the linear systems by direct methods, and loss of both practical and theoretical efficiency in solving the linear system by iteration—the Newton method, unadorned, cannot be considered a computational procedure at all for large systems, and can probably rarely be so considered for small systems.

3. ACCELERATED SUCCESSIVE REPLACEMENTS

For nonlinear algebraic systems, we have proposed the iterations

$$(6.5) \qquad x_i^{k+1} = x_i^k - \frac{f_i(x_1^k,\cdots,x_n^k)}{f_{i,i}(x_1^k,\cdots,x_n^k)}$$

and where $\omega \in R^1$,

$$(6.6) \qquad x_i^{k+1} = x_i^k - \omega \frac{f_i(x_1^{k+1},\cdots,x_{i-1}^{k+1},\, x_i^k,\cdots,x_n^k)}{f_{i,i}(x_1^{k+1},\cdots,x_{i-1}^{k+1},\, x_i^k,\cdots,x_n^k)}.$$

When the system is linear, so that

$$f_i(x_1,\cdots,x_n) = b_i - \sum_{j=1}^{n} a_{ij}x_j,$$

(6.5) reduces to simultaneous replacements, and (6.6) reduces to accelerated successive replacements as developed for linear systems. The method (6.6) is designed to combine in one iteration the Newton successive linearizations and the best method available for solving the linear systems in case the coefficient matrix is positive definite—namely, accelerated successive replacements.

EXERCISE

Show that (6.5) and (6.6) reduce to the linear methods claimed where the system is linear.

EXERCISE[1]

Give a linearized analysis of (6.6), showing that, if the system is 'nearly linear,' it will converge in a neighborhood of the root where the Jacobian matrix has the properties of the coefficient matrix required for convergence of the method for linear systems.

The method (6.6) was devised for use on Dirichlet problems for 'nearly linear' elliptic equations. It worked far better than expected on tests for the two-point boundary value problem for highly nonlinear ordinary differential equations. For a finite-difference replacement of $F(x,y,(dy/dx), (d^2y/dx^2)) = 0$, $y(a) \wedge y(b)$ given, we write

$$f_i(y_1,\cdots,y_n) = F\left(x_i,y_i, \frac{y_{i+1}-y_i}{h}, \frac{y_{i+1}-2y_i+y_{i-1}}{h^2}\right),$$

where x_i, $i = 0,\cdots,n$, $n + 1$, are points of a partition of $(a,b) \ni x_{i+1} - x_i = h \in R^1 \ \forall \ i \in \Omega_n$ and $x_0 = a$, $x_{n+1} = b$, $y_i = y(x_i)$. Putting $y_0 = y(a) \wedge$

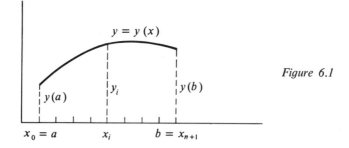

Figure 6.1

$y_{n+1} = y(b)$, we have the finite-difference analogue to be solved. Our iteration formula (6.6) provides one correction formula to be programmed and indexed as points are scanned repeatedly, say, from left to right, and corrected. Because of the ease of programming and proved reliability of the method, it has been used on a large number of problems including, recently, one in corn genetics [4]. Experience has shown that there is little difficulty in finding a workable ω if a systematic search is made, using large mesh size and large tolerance.

C. Bryan [3] has provided a rigorous analysis of (6.5), giving a neighborhood in which it will converge (under some conditions) and providing error bounds. Unfortunately these neighborhoods are

---

[1] Optional.

usually quite small. We are usually forced to find them in practice by performing a large number of iterations on (6.6) and by at least thinking of performing one last iteration on (6.5) to get an error bound, using the Bryan theorem to verify any apparent convergence that seems to arise in the computations.

EXERCISE

Show that if the Newton method for a real valued function of one real variable is accelerated, using a parameter that does not depend on the iteration (i.e., $\omega \in R^1$, not $\omega : \Omega \to R^1$), the iteration obtained is

$$x^{k+1} = x^k - \omega \frac{f(x^k)}{f'(x^k)}.$$

We now prescribe the analogue method associated with (6.6). From (6.6)

$$x_i^{k+1} - x_i^k =$$

$$- \omega \frac{f_i([x_1^{k+1} - x_1^k] + x_1^k, \cdots, [x_{i-1}^{k+1} - x_{i-1}^k] + x_{i-1}^k, x_i^k, \cdots, x_n^k)}{f_{i,i}([x_1^{k+1} - x_1^k] + x_1^k, \cdots, [x_{i-1}^{k+1} - x_{i-1}^k] + x_{i-1}^k, x_i^k, \cdots, x_n^k)}$$

and with our usual necessary approximate replacement, we look for asymptotic solutions $(t \to \infty)$ of

$$(6.7) \qquad \frac{dx_i}{dt} = - \omega \frac{f_i(x_1 + \dfrac{dx_1}{dt}, \cdots, x_{i-1} + \dfrac{dx_{i-1}}{dt}, x_i, \cdots, x_n)}{f_{i,i}\left(x + \dfrac{dx_1}{dt}, \cdots, x_{i-1} + \dfrac{dx_{i-1}}{dt}, x_1, \cdots, x_n\right)}$$

$i = 1, \cdots, n$. As in the linear case, the equations for $(dx_j/dt), j = 1, \cdots, i-1$, are used as function generators in equations for $(dx_j/dt), j = i, \cdots, n$. Of course, linearized analysis leads us to believe that convergence of (6.6) implies asymptotic stability of (6.7), but not vice versa. Liaponov methods, now classical for investigation of asymptotic stability of systems like (6.7), can perhaps be applied also to (6.6). (See [5] or [6].)

The student is asked to review the comments of Chapter 4, Sec. 4, relative to the possibility of using equation (6.7) on analogue equipment that communicates with digital equipment in order to determine an optimum acceleration parameter ω and a good set of initial values. The set of initial values are of paramount importance for iterative solution of nonlinear algebraic equations, unless global uniqueness happens to be available.

4. ITERATIVE MINIMIZATION FOR NONLINEAR LEAST SQUARES PROBLEMS

A method said to be due to Gauss for minimization of a quadratic integral or sum, with respect to parameters that appear nonlinearly, is similar enough to the Newton method to be sometimes confused with it. Statisticians refer to the Gauss-Newton method. For a set of points (x_i, y_i), $x_i \in R^1$, $y_i \in R^1$, $i = 1, \cdots, n$, we ask to determine $c_j \in R^1$, $j = 1, \cdots, m$ $(m < n) \ni$

$$Q(c_1, \cdots, c_m) = \sum_{i=1}^{n} [f(x; c_1, \cdots, c_m) - y_i]^2$$

is minimized where $f: E^{m+1} \to E^1 \wedge (\partial f / \partial c_j)$ exist $\forall j = 1, \cdots, m$. Instead of solving the system $(\partial Q / \partial c_j) = 0$, $j = 1, \cdots, m$, which will only carry us to some stationary point and will in general require iteration to solve, we guess values $c_1^0, c_2^0, \cdots, c_m^0$ and, given $c_1^k, \cdots, c_m^k$, minimize

$$Q_1(c_1^{k+1}, \cdots, c_m^{k+1}) = \sum_{i=1}^{n} \left[\sum_{j=1}^{m} \frac{\partial f^k}{\partial c_j}(x_i) \cdot (c_j^{k+1} - c_j^k) - (y_i - f^k(x_i)) \right]^2,$$

where $f^k(x_i) = f(x_i; c_1^k, \cdots, c_m^k)$, by solving the linear system $\partial Q_1 / \partial c_h^{k+1} = 0$, $h = 1, \cdots, m$. Of course, c_j^{k+1} is then computed from c_j^k. The linear system to be solved is

$$\sum_{j=1}^{m} \left[\sum_{i=1}^{n} \frac{\partial f^k(x_i)}{\partial c_j} \frac{\partial f^k(x_i)}{\partial c_h} \right] (c_j^{k+1} - c_j^k) = \sum_{i=1}^{n} (y_i - f^k(x_i)) \frac{\partial f^k(x_j)}{\partial c_h}$$

$h = 1, \cdots, n$. Here the linear system has a positive definite coefficient matrix at every iteration, so that the method of accelerated successive replacements is available for accurate solution. Experience has shown that, in using direct methods to solve the linear systems involved at each iteration, one is almost always plagued with a serious loss of accuracy in solving the linear systems as the sequence $\{c^k\}$ approaches its supposed limit, so that when used in this manner, the method seldom works. Because of this, the method has fallen into bad repute, and some method of steepest descent has often been substituted for it. It would seem that, with the suggested modification of solving the linearized systems by accelerated successive replacements, it is unnecessary to abandon an otherwise sound technique.

However, we once again find ourselves piling one iteration upon the other, so we now prescribe an iterative procedure that, like (6.6) for finding roots, should serve for our nonlinear least squares procedures to combine the linearization iterations with the accelerated successive replacements iterations for solving the linear systems involved after each linearization. It is

$$
(6.8) \quad c_h^{k+1} = c_h^k - \omega \frac{\sum_{i=1}^{n} \frac{\partial f}{\partial c_h}(x_i; c_1^{k+1}, \cdots, c_{h-1}^{k+1}, c_h^k, \cdots, c_m^k) \cdot [f(x_i; c_1^{k+1}, \cdots, c_{h-1}^{k+1}, c_h^k, \cdots, c_m^k) - y_i]}{\sum_{i=1}^{n} \left[\frac{\partial f}{\partial c_h}(x_i; c_1^{k+1}, \cdots, c_{h-1}^{k+1}, c_h^k, \cdots, c_m^k)\right]^2}.
$$

The method can be applied, of course, to finding roots of a system of equations $F_i(x_1, \cdots, x_m) = 0$, by replacing $f(x_i; c_1, \cdots, c_m)$ above by $F_i(x_1, \cdots, x_m)$, and considering minimization of

$$
Q = \sum_{i=1}^{n} F_i^2(x_1, \cdots, x_m).
$$

Our iterative method (6.8) then becomes

$$
(6.9) \quad x_h^{k+1} = x_h^k - \omega \frac{\sum_{i=1}^{m} F_{i,h}(x_1^{k+1}, \cdots, x_{h-1}^{k+1}, x_h^k, \cdots, x_n^k) F_i(x_1^{k+1}, \cdots, x_{h-1}^{k+1}, x_h^k, \cdots, x_n^k)}{\sum_{i=1}^{m} F_{i,h}^2(x_1^{k+1}, \cdots, x_{h-1}^{k+1}, x_h^k, \cdots, x_n^k)}
$$

which should be, considering its origin, almost a universally valid iteration for finding roots of nonlinear systems if such roots exist.

EXERCISE

Show that if $F_i(x_1, \cdots, x_m) = 0$ is the linear system $Ax = b$, then (6.9) is accelerated successive replacements applied to the system $A^T A x = A^T b$.

Let us see what the method amounts to when used in connection with approximation of the solution of the two-point boundary value problem for a nonlinear ordinary differential equation. We have

$$
G(x, y, y', y'') = 0, \; y(a) \wedge y(b) \quad \text{given},
$$

and immediately write

$$
F(x, y, y', y'') = G(x, y + w, y' + w', y'' + w'') = 0,
$$

by putting $y = y(x) - w(x)$, where w is some function $\ni w(a) = y(a) \wedge w(b) = y(b)$. Consider an approximating family $\{v^k(x)\} \ni v^k(a) = v^k(b) = 0 \; \forall \, k = 1, \cdots, n$. We determine

$$y^n(x) = \sum_{j=1}^{n} c_j v^j(x),$$

by asking that

$$Q(c_1, \cdots, c_n) = \int_a^b F^2(x, y^n(x), y^{n\prime}(x), \, y^{n\prime\prime}(x)) \, dx$$

be minimized. For our computation procedure we have

(6.10)
$$c_h^{k+1} = c_h^k - \omega \frac{\displaystyle\int_a^b \frac{\partial F^k}{\partial c_h} F^k \, dx}{\displaystyle\int_a^b \left(\frac{\partial F^k}{\partial c_h}\right)^2 dx}$$

where

$$F^k = F\left(x, \sum_{j=1}^{h-1} c_j^{k+1} v^j + \sum_{j=h}^{n} c_j^k v^j, \sum_{j=1}^{h-1} c_j^{k+1}(v^j)^\prime + \sum_{j=h}^{n} c_j^k(v^j)^\prime,\right.$$

$$\left.\sum_{j=1}^{h-1} c_j^{k+1}(v^j)^{\prime\prime} + \sum_{j=h}^{n} c_j^k(v^j)^{\prime\prime}\right),$$

and
$$\frac{\partial F^k}{\partial c_h} = \frac{\partial F^k}{\partial y} v^h + \frac{\partial F^k}{\partial y^\prime}(v^h)^\prime + \frac{\partial F^k}{\partial y^{\prime\prime}}(v^h)^{\prime\prime}.$$

There remains the question, knowing c^k, can the values of the indicated integrals be computed? If, for example, the v^j, $j = 1, \cdots, n$, and F are polynomials, they can be computed using the kind of algebraic routine indicated earlier for linear problems. Application to nonlinear partial differential equations is, of course, much more difficult, and not so much is known about existence of a solution as for ordinary differential equations.

5. MINIMIZATION OF MAXIMUM DEVIATION

We now propose that nonlinear methods might be useful in treatment of linear problems.

Consider a Dirichlet problem for the Laplace equation on a region A

satisfying $u = f$ on Σ, and choose a set $\{v^l\}$, $l = 1, \cdots, n$, of harmonic polynomials as approximating functions. We wish to find

$$u^n = \sum_{l=1}^{n} c_l v^l \ni$$

$$\max_{\Sigma} |u^n - f|$$

is minimized.

The student will recall the Cauchy-Riesz lemma,

$$\lim_{P \to \infty} \left(\int_R |F|^p \, dR \right)^{1/p} = \operatorname*{lub}_R |F|.$$

EXERCISE

Prove the Cauchy-Riesz lemma.

We choose a sequence $\{c^k\} \ni \forall \, k \in \Omega$, $c^k \in E^n$ and

$$Q^k = \int_{\Sigma} (u^n - f)^{2^{k+1}} \, ds$$

is minimized $\forall \, k = 0, 1, 2, \cdots$. The initial guess of the sequence $(c_1{}^0, \cdots, c_n{}^0)$ is thus obtained in the usual least squares way. For $k > 0$, we solve the nonlinear equations $(\partial Q^k / \partial c_j) = 0$ by our accelerated successive replacements (6.6), where $(c_1{}^{k-1}, \cdots, c_n{}^{k-1})$ are starting values in the iteration. When k is reached, so that the vector c^k (or the quantity Q^k) does not change in norm to some accuracy, we terminate the computation, presuming that the minimax fit has been achieved. If K 'over-all iterations' have been performed, the value of $(Q^K)^{2^{-(K+1)}}$ can be taken as approximately equal to

$$\max_{\Sigma} |u^n - f| = \max_{A \cup \Sigma} |u^n - f|,$$

giving a reliable estimate of accuracy. Of course, any bound for

$$\max_{\Sigma} |u^n - f|$$

still gives an error bound. It should be noted that by using $p = 2^{k+1}$ in the Cauchy-Riesz lemma we guarantee the existence of a unique minimum for each Q^k.

Of course, Q^k is already in a form

$$Q^k = \int_{\Sigma} F^2(c_1, \cdots, c_n) \, ds,$$

where
$$F = (u'' - f)^{2k}$$

so that we can apply (6.10) directly. Thus we put

$$c_h^{l+1} = c_h^l - \omega \frac{\int_\Sigma \frac{\partial F^l}{\partial c_h} F^l \, ds}{\int_\Sigma \left(\frac{\partial F^l}{\partial c_h}\right)^2 ds}$$

$$= c_h^l - \omega \frac{\int_\Sigma \left(\sum_{i=1}^{h-1} c_i^{l+1} v^i + \sum_{i=h}^n c_i^l v^i - f\right)^{2k+1-l} v^h \, ds}{2^k \int_\Sigma \left(\sum_{i=1}^{h-1} c_i^{l+1} v^i + \sum_{i=h}^n c_i^l v^i - f\right)^{2k+1-2}(v^h) \, ds}$$

If the v^k's are indeed polynomials, and f and Σ are of a 'simple' nature, these quantities are computable.

References

[1] B. Marcus, 'Solutions of polynomial systems by iteration,' *Rend. Circ. Matem. Palermo, Ser. II*, **XI**, (1962). 1–20.

[2] B. Marcus, 'Error bounds for solutions of infinite polynomial systems by iteration,' *Rend. Circ. Matem. Palermo, Ser. II*, **XIII**, (1964). 1–6.

[3] C. A. Bryan, 'On the convergence of the method of nonlinear simultaneous displacements,' *Rend. Circ. Matem. Palermo, Ser. II*, **XIII**, (1964), 177–191.

[4] W. D. Hanson, 'Effects of partial isolation (distance), migration, and differential fitness values among environmental niches upon steady state gene frequencies', *Biometrics*, 1966.

[5] S. Lefschetz, *Differential Equations: Geometric Theory*, Interscience Publishers, 2nd ed., New York, 1962.

[6] G. C. Rota, and G. Birkhoff, *Ordinary Differential Equations*, Ginn and Company, Boston, 1962.

CHAPTER 7

INITIAL VALUE PROBLEMS FOR ORDINARY DIFFERENTIAL EQUATIONS

1. DIFFERENCING DATA

It can be noted from the Taylor theorem that $f:[A,B] \to R^1$

$$\wedge \ f \in c^3[A,B] \wedge a,b \in [A,B] \wedge h = b - a$$

$$\Rightarrow \left(\frac{df(b)}{dx} = \frac{f(b) - f(a)}{h} + \varepsilon_1, \ |\varepsilon_1| \le Sh \right)$$

$$\wedge \left(\frac{df}{dx} \left(\frac{b+a}{2} \right) = \frac{f(b) - f(a)}{2h} + \varepsilon_2, \ |\varepsilon_2| \le Th^2 \right),$$

where

$$\max_{x \in [A,B]} f''(x) = S \wedge \max_{x \in [A,B]} f'''(x) = T.$$

Of course, the first term of the first expression may serve as well to approximate $(df(a)/dx)$. It becomes apparent, then, that in differencing a set of data that is presumed to represent a subset of a function having three continuous derivatives on a closed interval containing the domain of tabulation, central formulas are much preferred to one-sided formulas for approximating derivatives, unless there is available very precise information on the relative sizes of S, T, and h, indicating a contrary advantage. At least, although T may be much larger than S, we know by refinement of the mesh that the central difference formulation will give much higher accuracy or, really, that the bound given for ε_2 will be much smaller than that given for ε_1. If the mesh size is halved, the given error bound will be halved for one-sided differences and multiplied by $\frac{1}{4}$ for central differences. Moreover, for small h, we become involved in the pathological problem of numerical analysis where large numbers whose difference is small must be subtracted. Since we compute only with terminating decimals, this will be disastrous if h is not kept large enough. This, then, also favors central differences, since a larger h can be used to get a given accuracy.

There is to be considered, nonetheless, the classical balance between the error of ignoring the remainder term of the Taylor theorem for f and the error of truncating the Cauchy sequences representing the real number functional values. Reflecting inaccuracies in the mathematical thought of an earlier age, the latter has been called round-off error, and the former truncation error, though the former does not refer to a series except in special cases where f is analytic, and the latter does refer to a very genuine case of truncation of sequences or series.

Let

$$\sigma(n,h) = \frac{f(b) - f(a)}{h} - \frac{f_n(b) - f_n(a)}{h}$$

$$= (1/h)([f(b) - f(a)] - [f_n(b) - f_n(a)]),$$

where $h = b - a$, and $f_n(b)$, $f_n(a)$ are the first n decimals of the real numbers $f(b), f(a)$. For any given n, the absolute value of the difference between the first bracket $[f(b) - f(a)]$, and the second bracket $[f_n(b) - f_n(a)]$ is for any h less than or equal to a given number N_n; and we then have that

$$\lim_{h \to \infty} \sigma(n,h) = 0.$$

We presume that $\forall\, n \in \Omega \,\exists\, M_n \leq N_n \ni \forall\, h \in R^1$, *the absolute value of the difference between the first and second brackets is* $> M_n$. Although counterexamples could be proposed, this assumption forms a reasonable basis for any over-all assessment of the error due to computing with terminating decimals, since it represents the worst possible situation. From this assumption, it follows that

$$\lim_{h \to 0} \sigma(n,h) = \infty.$$

Any information on $\sigma(n,h)$ more precise than these limits will depend

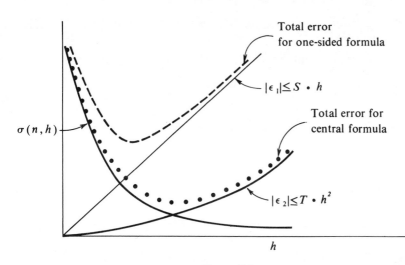

Figure 7.1

markedly on n and on details of f in a neighborhood of b or a. By plotting bounds of the Taylor remainder term for f' for the one-sided and central formulas on the same graph with $\sigma(n,h)$, it may be seen that an optimum h will very likely be larger for central than for one-sided formulas insofar as total error is concerned. Certainly the graphs show that central formulas are to be preferred in differencing data unless there is detailed information available on the data indicating the contrary.

Thus although there are immediate counterexamples to any rule that central formulas are always superior in differencing data (S small, T large), these examples are of negligible consequence in numerical practice. However, the careful investigator is warned to look for exceptions. It is doubtful that any serious investigator in the physical sciences would indeed be unaware that central differencing of data is almost always superior to one-sided differencing. However, for those working in biological and management areas, the handling of information in digital form may, at this time, be a new experience, for which they have no traditional guides.

2. STABILITY OF ORDINARY DIFFERENCE EQUATIONS

Surprisingly, it is found that central differences are not always preferable in making a finite-difference analogue of differential equations. If in so using central differences, one replaces an n-order differential equation by an $m > n$-order difference equation, he may introduce extraneous roots, and if these roots are unbounded, an unbounded error is introduced.

Consider the trivial intial value problem

$$y' = -y, \quad y(0) = 1,$$

where y' is replaced alternately by $(1/h)(y_n - y_{n-1})$ and by $(1/(2h)) \times (y_{n+1} - y_{n-1})$. We have

(7.1) $y_0 = 1, \quad y_n = y_{n-1} - hy_{n-1}$ (Euler)

and

(7.2) $y_0 = 1, \quad y_1 = (1 - h)y_0, \quad y_{n+1} = y_{n-1} - 2hy_n,$

where values $y_n = y(x_n)$, $x_n = nh$, are to be obtained successively for $n = 1,2,\cdots$. For (7.1), we find quickly that

$$y_n = (1 - h)y_{n-1} = (1 - h)^2 y_{n-2} = \cdots = (1 - h)^n y_0 = (1 - h)^n$$
$$= (1 - h)^{x/h} = [(1 - h)^{-1/h}]^{-x} = [(e^{-h} + O(h^2))^{-1/h}]^{-x},$$

or

$$\lim_{h \to 0} y_n(x) = e^{-x},$$

exactly as one expects. In fact, if z_0 is taken to be $1 + \delta$ and z_n satisfies (7.1), then $w_n = z_n - y_n$ satisfies

$$w_n = (1 - h)^n \delta,$$

and $\forall h \ni 0 < h < 2$ (h fixed),

$$\lim_{n \to \infty} w_n = 0.$$

Thus the Euler method is stable here. Any error in y_0, or in any successive y_n, is 'damped out' in computing successive values. Note carefully the difference in examining

$$\lim_{h \to 0} y_n,$$

which has to do with convergence of the solution of the difference equation to that of the differential equation, and in examining

$$\lim_{n \to \infty} y_n \quad \text{or} \quad \lim_{n \to \infty} w_n,$$

which has to do with asymptotic stability of the difference equation itself.

Now (7.2) provides a second-order differential equation with constant coefficients

$$y_{n+1} + 2hy_n - y_{n-1} = 0,$$

for which all solutions are linear combinations of the form $y_n = \xi^n$ (the theory of ordinary difference equations with constant coefficients is analogous to that of ordinary differential equations with constant coefficients). We have $e^{mx} = (e^{mh})^n = \xi^n$ where $\xi = e^{mh}$. Let $y_n = \xi^n$. Then

$$\xi^{n+1} + 2h\xi^n - \xi^{n-1} = \xi^{n-1}(\xi^2 + 2h\xi - 1) = 0$$

or $\xi = 0$ (trivial solution)

$$\vee \ \xi = -h + \sqrt{h^2 + 1} \ \vee \ \xi = -h - \sqrt{h^2 + 1},$$

so that

$$y_n = A(-h + \sqrt{h^2 + 1})^n + B(-h - \sqrt{h^2 + 1})^n,$$

and since

$$1 = y_0 = A + B,$$

$$y_n = A(-h + \sqrt{h^2 + 1})^n + (-1)^n(1 - A)(h + \sqrt{h^2 + 1})^n.$$

Using the binomial theorem,

$$\lim_{h \to 0}(-h + \sqrt{h^2 + 1})^n = e^{-x} \ \wedge \ \lim_{h \to 0}(h + \sqrt{h^2 + 1})^n = e^x.$$

EXERCISE

Prove the above limits.

If y_1 has been chosen so that $A = 1$ (i.e., $y_1 = -h + \sqrt{h^2 + 1}$, not $(1 - h)$ as in (7.2)) we have the correct solution. However, in computation, unless great care is taken, y_1 will be chosen $\ni A = 1 + \zeta$, where ζ arises from use of terminating decimals in computing. Then we have

$$y_n = (-h + \sqrt{h^2 + 1})^n + (-1)^n\zeta(h + \sqrt{h^2 + 1})^n.$$

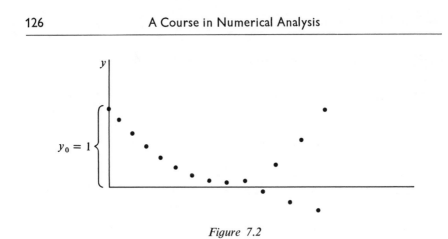

Figure 7.2

The error term is oscillatory and unbounded. It converges with h in absolute value to ζe^x. As n becomes large, it will begin to dominate the first term, masking the solution sought. In computation with small h, one will see for small n very good answers being produced, but eventually, as n (or x) becomes larger, a 'flowering' will take place as the oscillatory error term takes over. Soon the numbers intended as answers will become so large that the machine cannot continue to store them (exponent overflow), and the program will stop. This is typical of a method where numerical analysis is badly done—one does not even have the satisfaction of seeing numbers produced; it just doesn't work! For numerical detail, see the tabulation at the end of this section. Of course, a similar error ζ is introduced at every computation point. Our tabulation contains a sum of resulting (exponential) errors, while our analysis contains one only. Even though the evaluation of the initial point is carefully carried out so that $\zeta = 0$, such an error will be introduced at every point.

EXERCISE

Show that central difference replacement for $(dy/dt) = y$, $y(0) = 1$ introduces a bounded error converging in absolute value to ζe^{-x}, which is of no consequence, since the solution is e^x.

The student should carefully note an implied identity between numerical stability of a 'marching schema' for ordinary differential equations and convergence of iterative methods. Note also that the loss in accuracy is similar to that experienced in using direct methods on linear algebraic systems. The student should also notice that while the differential equation $y' = -y$ is asymptotically stable, and while $y' = y$ is asymptotically unstable, the situation is reversed for our (7.2) difference analogue of these equations. Thus, it is dangerous to identify stability of a differential equation with stability of a difference equation replacing it.

For a more penetrating and general analysis of the above, consider

$$\frac{dy}{dx} = f(x,y), \; y(0) = a,$$

which is asymptotically stable for $f_y < 0$ and asymptotically unstable for $f_y > 0$. A central difference replacement like that in (7.2) gives

(7.3) $$y_{n+1} = y_{n-1} + 2hf(x_n,y_n), \quad y_0 = a.$$

For numerical stability we consider asymptotic stability of the difference equation (7.3). Therefore, we consider a solution $z_n \ni z_0 = a + \delta$, and inquire about $\lim_{n \to \infty} w_n$, where $w_n = z_n - y_n$ for δ small. We have $\exists \; \eta_n$ between z_n and $y_n \ni$

$$w_{n+1} = w_{n-1} + 2h[f(x_n,z_n) - f(x_n,y_n)]$$
$$= w_{n-1} + 2hf_y(x_n,\eta_n)w_n.$$

Let $v_n = w_{n-1}$. Then we consider the first order system

$$v_{n+1} = w_n$$
$$w_{n+1} = v_n + 2hf_y(x_n,\eta_n)w_n$$

or

(7.4) $$U_{n+1} = A_n U_n = \cdots = \left(\prod_{k=1}^{n} A_k \right) U_0,$$

where

$$A_n = \begin{pmatrix} 0 & 1 \\ 1 & 2hf_y(x_n,\eta_n) \end{pmatrix} \wedge U_n = \begin{pmatrix} v_n \\ w_n \end{pmatrix} \wedge U_0 = \begin{pmatrix} w_{-1} \\ \delta \end{pmatrix}$$

Since $\forall \; k \in \Omega, \; |A_k| = -1$, and the determinant of any finite product of matrices is the product of determinants, it is impossible that

$$\lim_{n \to \infty} U_{n+1} = 0.$$

Thus for the case $f_y < 0$, we have again that (7.3) is asymptotically unstable, in spite of the fact that the differential equation is asymptotically stable.

The same conclusion of instability applies, of course, for $f_y > 0$, but this is due to the instability of the 'mother' differential equation. It is not convenient here to consider separating the solution of the difference equation into a term converging to the unstable solution of the differential equation and a stable error term, as in the exercise above for $y' = y$, though such analyses, or a percentage error analysis, can be undertaken.

Numerical stability for 'marching schema' for differential equations is now clearly identified with convergence for iterative methods represented by those finite-difference equations that can be regarded as recursions. If the differential equation is nonlinear, the iterative method also is nonlinear. To the extent that linearized analysis for convergence of iterative methods is not considered adequate in modern times, neither should linear analysis of stability for marching schema be considered adequate, but sometimes this is all we have to work with. The von Neumann criterion for numerical stability of initial value problems of partial differential equations proposes replacement of nonlinear difference equations by difference equations with constant coefficients for purposes of stability investigations.

The above analysis for the equation $y' = f(x,y)$ can be extended to almost all initial value problems of ordinary differential equations by letting $y \in E^n$ and $f(x,y) \in E^n$, but we would require a theory of Frechet differentials to consider f_y and the associated mean value theorem used above. For such a theory, one takes essentially that

$$f_y \cdot h = \lim_{\beta \to 0} \frac{f(x,y + \beta h) - f(x,y)}{\beta},$$

and the limit is considered in an appropriate norm. The theory is too sophisticated mathematically to be included here, and we are therefore content to remark that it gives the same results by the same methods shown above, only now for systems of differential equations.

Numerical instability of marching schema could have arisen from two entirely different sources: either from (1) the introduction of an extraneous and unbounded root in passing to the difference analogue, or from (ii) the requirement that eigenvalues of a certain matrix in the stability equation for the difference equation be less than one in modulus. Eigenvalues of the corresponding matrix in the stability equation for differential equations need only have a negative real part (see Chapter 5, sec. 4), and this is not as requiring. *The latter source of instability does not occur for ordinary differential equations.* Clearly,

An Example of Numerical Instability *

$$y' = -y,\ y(0) = 1$$

$$\frac{1}{2h}(y_{n+1} - y_{n-1}) = -y_n,\ y_1 = 1,\ h = 0.1$$

x_n	y_n	x_n	y_n
$0.20000000E + 00$	$0.81903260E + 00$	$0.48000000E + 01$	$0.17324955E - 01$
$0.30000000E + 00$	$0.74103048E + 00$	$0.49000000E + 01$	$-0.24712494E - 02$
$0.40000000E + 00$	$0.67082651E + 00$	$0.50000000E + 01$	$0.17819204E - 01$
$0.50000000E + 00$	$0.60686518E + 00$	$0.51000000E + 01$	$-0.60350902E - 02$
$0.60000000E + 00$	$0.54945348E + 00$	$0.52000000E + 01$	$0.19026222E - 01$
$0.70000000E + 00$	$0.49697449E + 00$	$0.53000000E + 01$	$-0.98403346E - 02$
$0.80000000E + 00$	$0.45005859E + 00$	$0.54000000E + 01$	$0.20994288E - 01$
$0.90000000E + 00$	$0.40696278E + 00$	$0.55000000E + 01$	$-0.14039192E - 01$
$0.10000000E + 01$	$0.36866604E + 00$	$0.56000000E + 01$	$0.23802126E - 01$
$0.11000000E + 01$	$0.33322958E + 00$	$0.57000000E + 01$	$-0.18799617E - 01$
$0.12000000E + 01$	$0.30202013E + 00$	$0.58000000E + 01$	$0.27562049E - 01$
$0.13000000E + 01$	$0.27282556E + 00$	$0.59000000E + 01$	$-0.24312026E - 01$
$0.14000000E + 01$	$0.24745502E + 00$	$0.60000000E + 01$	$0.32424454E - 01$
$0.15000000E + 01$	$0.22333456E + 00$	$0.61000000E + 01$	$-0.30796916E - 01$
$0.16000000E + 01$	$0.20278811E + 00$	$0.62000000E + 01$	$0.38583837E - 01$
$0.17000000E + 01$	$0.18277694E + 00$	$0.63000000E + 01$	$-0.38513683E - 01$
$0.18000000E + 01$	$0.16623273E + 00$	$0.64000000E + 01$	$0.46286573E - 01$
$0.19000000E + 01$	$0.14953040E + 00$	$0.65000000E + 01$	$-0.47770997E - 01$
$0.20000000E + 01$	$0.13632665E + 00$	$0.66000000E + 01$	$0.55840772E - 01$
$0.21000000E + 01$	$0.12226507E + 00$	$0.67000000E + 01$	$-0.58939151E - 01$
$0.22000000E + 01$	$0.11187364E + 00$	$0.68000000E + 01$	$0.67628602E - 01$
$0.23000000E + 01$	$0.99890350E - 01$	$0.69000000E + 01$	$-0.72464871E - 01$
$0.24000000E + 01$	$0.91895570E - 01$	$0.70000000E + 01$	$0.82121576E - 01$
$0.25000000E + 01$	$0.81511236E - 01$	$0.71000000E + 01$	$-0.88889186E - 01$
$0.26000000E + 01$	$0.75593323E - 01$	$0.72000000E + 01$	$0.99899413E - 01$
$0.27000000E + 01$	$0.66392572E - 01$	$0.73000000E + 01$	$-0.10886906E + 00$
$0.28000000E + 01$	$0.62314809E - 01$	$0.74000000E + 01$	$0.12167322E + 00$
$0.29000000E + 01$	$0.53929611E - 01$	$0.75000000E + 01$	$-0.13320370E + 00$
$0.30000000E + 01$	$0.51528887E - 01$	$0.76000000E + 01$	$0.14831396E + 00$
$0.31000000E + 01$	$0.43623834E - 01$	$0.77000000E + 01$	$-0.16286649E + 00$
$0.32000000E + 01$	$0.42804121E - 01$	$0.78000000E + 01$	$0.18088725E + 00$
$0.33000000E + 01$	$0.35063010E - 01$	$0.79000000E + 01$	$-0.19904394E + 00$
$0.34000000E + 01$	$0.35791519E - 01$	$0.80000000E + 01$	$0.22069603E + 00$
$0.35000000E + 01$	$0.27904707E - 01$	$0.81000000E + 01$	$-0.24318314E + 00$
$0.36000000E + 01$	$0.30210578E - 01$	$0.82000000E + 01$	$0.26933265E + 00$
$0.37000000E + 01$	$0.21862592E - 01$	$0.83000000E + 01$	$-0.29704967E + 00$
$0.38000000E + 01$	$0.25838060E - 01$	$0.84000000E + 01$	$0.32874258E + 00$
$0.39000000E + 01$	$0.16694980E - 01$	$0.85000000E + 01$	$-0.36279818E + 00$
$0.40000000E + 01$	$0.22499064E - 01$	$0.86000000E + 01$	$0.40130221E + 00$
$0.41000000E + 01$	$0.12195168E - 01$	$0.87000000E + 01$	$-0.44305862E + 00$
$0.42000000E + 01$	$0.20060031E - 01$	$0.88000000E + 01$	$0.48991393E + 00$
$0.43000000E + 01$	$0.81831620E - 02$	$0.89000000E + 01$	$-0.54104140E + 00$
$0.44000000E + 01$	$0.18423399E - 01$	$0.90000000E + 01$	$0.59812221E + 00$
$0.45000000E + 01$	$0.44984822E - 02$	$0.91000000E + 01$	$-0.66066584E + 00$
$0.46000000E + 01$	$0.17523703E - 01$	$0.92000000E + 01$	$0.73025537E + 00$
$0.47000000E + 01$	$0.99374160E - 03$	$0.93000000E + 01$	$-0.80671691E + 00$

* Numbers following E after table entries are powers of 10 factors.

x_n	y_n	x_n	y_n
$0.94000000E + 01$	$0.89159875E + 00$	$0.14800000E + 02$	$0.19562634E + 03$
$0.95000000E + 01$	$-0.98503666E + 00$	$0.14900000E + 02$	$-0.21616466E + 03$
$0.96000000E + 01$	$0.10886060E + 01$	$0.15000000E + 02$	$0.23885927E + 03$
$0.97000000E + 01$	$-0.12027578E + 01$	$0.15100000E + 02$	$-0.26393651E + 03$
$0.98000000E + 01$	$0.13291575E + 01$	$0.15200000E + 02$	$0.29164657E + 03$
$0.99000000E + 01$	$-0.14685893E + 01$	$0.15300000E + 02$	$-0.32226582E + 03$
$0.10000000E + 02$	$0.16228753E + 01$	$0.15400000E + 02$	$0.35609973E + 03$
$0.10100000E + 02$	$-0.17931643E + 01$	$0.15500000E + 02$	$-0.39348576E + 03$
$0.10200000E + 02$	$0.19815081E + 01$	$0.15600000E + 02$	$0.43479688E + 03$
$0.10300000E + 02$	$-0.21894659E + 01$	$0.15700000E + 02$	$-0.48044513E + 03$
$0.10400000E + 02$	$0.24194012E + 01$	$0.15800000E + 02$	$0.53088590E + 03$
$0.10500000E + 02$	$-0.26733461E + 01$	$0.15900000E + 02$	$-0.58662231E + 03$
$0.10600000E + 02$	$0.29540704E + 01$	$0.16000000E + 02$	$0.64821036E + 03$
$0.10700000E + 02$	$-0.32641601E + 01$	$0.16100000E + 02$	$-0.71626438E + 03$
$0.10800000E + 02$	$0.36069024E + 01$	$0.16200000E + 02$	$0.79146323E + 03$
$0.10900000E + 02$	$-0.39855405E + 01$	$0.16300000E + 02$	$-0.87455702E + 03$
$0.11000000E + 02$	$0.44040105E + 01$	$0.16400000E + 02$	$0.96637463E + 03$
$0.11100000E + 02$	$-0.48663426E + 01$	$0.16500000E + 02$	$-0.10678319E + 04$
$0.11200000E + 02$	$0.53772790E + 01$	$0.16600000E + 02$	$0.11799410E + 04$
$0.11300000E + 02$	$-0.59417984E + 01$	$0.16700000E + 02$	$-0.13038201E + 04$
$0.11400000E + 02$	$0.65656386E + 01$	$0.16800000E + 02$	$0.14407050E + 04$
$0.11500000E + 02$	$-0.72549261E + 01$	$0.16900000E + 02$	$-0.15919611E + 04$
$0.11600000E + 02$	$0.80166238E + 01$	$0.17000000E + 02$	$0.17590972E + 04$
$0.11700000E + 02$	$-0.88582508E + 01$	$0.17100000E + 02$	$-0.19437805E + 04$
$0.11800000E + 02$	$0.97882739E + 01$	$0.17200000E + 02$	$0.21478533E + 04$
$0.11900000E + 02$	$-0.10815905E + 02$	$0.17300000E + 02$	$-0.23733511E + 04$
$0.12000000E + 02$	$0.11951454E + 02$	$0.17400000E + 02$	$0.26225235E + 04$
$0.12100000E + 02$	$-0.13206195E + 02$	$0.17500000E + 02$	$-0.28978558E + 04$
$0.12200000E + 02$	$0.14592693E + 02$	$0.17600000E + 02$	$0.32020946E + 04$
$0.12300000E + 02$	$-0.16124733E + 02$	$0.17700000E + 02$	$-0.35382747E + 04$
$0.12400000E + 02$	$0.17817639E + 02$	$0.17800000E + 02$	$0.39097495E + 04$
$0.12500000E + 02$	$-0.19688260E + 02$	$0.17900000E + 02$	$-0.43202246E + 04$
$0.12600000E + 02$	$0.21755291E + 02$	$0.18000000E + 02$	$0.47737944E + 04$
$0.12700000E + 02$	$-0.24039318E + 02$	$0.18100000E + 02$	$-0.52749834E + 04$
$0.12800000E + 02$	$0.26563154E + 02$	$0.18200000E + 02$	$0.58287910E + 04$
$0.12900000E + 02$	$-0.29351948E + 02$	$0.18300000E + 02$	$-0.64407416E + 04$
$0.13000000E + 02$	$0.32433543E + 02$	$0.18400000E + 02$	$0.71169393E + 04$
$0.13100000E + 02$	$-0.35838656E + 02$	$0.18500000E + 02$	$-0.78641294E + 04$
$0.13200000E + 02$	$0.39601274E + 02$	$0.18600000E + 02$	$0.86897651E + 04$
$0.13300000E + 02$	$-0.43758910E + 02$	$0.18700000E + 02$	$-0.96020824E + 04$
$0.13400000E + 02$	$0.48353056E + 02$	$0.18800000E + 02$	$0.10610181E + 05$
$0.13500000E + 02$	$-0.53429521E + 02$	$0.18900000E + 02$	$-0.11724118E + 05$
$0.13600000E + 02$	$0.59038960E + 02$	$0.19000000E + 02$	$0.12955004E + 05$
$0.13700000E + 02$	$-0.65237313E + 02$	$0.19100000E + 02$	$-0.14315118E + 05$
$0.13800000E + 02$	$0.72086422E + 02$	$0.19200000E + 02$	$0.15818027E + 05$
$0.13900000E + 02$	$-0.79654597E + 02$	$0.19300000E + 02$	$-0.17478723E + 05$
$0.14000000E + 02$	$0.88017341E + 02$	$0.19400000E + 02$	$0.19313771E + 05$
$0.14100000E + 02$	$-0.97258065E + 02$	$0.19500000E + 02$	$-0.21341477E + 05$
$0.14200000E + 02$	$0.10746895E + 03$	$0.19600000E + 02$	$0.23582066E + 05$
$0.14300000E + 02$	$-0.11875185E + 03$	$0.19700000E + 02$	$-0.26057890E + 05$
$0.14400000E + 02$	$0.13121932E + 03$	$0.19800000E + 02$	$0.28793644E + 05$
$0.14500000E + 02$	$-0.14499571E + 03$	$0.19900000E + 02$	$-0.31816618E + 05$
$0.14600000E + 02$	$0.16021846E + 03$	$0.20000000E + 02$	$0.35156967E + 05$
$0.14700000E + 02$	$-0.17703940E + 03$		

we have not provided a proof of this contention, but we have covered essentially all possibilities above by considering a very unstable method and indicating its handling for almost all equations. In the case of initial value problems for partial differential equations, the situation will not be nearly so simple, the source (ii) playing a dominant role.

For ordinary differential equation initial value problems, it is possible to find methods where first-order systems of differential equations are replaced by first-order systems of difference equations, so that no extraneous roots are introduced, and yet so that the error is as small as $O(h^5)$! These are the Runge-Kutta procedures which, as we have indicated, are unconditionally stable. Why then should we concern ourselves with methods that are at best conditionally stable and yet do not give a higher-order error term? The literature is full of so-called predictor-corrector formulas that, although they require iteration at each step to solve the difference equation, even then are only conditionally stable and offer no higher accuracy than ordinary Runge-Kutta, which is, incidentally, also saving of storage. There are then good reasons why American computing laboratories have been sold on the use of Runge-Kutta for initial value problems of ordinary differential equations. In integration of trajectories over long time periods, as in modern satellite and astronaut requirements, methods of much higher accuracy than $O(h^5)$ are desirable. It is possible to conceive of such methods, but they have not been tested and are not appropriate to this book's treatment. Of course, we are still hopeful that general methods yielding computable (and realistic) error bounds will be found. Finite-difference methods offer no real possibilities for this standard.

3. UNCONDITIONAL STABILITY

As it has developed above, then, the Runge-Kutta method, since it replaces a first-order ordinary differential equation by a first-order ordinary difference equation, always can be expected to be stable if the difference equation is asymptotically stable. If the differential equation is asymptotically unstable, it essentially adds nothing to the instability, since it can be shown that percentage error does not increase with n. That is, solving $y' = y$, $y(0) = 1$ with the Euler method causes no difficulty, although the equation *and* its finite-difference replacement are unstable, because only a finite number of digits is retained. We speak of Runge-Kutta, then, as unconditionally stable, to distinguish it from many other methods for which stability depends on certain conditions on the differential equation being satisfied. We will examine Runge-Kutta for one first-order equation $y' = f(x,y)$, but this can be extended to virtually all ordinary differential equations by regarding it as a vector equation. Once again, our analysis involves the expression $f_y(x,y)$, so that the theory of Frechet differentials becomes essential in extension of the analysis of Runge-Kutta procedures to vector equations, just as it was essential for the stability analysis above. *The Runge-Kutta computations, however, do not involve the expression f_y, and the results of the indicated analysis are such that one may use these equations unaltered when y and $f(x,y) \in E^n \; \forall \; n \in \Omega$.*

4. DERIVATION OF A RUNGE-KUTTA FORMULA OF $O(h^3)$ ACCURACY

Let $f: I \times E^1 \to E^1$, $I \subset E^1$, $f \in C^2(\bar{I} \times E^1)$ and $\sigma \ni y: I \to E^1$, $y \in C^2(\bar{I}) \ni$ $y' = f(x,y) \wedge y(x_0) = y_0 \in E^1$ where $x_0 \in I$. We ask to determine $\alpha_0, \alpha_1, \mu, \lambda \in R^1 \ni$

(7.5)
$$y_{n+1} = y_n + \alpha_0 k_0 + \alpha_1 k_1$$
$$k_0 = hf(x_n, y_n)$$
$$k_1 = hf(x_n + \mu h, y_n + \lambda k_0)$$

gives an expression of y_{n+1} correct to $O(h^3)$ *if y_n is known exactly.* Applied to the function y, the Taylor theorem gives

$$y_{n+1} = y_n + y_n'h + y_n''\frac{h^2}{2!} + O(h^3)$$

$$= y_n + f(x_n,y_n)h + [f_x(x_n,y_n) + f_y(x_n,y_n)f(x_n,y_n)]\frac{h^2}{2!}$$
$$+ O(h^3).$$

Applied to k_1 (or really to f), the Taylor theorem gives

$$k_1 = h\{f(x_n,y_n) + [\mu h f_x(x_n,y_n) + \lambda k_0 f_y(x_n,y_n)]\} + O(h^3)$$

and from (7.5)

$$y_{n+1} = y_n + h \cdot (\alpha_0 + \alpha_1) \cdot f(x_n,y_n) + h^2 \cdot \alpha_1[\mu f_x(x_n,y_n)$$
$$+ \lambda f(x_n,y_n)f_y(x_n,y_n)] + O(h^3).$$

Our requirements will be met if we choose $\alpha_0, \alpha_1, \mu, \wedge \lambda \ni$

(7.6) $$\alpha_0 + \alpha_1 = 1, \quad \alpha_1 \mu = \tfrac{1}{2}, \quad \lambda \alpha_1 = \tfrac{1}{2}.$$

With α_1 arbitrary $\alpha_0 = 1 - \alpha_1 \wedge \lambda = \mu = 1/(2\alpha_1)$. A convenient choice is $\alpha_1 = \tfrac{1}{2}$, so that

$$\alpha_0 = \alpha_1 = \tfrac{1}{2} \wedge \lambda = \mu = 1.$$

5. RUNGE-KUTTA FORMULAS

We have, then,

$$y_{n+1} = y_n + \tfrac{1}{2}(k_0 + k_1) + O(h^3),$$

where $$k_0 = hf(x_n, y_n)$$

$$k_1 = hf(x_n + h, y_n + k_0),$$

where, however, there is one degree of freedom available in choice of computing parameters that one may want to use in reducing the magnitude of the $O(h^3)$ function. Methods of analysis of Runge-Kutta methods for higher-order accuracy are identical, except that the systems of equations (7.6) for the parameters are larger, and that the nonlinearity offers more freedom in the choice of parameters. When accuracy higher than $O(h^5)$ is sought, it has been generally accepted that the problem of solving this system for an acceptable list of parameters is prohibitively difficult. In view of modern advances in solving nonlinear systems, this decision may need to be re-examined, but we quote here the classic formulas for $O(h^4)$ and $O(h^5)$:

$$y_{n+1} = y_n + \tfrac{1}{6}(k_0 + 4k_1 + k_2) + O(h^4),$$

where $$k_0 = hf(x_n, y_n)$$
$$k_1 = hf(x_n + \tfrac{1}{2}h, y_n + \tfrac{1}{2}k_0)$$
$$k_2 = hf(x_n + h, y_n + 2k_1 - k_0)$$

and $$y_{n+1} = y_n + \tfrac{1}{6}(k_0 + 2k_1 + 2k_2 + k_3) + O(h^5),$$

where $$k_0 = hf(x_n, y_n)$$
$$k_1 = hf(x_n + \tfrac{1}{2}h, y_n + \tfrac{1}{2}k_0)$$
$$k_2 = hf(x_n + \tfrac{1}{2}h, y_n + \tfrac{1}{2}k_1)$$
$$k_3 = hf(x_n + h, y_n + k_2).$$

Of course, these formulas are valid for $f \in C^3(\bar{I} \times E^1)$, $y \in C^3(\bar{I})$ and $f \in C^4(\bar{I} \times E^1)$, $y \in C^4(\bar{I})$, respectively. We note that the originators of these methods had geometric arguments for the assumed form, and that the student would do well, in attempting to extend them, to start with a form that has a geometric significance, if he expects success in determining a valid list of parameters.

RESEARCH EXERCISE

Utilizing computation techniques for large nonlinear algebraic systems, devise a routine to give Runge-Kutta formulas for any given order accuracy.

6. A FINITE FORM

As already noted the Runge-Kutta formulas, since they involve no derivatives f_y, explicitly, can be simply adopted for the cases $y \in E^n \wedge f(x,y) \in E^n$, although their validity in case $n > 1$ is established on the basis of a somewhat more sophisticated analysis. For almost any initial value problem for ordinary differential equations, then, 'marching' from one point to the next with order accuracy $O(h^5)$ can be accomplished if $f(x_n, y_n)$ can be evaluated at each point (x_n, y_n). Of course, we say nothing about the order accuracy of the function y, approximated over a number of time steps, or about computational error bounds, which cannot be made available, but we rely to some extent on the fact that, for stable difference equations, small errors at one point do not cause large errors later, and that successive mesh refinements will yield useful assessments of the magnitude of the error. The evaluation of $f(x_n, y_n)$ can involve large computation times. If repeated every small step length h over a large distance x, even evaluations of trigonometric and exponential functions consume large amounts of time, but this can almost always be avoided, albeit at the expense of integrating a larger system.

Definition

Let Φ_0 be the set of all functions $\varphi_0 : I \to E^1$, $I \subset E^1$, $\ni \varphi_0$ is a solution of some ordinary differential equation (of finite order) with constant coefficients. Let Φ_{k+1} be the set of functions $\varphi_{k+1} : I \to E^1 \ni \varphi_{k+1}$ is a solution of a (finite) system of differential equations $y' = F(x,y)$ where F can be expressed as an n-tuple of finite sums, products, and quotients of elements of Φ_k. Any element of the inductively defined sequence

$\{\Phi_k\}$ is said to be the class of k differentially generated functions. An element of any class of k differentially generated functions is said to be a finitely differentially generated function.

Proposition

Consider the initial value problem $y' = f(x,y)$, $y(x_0) = y^0 \in E^n$, where $f(x,y)$ is expressed as an n-tuple of finite sums, products, and quotients of finitely differentially generated functions. Then, allowing for possibly infinite initial values, an initial value problem for an $m > n$ order system of differential equations $z' = G(z)$, $z(x_0) = z_0 \in E^m$ can be found, such that $G(z)$ is an m-tuple of polynomials in the components $z_1, \cdots, z_m$ of z, and the first components of the solutions of $z' = G(z)$, $z(x_0) = z^0$, which is unique where it exists, satisfies $y' = f(x,y)$, $y(x_0) = y^0 \in E^n$.

Note that the systems obtained, besides being in a closed form, are also autonomous, i.e., $G_z = 0$.

Example: Suppose

(7.7) $$y'' = \frac{1}{x^2} e^{\cos[y'(\ln y)^2]}, \quad y'(1) = y(1) = 1.$$

Let $y_1 = y$, $y_2 = y' = y_1'$, $y_3 = \frac{1}{x^2}$, $y_4 = y_3' = -\frac{2}{x^3}$, $y_3'' = 6x^{-4} = 6y_3^2$.

Then (7.7) becomes

(7.8)
$$
\begin{aligned}
y_1' &= y_2 & y_1(1) &= 1 \\
y_2' &= y_3 e^{\cos[y_2(\ln y_1)^2]} & y_2(1) &= 1 \\
y_3' &= y_4 & y_3(1) &= 1 \\
y_4' &= 6y_3^2 & y_4(1) &= -2.
\end{aligned}
$$

Continuing, let $y_5 = \ln y_1$ or $y_5' = y_1'/y_1 = y_2/y_1$, $y_6 = y_2 y_5^2$ or $y_6' = 2y_2 y_5 y_5' + y_5^2 y_2' = 2y_2^2 y_5/y_1 + y_5^2 y_2'$. Then (7.8) becomes

$$
\begin{aligned}
y_1' &= y_2 & y_4' &= 6y_3^2 \\
y_2' &= y_3 e^{\cos y_6} & y_5' &= y_2/y_1 \\
y_3' &= y_4 & y_6' &= 2y_5 y_2^2/y_1 + y_5^2 y_3 e^{\cos y_6}.
\end{aligned}
$$

Now, let $y_7 = \cos y_6$ and $y_8 = \sin y_6$. Then $y_7' = -(\sin y_6)y_6' = -2y_8y_2^2y_5/y_1 - y_8y_5^2y_3\,e^{y_7}$, $\quad y_8' = (\cos y_6)y_6' = y_7y_6' = 2y_7y_2^2y_5/y_1 + y_7y_5^2y_3\,e^{y_7}$. Let $y_9 = e^{y_7}$, $y_9' = y_7'y_9$, or $y_9' = -2y_2^2y_5y_8y_9/y_1 - y_3y_5^2y_8y_9^2$. Let $y_{10} = 1/y_1$ or, eliminating solutions that are zero on a set with a limit point,[1] $y_{10}' = -y_1'/y_1^2 = -y_2y_{10}^2$, so that finally we have

$$y_1' = y_2 \qquad\qquad\qquad\qquad y_1(1) = 1$$

$$y_2' = y_3y_9 \qquad\qquad\qquad\quad y_2(1) = 1$$

$$y_3' = y_4 \qquad\qquad\qquad\qquad y_3(1) = 1$$

$$y_4' = 6y_3^2 \qquad\qquad\qquad\quad y_4(1) = -2$$

$$y_5' = y_2y_{10} \qquad\qquad\qquad\quad y_5(1) = 0$$

$$y_6' = 2y_2^2y_5y_{10} + y_5^2y_3y_9 \qquad\quad y_6(1) = 0$$

$$y_7' = -2y_2^2y_5y_8y_{10} - y_3y_5^2y_8y_9 \qquad y_7(1) = 1$$

$$y_8' = 2y_2^2y_5y_7y_{10} + y_3y_5^2y_7y_9 \qquad\; y_8(1) = 0$$

$$y_9' = -2y_2^2y_5y_8y_9y_{10} - y_3y_5^2y_8y_9^2 \quad y_9(1) = e$$

$$y_{10}' = -y_2y_{10}^2 \qquad\qquad\qquad\; y_{10}(1) = 1.$$

This simple technique, though it has probably never appeared in a mathematics textbook, is extremely useful; it is, in fact, stock-in-trade in every American computing laboratory that is active in differential equations. Its limits of validity beyond the sufficient condition given above (and the fact that it can be done piecewise on functions that have these properties piecewise) seem not to be known.

RESEARCH EXERCISE

Give a necessary and sufficient condition under which an initial value problem can be reduced to a closed form (involving finite sums of finite products).

RESEARCH EXERCISE

For differential equations in finite form, develop recursion relations for coefficients in the Taylor series expansions of the solution functions, thus giving a higher-order Runge-Kutta technique, but one where tabulated functions cannot be used.

---

[1] At an isolated point, y_{10}' could be defined $-y_2y_{10}^2$ by continuity.

In our example, were we to choose $x_0 = 0$ rather than $x_0 = 1$, a question would arise concerning existence. In the finite form, existence would come into question, not in the differential equation for which a Lipschitz condition is satisfied, but in the initial condition $y_3(0)$. When an initial condition of the original problem gives rise to a condition where one component of the solution of the closed form is unbounded at the initial point, a Taylor theorem of order equal to that of the Runge-Kutta formula to be utilized is applied to that component, minus the appropriate singular function (in the example, to $y_3(x) = 1/x^2$), and to all other components that are to be regular at the initial point. One thus proceeds one step size h away from the initial point and then uses the usual Runge-Kutta formulation. Of course, although general Runge-Kutta formulas for this contingency can be derived, they will be possible only when solutions exist that have the assumed properties. Reduction to finite form may sometimes be an aid in deciding questions of existence or even uniqueness, if the solutions eliminated in the reduction process are carefully noted.

We give a simple example of the latter. Consider the initial value problem

$$y' = y^{1/2}, \quad y(0) = 0.$$

Two solutions are $y = 0$ and $y = (\frac{1}{4})x^2$, and this case is often quoted to show that for uniqueness, $f(x,y)$ must satisfy a Lipschitz condition in a neighborhood of the initial point in E^2. Reducing to closed form, $y_2 = y_1^{1/2}$

$$y_1' = y_2$$
$$y_2' = \tfrac{1}{2}y_1^{-1/2}y_1' = \tfrac{1}{2}y_1^{-1/2}y_2 = \tfrac{1}{2}y_1^{-1/2}y_1^{1/2} = \tfrac{1}{2}$$
$$y_1(0) = 0 \qquad y_2(0) = 0,$$

where the solution $y(x) = y_1(x) = 0$ (or any other that is zero on a set with limit point) has been eliminated. Since the finite form satisfies a Lipschitz condition on any finite rectangle in E^2, $y_1 = \frac{1}{4}x^2$, $y_2 = \frac{1}{2}x$ is *the unique solution* of the closed form problem.

In considering existence, one should note that in getting rid of quotients one may easily introduce functions that have a singularity at some finite point of the plane that is not an initial point. In our example, $y_3 = 1/x^2$ is such a function. Were we to attempt solving step by step the problem

$$y_3' = y_4 \qquad y_3(1) = 1$$
$$y_4' = 6y_3^2 \qquad y_3(1) = 2$$

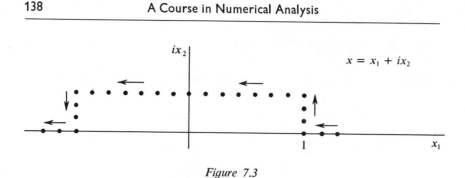

Figure 7.3

for $x < 1$, we would find the solution becoming unbounded in a neighborhood of $x = 0$. A well-honored method here is to consider the domain of the solution function extended to the complex plane and choose another path (rectangular for numerical convenience) in the complex plane to get around $x = 0$. In the example at hand, since there is no singularity other than $x = 0$ in the complex plane for $y_3(x) = 1/x^2$, any path will do. The same difficulty would arise and the same resolution be proposed if the function $y_3 = 1/x^2$ had not been introduced in our first example. But it would arise, then, in evaluation of a function $f(x,y)$ near $x = 0$, not in the existence of y_3, which is a component of the solution function in the finite form equation. Thus it would not cause us difficulty in stating existence but only in computation.

7. RUNGE-KUTTA AS A TOOL FOR TWO-POINT PROBLEMS

Consider the two-point boundary value problem

$$(7.9) \qquad y'' = f(x,y,y'), \quad y(a) = A \in R^1, \quad y(b) = B \in R^1.$$

Of course, such problems can become far more complex, involving linear combinations of y and its first derivatives at end points, or involving higher-order equations and, perhaps, data at more than two points. We make this problem suffice as an example of its type. If f is linear in y and y', we have the equivalent first-order system

$$(7.10) \qquad Y' = M(x)Y + H(x), \quad Y = \begin{pmatrix} y \\ y' \end{pmatrix}.$$

Let $Y_1 = \begin{pmatrix} y_1 \\ y_1' \end{pmatrix}$ and $Y_2 = \begin{pmatrix} y_2 \\ y_2' \end{pmatrix}$ satisfy the following initial value problems.

$$(7.11) \quad \begin{aligned} Y_1' &= M(x)\,Y_1 + (1/A)H(x) \quad & Y_1(a) &= \binom{1}{0} \\[2mm] Y_2' &= M(x)\,Y_2 & Y_2(a) &= \binom{0}{1} \end{aligned}$$

Then $\forall \; \alpha, \; \beta \in R^1$, $\alpha Y_1 + \beta Y_2$ satisfies the differential equation

$$(\alpha Y_1 + \beta Y_2)' = M(x)(\alpha Y_1 + \beta Y_2) + \alpha(1/A)H(x).$$

Putting $\alpha = A$, we have $\alpha Y_1 + \beta Y_2$ satisfies (7.10) and

$$\begin{aligned} \alpha y_1(a) + \beta y_2(a) &= \alpha \cdot 1 + \beta \cdot 0 = A \\ \alpha y_1(b) + \beta y_2(b) &= A y_1(b) + \beta y_2(b) = B, \end{aligned}$$

if $\beta = (1/y_2(b))(B - Ay_1(b))$.

Thus solutions of linear initial value problems (7.11) are to be approximated by, let us say, using Runge-Kutta. Then, provided it does not happen that $y_2(b) = 0$, the linear combination $Ay_1(x) + (1/y_2(b))$ $(B - Ay_1(b))y_2(x)$ is the solution of our two-point boundary value problem. One could also solve the initial value problem (7.10) with $Y(a) = \binom{A}{\tau}$ and adjust τ until a solution $Y(b)$ is obtained such that $y_1(b) = B$. Since in this consideration $y(b)$ is a linear function of τ, successive trials and linear interpolation are almost certain to meet with success. We call the latter the 'ballistic method.' Even for linear equations it must be warned that, despite stability considerations, if $b - a$ is large, there is a possibility of large accumulations of error in marching by small steps from b to a, and that some independent check of accuracy would be well worth undertaking.

For nonlinear equations, the linear combination method is hardly relevant. It would seem that the ballistic method could be taken over simply by noting that, in the above notation, $y(b)$ is a possible nonlinear function of τ. One might even expect to enhance the technique by using a Newton method of chords to find a root for the nonlinear function $y(b;\tau) - B$. In practice, it is often (perhaps usually) found that the value of $y(b)$ is so sensitive to τ that tiny variations of τ cause wide variations of $y(b;\tau) - B$ in a neighborhood of its root. We have thus indicated in our section on iterative methods for nonlinear algebraic systems, that the system of finite-difference equations over the interval (a,b) be solved by iterative methods. This computation does not involve

Runge-Kutta and, in fact, the form (7.9)—or a second-order system—is a preferred computational form to that of (7.10)—or to a first-order system.

In connection with the fact that the ballistic method is often inoperable for two-point boundary value problems of nonlinear differential equations, we call attention to a type of stability consideration that is somewhat different from the type so far discussed. For an initial value problem, if for every x in an interval where the solution exists, a solution $y(x;\tau)$ is a continuous function of the initial data τ, then the solution y is said to be continuously dependent on the data. Sometimes, however, even though y is continuously dependent on the data, we have a condition of virtual or 'practical' instability in that a small change in the initial data gives a large change in the solution at a point x; in fact, where x_0 is the initial x and $x - x_0$ is very large, this is almost certain to be the case. The differential equations governing rocket trajectories are such that solutions are continuously dependent on the data, but if no adjustments of trajectory are made in flight, the accuracy requirements on initial velocity, in order to hit a distant target like the moon, are fantastic. The early American moon shots were made with rockets designed for ballistic-missile use, and their thrust was sufficient to make a moon shot possible only if high accuracy were obtained. The successful early Russian shots, and later successful American shots, utilized higher thrusts to reduce the 'practical instability.' Applied to difference equations instead of differential equations, we can have a similar 'practical numerical instability' or, shall we say, 'sensitive dependence,' and this seems to be responsible for the usual failure of the ballistic method applied to the two-point boundary value problem.

We offer our heartfelt sympathy and a limited supply of aspirin to all those many young computors who will scoff at our words of warning and try to use the ballistic method on nonlinear two-point problems. We were young once, too, and believed life could not be difficult.

CHAPTER 8

METHOD OF CHARACTERISTICS

1. THEORY OF CHARACTERISTICS FOR QUASI-LINEAR EQUATIONS IN TWO INDEPENDENT VARIABLES

Let I be an interval of R^1, and let δD be the boundary of a region D of E^2, containing a segment (or segments)

$$K = \{(x,y) \mid (y = k(x)) \wedge (k : I \to R^1) \wedge (k \in C^1(I))\}.$$

Let $U : K \to E^n$ where $U = \begin{pmatrix} u_1 \\ \vdots \\ u_n \end{pmatrix}$ and $\dfrac{d}{dx} u_i(x, k(x))$ exists $\forall\ i = 1, \cdots, n.$

Let

$$A = (a_{ij}(x,y,u_1,\cdots,u_n)), \quad B = (b_{ij}(x,y,u_1,\cdots,u_n)), \quad H = (h_j(x,y,u_1,\cdots u_n))$$

where

$$a_{ij} \in C((D \cup K) \times E^n), \quad b_{ij} \in C((D \cup K) \times E^n),$$
$$h_j \in C((D \cup K) \times E^n)\ \forall\ i,j = 1,\cdots,n.$$

We ask if there exist segments $K \ni$ the domain of U is not uniquely extended to some region $E \ni D \cup K \supset E \not\supseteq K$ by requiring that on K

(8.1) $$AU_x + BU_y = H.$$

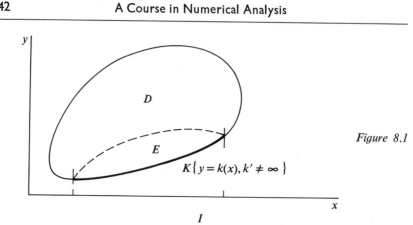

Figure 8.1

If such curve segments exist, we call them characteristics of equation (8.1), since they serve to characterize segments of the boundary of the largest region in E^2 to which particular solutions of (8.1) can be uniquely extended. From this property arise others of great importance, providing in some cases a bounded region in which the solution of a boundary value problem is uniquely determined, even when data is prescribed on a finite segment of a curve.

If such characteristics K exist, they must be such that, if U is given on K, U_y is not uniquely determined on K by (8.1) for, remembering that $k \in C^1(I)$, a given extension of U determines U_y uniquely as a limit of (vertical) difference quotients. Thus if U allows more than one extension (i.e., K is a characteristic), then U determines more than one value of U_y on K.

If $U(x,k(x))$ is given on K, then so is

$$\frac{dU}{dx} = \frac{d}{dx} U(x,k(x)) = U_x(x,k(x)) + k'U_y(x,k(x)).$$

From (8.1)

(8.2) $$(B - k'A)U_y = H - A\frac{dU}{dx},$$

for which the solution U_y is not unique, if

(8.3) $$|B - k'A| = 0.$$

We see then that characteristic directions k' of (8.1) are eigenvalues of the matrix B with respect to A. We call the roots of (8.3) k_i', $i = 1,2,\cdots,n$.

If U is known in a region of E^2, these give differential equations for n families of characteristic curves, real if k_i' is real,

$$\frac{dy}{dx} = k_i'(x,y,u_1(x,y),u_2(x,y),\cdots,u_n(x,y)),$$

$i = 1,2,\cdots,n$. For solutions U_y of (8.2) to exist on a characteristic, and thus for an extension of U across a characteristic, albeit not unique, to exist to a region E, the rank of the augmented matrix

$$(8.4) \qquad\qquad \left(B - k_i'A,\ H - A\frac{dU}{dx}\right)$$

must be equal to the rank $(< n)$ of the coefficient matrix

$$(B - k_i'A).$$

The equation (8.3) is called the characteristic equation, whereas rank conditions on (8.4) are sometimes called compatibility relations, since they provide ordinary differential equations[1] relating components of U, and these relations must be satisfied if a solution is to exist on a characteristic.

EXERCISE

Work out the characteristic equation and compatibility relations for the $n = 2$ case. (Note that there are only two, not four, independent compatibility relations.)

EXERCISE

For the wave equation $f_{xx} - f_{yy} = 0$, write an equivalent first-order system by putting $v = f_x$, $u = f_y$, and, assuming $f \in C^2$, putting $v_y - u_x = 0$. Find the characteristic families.

EXERCISE

Find the characteristic directions of the Laplace equation $u_{xx} + u_{yy} = 0$.

---

[1] An alternate derivation of characteristics asks for curves on which these ordinary differential relations replace the partial differential equations. Authors who prefer this development usually call the rank conditions (8.4) 'characteristic equations,' which introduces some confusion in the literature.

EXERCISE

Find the characteristic family for the heat equation $u_{xx} - u_y = 0$.

For the $n = 2$ case, there are three possibilities: $k_1' \neq k_2'$, are both real, $k_1' \neq k_2'$ are complex conjugates, and $k_1' = k_2'$, the common value of which is real. These are called, respectively, 'hyperbolic,' 'elliptic,' and 'parabolic' type.

EXERCISE

By writing an equivalent first-order system for the equation

$$au_{xx} + 2bu_{xy} + cu_{yy} = d,$$

where $a = a(x,y,u_x,u_y)$, $b = b(x,y,u_x,u_y)$, $c = c(x,y,u_x,u_y)$, $d = d(x,y,u_x,u_y)$, classify it according as $b^2 - ac \gtreqless 0$.

EXERCISE

Write the Euler equations[2] for inviscid, compressible, two-dimensional, or axially symmetric flow, where the velocity is independent of time, assuming that the entropy $S = S(r,z)$ satisfies the relation

$$\frac{ds}{dt} = uS_r + vS_z = 0,$$

where u and v are velocity components in the r and z directions.
Let the adiabatic law $p = K\rho^\gamma$ apply between pressure and density (functions of r and z), where K and γ are real numbers. Show that the streamlines, given by $dz/dr = v/u$ are characteristics, and find two compatibility relations on them that may be integrated to give certain quantities that are constant on the streamlines. *Hint:* The total energy or enthalpy h satisfies the equation $\frac{dh}{d\zeta} = \frac{1}{\rho}\frac{dp}{d\zeta} + T\frac{dS}{d\zeta}$, where ζ is any curve parameter. Find the other characteristics, called mach lines, and show that they are real when

$$M^2 = \frac{u^2 + v^2}{dp/d\rho} = \frac{u^2 + v^2}{\gamma p/\rho} > 1$$

(that is, when the flow is supersonic).

---

[2] The student may wish to look ahead to Chapter 10 at this point to find the Euler equations.

EXERCISE

Assuming isentropic ($s = $ constant) flow, introduce a stream function ψ (a function that is constant on streamlines, and such that the continuity equation is satisfied by requiring that it have two continuous derivatives) in the above, and find a second-order equation of the form

$$a\psi_{rr} + 2b\psi_{rz} + c\psi_{xx} = d$$

which it satisfies. Show that this equation is hyperbolic if $M^2 > 1$, and elliptic if $M^2 < 1$.

Notice in (8.3) above that if A, B depend only on x and y, the equations

$$\frac{dy}{dx} = k_1'(x,y), \cdots, \frac{dy}{dx} = k_n'(x,y)$$

determine characteristic families without knowledge of U if functions k_i' satisfy the well-known Lipschitz conditions. The case is known as linear if H is a linear function. In the general case (said to be quasilinear since the highest-order derivatives appear linearly) where A and B depend on $x,y,u_1,\cdots,u_n$, one cannot even tell if a given curve is characteristic without specification of $u_1,\cdots,u_n$ on the curve.

A Cauchy or initial value problem is said to be posed when $u_1,\cdots,u_n$ is given on a finite segment of a curve. Obviously, if a Cauchy problem is to be posed on a characteristic in such a way that a solution exists, the data cannot be given arbitrarily, but must satisfy compatibility relations. Moreover, even then the solution will not be uniquely determined.

EXERCISE

Discuss the problem of determining if a given curve in a compressible flow problem is an appropriate initial value (or Cauchy problem) line.

2. METHOD OF CHARACTERISTICS

Consider the quasilinear second-order equation

$$a\psi_{xx} + 2b\psi_{xy} + c\psi_{yy} = d$$

in $D \subset E^2$, where $\psi \in C^2(D)$ $\wedge$

$$a = a(x,y,\psi_x,\psi_y) \wedge b = b(x,y,\psi_x,\psi_y) \wedge c = c(x,y,\psi_x,\psi_y)$$
$$\wedge\, d = d(x,y,\psi_x,\psi_y).$$

Let $u = \psi_x$, $v = \psi_y$. Then

(8.5)
$$u_y - v_x = 0$$
$$au_x + bu_y + bv_x + cv_y = d$$

is a first-order system of the form (8.1) equivalent to our second-order equation. If a, b, c, and d depend also on ψ, we addend to the system an equation

$$\frac{d\psi(x,\gamma(x))}{dx} = u + \gamma' v,$$

where, for I the projection of D on the x-axis, γ is any function $\ni \gamma : I \to R^1 \wedge \gamma \in C^1(I)$. In this same manner, any partial differential equation or system of partial differential equations on a region of E^2 can be written as an equivalent system of the form (8.1). The converse is not true (although with entirely minor reservations the converse of the relevant statement for ordinary differential equations is true).

EXERCISE

Find a system of two first-order partial differential equations that cannot be written as one second-order equation.

We have from (8.5), putting

$$\begin{pmatrix} u \\ v \end{pmatrix}_x = \frac{d}{dx}\begin{pmatrix} u \\ v \end{pmatrix} - k'\begin{pmatrix} u \\ v \end{pmatrix}_y,$$

$$\left[\begin{pmatrix} 1 & 0 \\ b & c \end{pmatrix} - k'\begin{pmatrix} 0 & -1 \\ a & b \end{pmatrix}\right]\begin{pmatrix} u \\ v \end{pmatrix}_y = \begin{pmatrix} 0 \\ d \end{pmatrix} - \begin{pmatrix} 0 & -1 \\ a & b \end{pmatrix}\begin{pmatrix} du/dx \\ dv/dx \end{pmatrix},$$

so that the characteristic equation is

$$\begin{vmatrix} 1 & k' \\ b - k'a & c - k'b \end{vmatrix} = 0 \Rightarrow a(k')^2 - 2bk' + c = 0$$

or, for $a \neq 0$,

$$k_1' = \frac{b + \sqrt{b^2 - ac}}{a} = \alpha, \quad k_2' = \frac{b - \sqrt{b^2 - ac}}{a} = \beta.$$

Let $b^2 - ac$ be positive, so that our equation is of hyperbolic type, and pose a Cauchy problem on a finite segment Γ of a noncharacteristic curve; $\Gamma = \{(x,y) \mid y = \varphi(x) \wedge \varphi \in C^1(I)\}$. That is, let u and v be given on $\Gamma \ni$

$$\alpha(x,\varphi(x),u(x,\varphi(x)),v(x,\varphi(x))) \neq \varphi'(x)$$

$$\wedge \ \beta(x,\varphi(x),u(x,\varphi(x)),v(x,\varphi(x))) \neq \varphi'(x) \ \forall \ x \in I.$$

Then, under appropriate conditions on a, b, c, and d, $\forall \ (x,y) \in \Gamma \ \exists$ two characteristic directions α, β, not tangent to the curve represented by $y = \varphi(x)$ at (x,y). By selecting a partition of I (say, with equal mesh h), we choose a discrete set of points of Γ. For any consecutive pair of points 1, and 2, we agree to use subscripts to indicate evaluations at

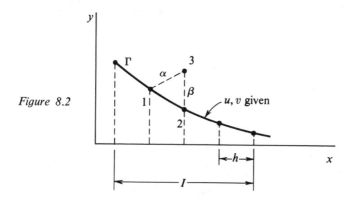

Figure 8.2

numbered points. It will be our task to compute u and v at some point 3 off the curve Γ in such a way that an $O(h)$ finite-difference analogue of our differential equation is satisfied. The characteristic equations become

$$O(h) + \frac{y_3 - y_1}{x_3 - x_1} = \alpha_1; \quad O(h) + \frac{y_3 - y_2}{x_3 - x_2} = \beta_2,$$

which are to be solved for (x_3,y_3), ignoring functions $O(h)$. From the compatibility equation

$$\begin{vmatrix} 1 & dv/dx \\ b - k'a & d - a\,du/dx - b\,dv/dx \end{vmatrix} = 0,$$

valid for $(k' = \alpha) \wedge (k' = \beta)$, we have, ignoring functions $O(h)$,

$$\begin{vmatrix} 1 & \dfrac{v_3 - v_1}{x_3 - x_1} \\[2ex] b_1 - \alpha_1 a_1 & d - a_1 \dfrac{u_3 - u_1}{x_3 - x_1} - b_1 \dfrac{v_3 - v_1}{x_3 - x_1} \end{vmatrix} = 0$$

and

$$\begin{vmatrix} 1 & \dfrac{v_3 - v_1}{x_3 - x_1} \\[2ex] b_2 - \beta_2 a_2 & d - a_2 \dfrac{u_3 - u_2}{x_3 - x_2} - b_2 \dfrac{v_3 - v_2}{x_3 - x_2} \end{vmatrix} = 0,$$

which are to be solved for u_3 and v_3. Computing (x_3, y_3, u_3, v_3) from each pair of the discrete set on Γ, we obtain another discrete set of points with one less element. Continuing in this manner, we cover a 'triangle' bounded by the initial line and by two approximations of characteristics generated from $O(h)$ finite-difference replacements of

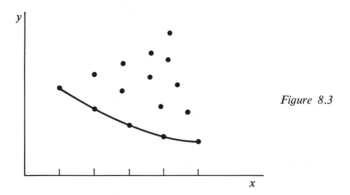

Figure 8.3

their differential equations. This is the method of characteristics. Notice that, as with ordinary differential equations (to which, so to speak, our partial differential equation initial value problem has been step-by-step reduced), for the purely computational task, it makes no difference whether the equations are linear or nonlinear. This fact specifically is said to have motivated the great mathematician von Neumann to invent or at least develop the internally programmed computers. He wanted to be able to get some 'tack' on our nonlinear problems that seemed so difficult as to defy analysis. We will take pains to show the versatility of the method of characteristics for fluid dynamic problems. It is almost evidently stable, being based on replacement of first-order ordinary differential equations by first-order ordinary difference equations. But, of course, no error bounds are provided, and it will be seen that its use, without very careful attention to technique and to conditions satisfied by the data, is restricted to hyperbolic type.

If, as the march proceeds, the characteristics coalesce (form an envelope), one cannot use the method further without alteration, for at each step the new 'data line' comes closer and closer to characteristic. Intuition then indicates the development of a 'threefold' surface on which the solution function could be defined, but to pursue this further, there would have to be formulated a relevant theory of differential forms. In fluid dynamics where one wishes to assign, for example, one value of pressure at a point in E^2 or E^3, functions defined on such a manifold are not wanted (unless prescription can be given as to which branch values to select), so the practice has been to place a shock, or condition for discontinuity of pressure (see Chapter 10, Sec. 3 and Chapter 12, Sec. 1), on such an envelope.

It very often happens in modern technology that one wishes to treat a system (8.1) of order $n > 2$, where all roots of the characteristic equations are real and more than two are distinct. It is tempting, then, to consider integrating the compatibility relations on each of the distinct characteristics. Since $n > 2$ linear characteristic approximations from two points will not intersect at one point, this involves intersecting the 'outside' characteristics from two points, 1 and 2, where the solution is known, and then 'sending down' the remaining characteristics from this intersection to points between 1 and 2, where a linear interpolation is made for the requisite values of the solution. Since the interpolated values are determined to $O(h)$, there is no objection to accuracy in such

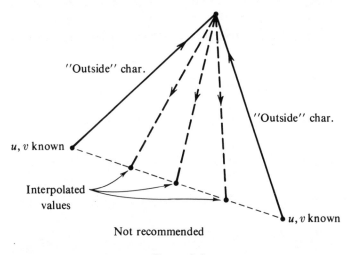

Figure 8.4

a usage, but the method is computationally clumsy. A cleaner development of successive values is possible if one writes partial difference analogues of the original system (8.1) without resolution into compatibility relations along characteristics. For numerical stability, one is then required to march from two points to a third that lies within the 'outside' characteristics. Unfortunately, a view of characteristics as having physical existence has often caused aeronautical engineers to ignore this easier computation possibility.

It will be noticed once more than our 'marching schemes' can be regarded as iterative methods, and that stability of the march can be virtually, though not entirely, identified with convergence of the iterative method. This point will be fully developed later. The prospect noted above, then, that nonlinear equations can be integrated step by step without noticing that the system is nonlinear, is deceiving, since it merely remarks that iterative methods for nonlinear systems are constructed so that values at the $k + 1$ iteration are computed in terms of values at the k and previous iterations. It leaves unmentioned the very difficult problems of convergence of iterative methods for nonlinear systems, which are reflected as stability problems.

These matters have been considered only in the context of the discretized problems, without considering either convergence to solution of the differential equation initial value problem or the computation of error bounds. Methods for nonlinear initial value problems that meet the high standards envisioned in that they yield computable error bounds and involve computations utilizing either convergent iterative methods or stable marching schemes have, with the exception of some special cases, never been developed. The least squares or Galierkin procedure would seem to offer promise in this direction if accompanied with the use of the iterative methods for nonlinear systems proposed earlier.

3. D'ALEMBERT SOLUTION OF THE CAUCHY PROBLEM FOR THE WAVE EQUATION[3] IN E^2

Consider the problem

$$\psi_{xx} - \psi_{yy} = 0$$
$$\psi(x,0) = f(x), \quad f \in C^2(a,b)$$
$$\psi_y(x,0) = g(x), \quad g \in C^1(a,b)$$

---

[3] For a variational argument that this is the equation for the displacement of a vibrating string, see Appendix D.

to be solved in a region of E^2 where $y \geq 0$. Putting $\xi = \frac{1}{2}(x + y)$, $\eta = \frac{1}{2}(x - y)$, we see that $\psi_{\xi\eta} = \psi_{xx} - \psi_{yy}$, so that all solutions of the differential equation are of the form

$$\psi(x,y) = F(x + y) + G(x - y).$$

Moreover, if for some interval $I \subset E^1$, $F \in C^2(I) \wedge G \in C^2(I)$, then the above is a regular solution of the differential equation in the isosceles triangle T contained in the upper-half plane with base I on the x-axis. Determining F and G from the boundary conditions in terms of f and g, it follows that

(8.6) $\psi(x,y) = \frac{1}{2}[f(x + y) + f(x - y)] + \frac{1}{2} \int_{x-y}^{x+y} g(s) \, ds$

is a regular solution in the isosceles triangle T contained in the upper-half plane with base (a,b). Using the fact that all solutions of the differential equation are of the form indicated, and putting $f = g = 0$, it is easily established that this solution is unique.

EXERCISE

Prove that $u_{\xi\eta} = u_{xx} - u_{yy}$.

EXERCISE

Prove the above statements that (8.6) is a solution of the Cauchy problem and that it is unique.

One sees that, for a point $(x,y) \in T$, the solution is determined by evaluating f at the intersection of the line $x - y = \text{constant}$ and the x-axis, by evaluating f at the intersection of $x + y = \text{constant}$ and the x-axis, by averaging these values, and by adding on the integral of g between the two intersections. Thus the solution is indeed determined in T, and, as it has been indicated, uniquely. Thus T, being the largest domain in which the solution of the initial value problem on (a,b) is uniquely defined, is called the domain of determination of (a,b). That this domain cannot be extended in the upper-half plane is seen by taking a point (x,y) in the upper-half plane outside T and noting that $\psi(x,y)$ then depends on data outside the interval (a,b). Since $x - y = \text{constant}$ and $x + y = \text{constant}$ are characteristics of the differential equation, this result is consistent with our development of the theory of characteristics. In this regard, notice that the domain of determination in the

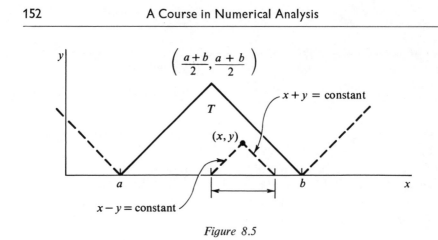

Figure 8.5

lower-half plane is a reflection of T, so that the largest domain in which a solution may be uniquely extended is bounded by segments of characteristics. This example is intended to elucidate the general theory and this theory should be reviewed now in this light by the student. Although the difficult questions of existence and uniqueness for quasi-linear equations have been avoided, we have seen here that in a purely hyperbolic region, characteristic segments bound whatever region of determination exists.

In our simple wave-equation problem, the unbounded region of the upper-half plane contained between the characteristics $x + y = a$ and $x - y = b$ is called the region of influence of (a,b), since an alteration of data in (a,b) results in an alteration of the solution at every point. Conversely to our comment on the region of determination of (a,b), the subinterval of (a,b), which forms the base of an isosceles triangle with vertex at the point (x,y), is called the 'domain of dependence of the solution at (x,y).' *Hyperbolic equations are to some extent characterized by having a finite domain of dependence.*

4. STABILITY OF A DIRECT FINITE-DIFFERENCE METHOD

Reconsider now the simple Cauchy problem (Chapter 8, Sec. 3). Letting $u_1 = \psi_x$, $u_2 = \psi_y$, an equivalent problem is

$$\begin{cases} u_{2x} - u_{1y} = 0 \\ u_{1x} - u_{2y} = 0 \end{cases} \quad \text{or} \quad \begin{pmatrix} u_1 \\ u_2 \end{pmatrix}_y = \begin{pmatrix} 0 & 1 \\ 1 & 0 \end{pmatrix} \begin{pmatrix} u_1 \\ u_2 \end{pmatrix}_x,$$

where $u_1(x,0) = f'(x) \wedge u_2(x,0) = g(x) \wedge f', g \in C^1(a,b)$. We write

$$U_y = BU_x \quad \text{where} \quad B = \begin{pmatrix} 0 & 1 \\ 1 & 0 \end{pmatrix} \wedge U = \begin{pmatrix} u_1 \\ u_2 \end{pmatrix},$$

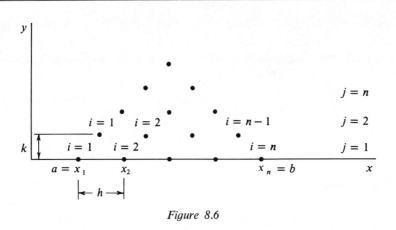

Figure 8.6

and it will be noteworthy that $B^2 = I$ where I is the (2×2) identity matrix. We partition (a,b), and consider a march to determine $U = \begin{pmatrix} u_1 \\ u_2 \end{pmatrix}$ at points on lines parallel to and above (a,b). We put

$$\frac{1}{k}[U_i^{j+1} - \tfrac{1}{2}(U_i^j + U_{i+1}^j)] = \frac{1}{h}B(U_{i+1}^j - U_i^j)$$

(with error in replacement of the differential equation $O(h) + O(k)$) or

(8.7) $$\boxed{U_i^{j+1} = \tfrac{1}{2}(U_i^j + U_{i+1}^j) + sB(U_{i+1}^j - U_i^j),}$$

where $s = k/h$. Letting $i = 1, \cdots, N$ on line $j = J$, we have that

(8.8)
$$\begin{pmatrix} U_1 \\ U_2 \\ \vdots \\ U_{N-1} \end{pmatrix}^{J+1}$$

$$= \begin{pmatrix} (\tfrac{1}{2}I - sB) & (\tfrac{1}{2}I + sB) & 0 & \cdots & 0 \\ 0 & (\tfrac{1}{2}I - sB) & (\tfrac{1}{2}I + sB) & \cdots & 0 \\ \vdots & \vdots & \vdots & & \vdots \\ 0 & 0 & 0 & \cdots & (\tfrac{1}{2}I - sB) \end{pmatrix} \begin{pmatrix} U_1 \\ U_2 \\ \vdots \\ U_{N-1} \end{pmatrix}^J$$

$$+ \begin{pmatrix} 0 \\ 0 \\ \vdots \\ (\tfrac{1}{2}I + sB)U_N^J \end{pmatrix}.$$

This now appears as a Picard iteration. Let $\delta_i{}^J$ be a perturbation vector of the values U_i on line $J \ni \delta_N{}^J = 0$, and let $\delta_i{}^{J+1}$ be the resulting perturbation vector on line $J + 1$. Then if A_N is the above $2(N - 1) \times 2(N - 1)$ matrix of real numbers,

$$
\begin{pmatrix} U_1 + \delta_1 \\ U_2 + \delta_2 \\ \vdots \\ U_{N-1} + \delta_{N-1} \end{pmatrix}^{J+1} = A_N \begin{pmatrix} U_1 + \delta_1 \\ U_2 + \delta_2 \\ \vdots \\ U_{N-1} + \delta_{N-1} \end{pmatrix}^J + \begin{pmatrix} 0 \\ 0 \\ \vdots \\ (\tfrac{1}{2}I + sB)U_N{}^J \end{pmatrix}
$$

or, subtracting (8.8),

$$
\begin{pmatrix} \delta_1 \\ \delta_2 \\ \vdots \\ \delta_{N-1} \end{pmatrix}^{J+1} = A_N \begin{pmatrix} \delta_1 \\ \delta_2 \\ \vdots \\ \delta_{N-1} \end{pmatrix}^J ,
$$

so that we achieve asymptotic stability of the difference equation—which is now identified with numerical stability of the marching schema—if Picard iteration of A_N converges where the limit is to be examined either by refining the mesh or extending the interval (a,b). Geometrically, one may wish to think of looking for stability by following out a strip between parallel lines of the first N-points, counting from the left of each row, and assuming that values to the right of the strip are not disturbed. To get the best condition for convergence, we use, of course, the spectral norm condition on A_N. Letting λ_i, $i = 1, \cdots, 2N - 2$, be any eigenvalue of A_N, and developing the determinant $|A_N - \lambda_i I|$ by (2×2) minors from the upper left

$$
|A_N - \lambda_i I| = 0 \Leftrightarrow |(\tfrac{1}{2} - \lambda_i)I - sB|^{N-1} = 0,
$$

or

$$
\left| \left(\frac{\tfrac{1}{2} - \lambda_i}{s} \right) I - B \right| = 0.
$$

But since $B^2 = I$, all squared eigenvalues of B are one (i.e., if μ is an eigenvalue of B and x an eigenvector, $Ix = B^2x = B(Bx) = B(\mu x) = \mu(Bx) = \mu^2 x$), so that

$$
\left(\frac{\tfrac{1}{2} - \lambda_i}{s} \right)^2 = 1 \quad \text{or} \quad \lambda_i = \tfrac{1}{2} \pm s
$$

and

$$
0 < \frac{k}{h} = s < \tfrac{1}{2} \Rightarrow \max |\lambda_i| = s(A_N) < 1.
$$

The march must be conducted so that from two points on line J a point on line $J + 1$ is obtained inside the characteristic triangle whose base is the interval between the two points on line J. Since the solution is uniquely determined for the differential equation no farther than the characteristic triangle on (a,b), we could not obtain any better results except by using $s = \frac{1}{2}$, so that $s(A_N) = 1$. For stability of a march, we should be willing to use this marginal condition, although the condition would be avoided if the march were regarded strictly as an iteration and only convergence were considered to be at stake. In using such a condition for stability of a marching schema, we allow for an asymptotic factor of reduction of the perturbations of one. Also, note that we could do simply with a condition for contraction of A_N; namely, that in some norm $\|A_N\| < 1$. We will resort to this for nonlinear problems. For linear problems, we would not be sure that we had the best possible results unless we used the spectral norm condition.

A strong word of warning must be issued in using the preceding analysis. We tacitly assumed above that solutions of the difference equation exist for any perturbation we wish to make of a line of data regarded as initial data, and that these solutions converge with refinement of mesh to the solution of the initial value problem of the differential equation for any perturbation of initial values. Returning to Chapter 8, Sec. 3, it is evident that solutions of our problem do exist for perturbations δ of f and η of $g \ni \delta \in C^2(a,b) \wedge \eta \in C^1(a,b)$, since the resulting displacement v, of our solution ψ, satisfies

$$v_{xx} - v_{yy} = 0 \wedge v(x,0) = \delta(x) \wedge v_y(x,0) = \eta(x),$$

for which our D'Alembert solution can be given in the characteristic traingle.[4] But now suppose our wave equation $\psi_{xx} - \psi_{yy} = 0$ is replaced by the Laplace equation $\psi_{xx} + \psi_{yy} = 0$. If the marching schema above is analyzed for stability, the only point of departure from the above is that the matrix B is replaced by

$$B = \begin{pmatrix} 0 & 1 \\ -1 & 0 \end{pmatrix} \quad \text{and} \quad B^2 = -I.$$

Then all squared eigenvalues of B are minus one (i.e., $-Ix = B^2x = B(\mu x) = \mu(Bx) = \mu^2 x$), so that

$$\left(\frac{\frac{1}{2} - \lambda_i}{s}\right)^2 = -1 \quad \text{or} \quad \lambda_i = \tfrac{1}{2} \pm is \quad \text{or} \quad |\lambda_i|^2 = \tfrac{1}{4} + s^2,$$

---

[4] With respect to certain extended interpretations of existence, this statement is even valid for a much larger class of perturbations.

or $$0 < \frac{h}{k} = s < \frac{\sqrt{3}}{2} \Rightarrow \max_i |\lambda_i| = s(A_N) < 1.$$

The apparent implication, however, that the march is numerically stable is fallacious, for it will be shown later (see Chapter 10, Sec. 1) that solutions to the initial value problem for the Laplace differential equation exist only if perturbations are taken to be functions that are analytic in a suitable domain of the complex plane. Thus the tacit assumptions of such an analysis as given above are grossly violated when performed on the Laplace equation, which itself is stable only to a restricted class of perturbations of data. Unless we take steps to ensure, as we will later (see Chapter 10, Sec. 2), that computational perturbations belong to, or are at least 'close' to, this very restricted class, we can expect that for a large mesh the march will produce reasonable solutions of the difference equations near the data line, but that as the mesh is refined so that a solution of the differential equation is approached, it will give fallacious values. Since small mesh or large distance from the data line is hardly to be distinguished for our difference equation, one expects that, for large mesh, inaccuracies will develop farther away from the data line. Thus one expects that as the error of replacement of the differential equation by the difference equation is reduced, the errors due to instabilities are increased, and this is exactly what is observed in computations. It is evident from this that one cannot really 'win'. However, one might learn to lose less noticeably; i.e., it should be noted that some work has been done to modify the march so that the effects of onset of instability are delayed and fairly good answers are obtained quite close to the data line [1][2]. In Chapter 11, a direct extension of the results we have shown for the wave and Laplace equations is obtained by introducing rotated characteristic coordinates where a more intricate matrix B plays an identical role to the above.

Returning to the wave equation problem, it must be noted that the stability analysis is often given in other terms. In (8.7), we have $\forall\, i = 1, \cdots, N - 1$

$$\delta_i^{j+1} = (\tfrac{1}{2}(I + sB))\delta_{i+1}^{j} + (\tfrac{1}{2}(I - sB))\delta_i^{j}.$$

We now examine stability of an arbitrary point on the line $J + 1$ to a perturbation of one only of the two points just below it on line J. Thus if $\delta_i^J = 0$, then

$$\delta_i^{J+1} = (\tfrac{1}{2}I + sB)\delta_{i+1}^{J}$$

or, if $\delta_{i+1}{}^J = 0$, then

$$\delta_i{}^{J+1} = (\tfrac{1}{2}I - sB)\delta_i{}^J.$$

In either case, using the maximum norm on the (2×2) correction matrix, we see that the error is reduced at every iteration if $s < \frac{1}{2}$, or we could use as before the spectral norm condition to show that powers of the correction matrix tend to zero.

Although this kind of stability analysis is obviously suitable here, since displacements due to independent perturbations are additive, it is open to serious question when applied to nonlinear equations. Besides the violation of additivity, for nonlinear equations the matrix will be replaced by one that depends on the solution. For nonlinear equations, evaluating B at i or $i + 1$ as desired, and, for the purpose of the examination of 'local stability,' treating it as a matrix of constants, we obtain the celebrated von Neumann criterion. Imperfect as it is logically—and this imperfection was quite as well understood by its author as by any other—it has provided virtually the only useful framework for judging stability of computations in nonlinear problems. In fact, the criterion has never been reported to fail in so obvious a way as to be associated with rapid oscillations in computed values when it indicated the march was stable. Nevertheless, unless we are ready to accept linearized analysis of convergence of iterative methods for nonlinear equations, the criterion cannot be regarded as meeting modern standards. We will show that modern methods of analysis of iterative procedures allow for some improvement of the von Neumann criterion. Specifically, in Chapter 11, Sec. 5, we will propose replacement of the von Neumann criterion, in cases where that is feasible, by asking that a march from one line to the next be given by a contractive map.

REFERENCES

[1] Fritz John, 'Numerical solution of problems which are not well-posed in the sense of Hadamard,' Proc. Rome Symposium (28–29–30 Jan., 1959) organized by the Provisional International Center, Libreria Eredi Virgilio Veschi, Rome, pp. 103–116.

[2] M. D. Van Dyke, 'The supersonic blunt body problem, review and extension,' *J. Aero. Space Sci.*, **25**, (1958), 485–496.

CHAPTER 9

STABILITY OF DIFFERENCE
METHODS FOR PARABOLIC
EQUATIONS

1. FORWARD DIFFERENCES FOR THE SLAB PROBLEM

We consider the problem to find[1] $u \; \forall \; x \in (0,l) \wedge t \in (0,T), T \in R_+{}^1$ ∋.

$$u_{xx} = u_t \wedge u(x,0) = f(x) \wedge u(0,t) = g_0(t) \wedge u(l,t) = g_1(t).$$

Partitioning $(0,l)$ and $(0,T)$ with equal meshes h and k, we discretize the problem by asking for values of u on the discrete set indicated in Figure 9.1 where our finite-difference replacement is

$$\frac{1}{k}(u_i^{j+1} - u_i^j) = \frac{u_{i-1}^j - 2u_i^j + u_{i+1}^j}{h^2}$$

or $\qquad u_i^{j+1} = u_i^j + r(u_{i-1}^j - 2u_i^j + u_{i+1}^j) \qquad$ where $\qquad r = k/h^2.$

Then

$$
\begin{pmatrix} u_1 \\ u_2 \\ u_3 \\ \vdots \\ u_n \end{pmatrix}^{j+1}
=
\begin{pmatrix}
1-2r & r & 0 & 0 & \cdots & 0 & 0 \\
r & 1-2r & r & 0 & \cdots & 0 & 0 \\
0 & r & 1-2r & r & \cdots & 0 & 0 \\
\vdots & \vdots & \vdots & \vdots & & \vdots & \vdots \\
0 & 0 & 0 & 0 & \cdots & r & 1-2r
\end{pmatrix}
\begin{pmatrix} u_1 \\ u_2 \\ u_3 \\ \vdots \\ u_n \end{pmatrix}^{j}
+
\begin{pmatrix} ru_0^j \\ 0 \\ 0 \\ \vdots \\ ru_{n+1}^j \end{pmatrix}.
$$

Of course, the marching schema is a Picard iteration, and a perturbation vector δ_i^j of u_i^j with $\delta_0^j = \delta_{n+1}^j = 0$ satisfies the relation

---

[1] To get a regular solution, we must require at least that $f \in C(0,l)$, $g_0 \in C(0,T)$, $g_1 \in C(0,T)$, $\lim_{x\to 0} f(x) = \lim_{t\to 0} g_0(t) \wedge \lim_{x\to l} f(x) = \lim_{t\to 0} g_1(t).$

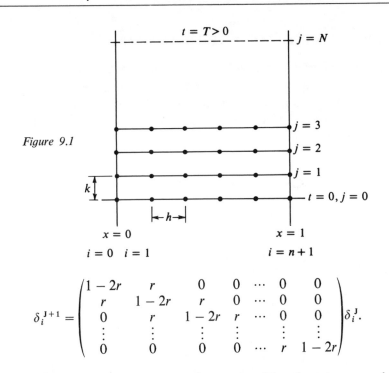

Figure 9.1

$$\delta_i^{J+1} = \begin{pmatrix} 1-2r & r & 0 & 0 & \cdots & 0 & 0 \\ r & 1-2r & r & 0 & \cdots & 0 & 0 \\ 0 & r & 1-2r & r & \cdots & 0 & 0 \\ \vdots & \vdots & \vdots & \vdots & & \vdots & \vdots \\ 0 & 0 & 0 & 0 & \cdots & r & 1-2r \end{pmatrix} \delta_i^J.$$

For simplicity of treatment, we restrict our considerations to cases where $n+1$ is divisible by three. Then using the spectral norm condition again, and developing the relevant secular determinant by two row minors, every λ_i that is an eigenvalue of the correction matrix satisfies

$$\begin{vmatrix} 1-2r-\lambda_i & r \\ r & 1-2r-\lambda_i \end{vmatrix} = 0,$$

or

$$\lambda_i = -2r \pm r + 1.$$

Then

$$0 < \frac{k}{h^2} = r < \frac{2}{3} \Rightarrow \max_i |\lambda_i| < 1.$$

Since it is frequently required to use h small—e.g., if $\exists\, x \in (0,l) \ni f'(x)$ is large—in order to approximate well the solution of the differential equation, the restriction $k < (2/3)h^2$ on the t-step necessary for stability of forward differences can be very limiting. To use h small may restrict the t-step so severely that little progress in the t-direction is made for large computing times. Moreover, for some similar equations of the parabolic type (e.g., $(k(x)u_x)_x = u_t$, where k is the coefficient of heat conduction, or see [1]), a parameter or function appearing in the equation can further restrict the t-step size.

2. IMPLICIT METHOD FOR THE SLAB PROBLEM

A better method, universally stable without restriction on the t-step, and requiring no more computing time per line, has completely replaced this method in numerical practice. Two oil engineers, J. Crank and P. Nicolson [2], first used the method. Our finite-difference replacement here is

$$\frac{1}{k}(u_i{}^{j+1} - u_i{}^j) = \frac{1}{2}\frac{1}{h^2}[(u_{i-1}{}^j - 2u_i{}^j + u_{i+1}{}^j) + (u_{i-1}{}^{j+1} - 2u_i{}^{j+1} + u_{i+1}{}^{j+1})],$$

or

$$-\frac{r}{2}u_{i-1}{}^{j+1} + (1+r)u_i{}^{j+1} - \frac{r}{2}u_{i+1}{}^{j+1} = \frac{r}{2}u_{i-1}{}^j + (1-r)u_i{}^j + \frac{r}{2}u_{i+1}{}^j,$$

or

$$
\begin{pmatrix} -\dfrac{r}{2}u_0 \\ 0 \\ 0 \\ \vdots \\ -\dfrac{r}{2}u_{n+1} \end{pmatrix}^{j+1}
+
\begin{pmatrix}
1+r & -\dfrac{r}{2} & 0 & 0 & \cdots & 0 \\
-\dfrac{r}{2} & 1+r & -\dfrac{r}{2} & 0 & \cdots & 0 \\
0 & -\dfrac{r}{2} & 1+r & -\dfrac{r}{2} & \cdots & 0 \\
\vdots & \vdots & \vdots & \vdots & & \vdots \\
0 & 0 & \cdots & & -\dfrac{r}{2} & 1+r
\end{pmatrix}
\begin{pmatrix} u_1 \\ u_2 \\ u_3 \\ \vdots \\ u_n \end{pmatrix}^{j+1}
$$

(9.1)

$$
=
\begin{pmatrix} \dfrac{r}{2}u_0 \\ 0 \\ 0 \\ \vdots \\ \dfrac{r}{2}u_{n+1} \end{pmatrix}^{j}
+
\begin{pmatrix}
1-r & \dfrac{r}{2} & 0 & 0 & \cdots & 0 \\
\dfrac{r}{2} & 1-r & \dfrac{r}{2} & 0 & \cdots & 0 \\
0 & \dfrac{r}{2} & 1-r & \dfrac{r}{2} & \cdots & 0 \\
\vdots & \vdots & \vdots & & & \vdots \\
0 & 0 & \cdots & & \dfrac{r}{2} & 1-r
\end{pmatrix}
\begin{pmatrix} u_1 \\ u_2 \\ u_3 \\ \vdots \\ u_n \end{pmatrix}^{j},
$$

which can be written in the form

$$b^{j+1} + Bu^{j+1} = -Cu^j + b^j.$$

We now perturb the values of u_i^j on line j by amounts δ_i^j, where $\delta_0^j = \delta_{n+1}^j = 0$, and look for the resulting displacement on line $j + 1$. Then

$$B\delta^{j+1} = -C\delta^j,$$

so that for asymptotic stability of the difference equation with respect to the initial data $f(x_i)$—not the 'side' data $g_0(t)$, $g_1(t)$—it will suffice to show that the eigenvalues of $-B^{-1}C$ are less than one in absolute value (see Chapter 4, Sec. 2). We have

$$0 = |\lambda_i B + C|$$

$$=
\begin{vmatrix}
(1 + r)\lambda_i + (-1 + r) & -\dfrac{r}{2}(\lambda_i + 1) & 0 & \cdots \\[2ex]
-\dfrac{r}{2}(\lambda_i + 1) & (1 + r)\lambda_i + (-1 + r) & -\dfrac{r}{2}(\lambda_i + 1) & \cdots \\[2ex]
\vdots & \vdots & \vdots & \\[2ex]
0 & -\dfrac{r}{2}(\lambda_i + 1) & (1 + r)\lambda_i + (-1 + r) & \cdots
\end{vmatrix}.$$

Again, for simplicity, restricting our considerations to cases where $n + 1$ is divisible by three,

$$
\begin{vmatrix}
(1 + r)\lambda_i + (-1 + r) & -\dfrac{r}{2}(\lambda_i + 1) \\[2ex]
-\dfrac{r}{2}(\lambda_i + 1) & \lambda_i(1 + r) + (-1 + r)
\end{vmatrix}
= 0,$$

or

$$(1 + r)\lambda_i + (r - 1) = \pm\frac{r}{2}(\lambda_i + 1),$$

or

$$\lambda_i = \frac{1 - r \pm r/2}{1 + r \mp r/2} = \frac{1 - r/2}{1 + r/2} \quad \text{or} \quad \frac{1 - (3/2)r}{1 + (3/2)r},$$

so that $\forall\, r > 0,\ \max_i |\lambda_i| < 1$.

By letting r be negative it is seen that both the forward difference and Crank-Nicolson methods will be unstable if the problem of Chapter 9, Sec. 1, is posed for $T < 0$: i.e., if it is posed in the lower-half plane. Here, unlike the case of the Laplace equation, asymptotic stability of the difference equation corresponds to that of the differential equation. To see this, perturb the initial data $f(x)$ in the slab (differential equation) problem as posed in Chapter 9, Sec. 1 by a function $\delta(x)$, leaving the 'side' data $g_0(t)$ and $g_1(t)$ unchanged. The resulting displacement v of the solution u satisfies

$$v_{xx} = v_t,$$
$$v(x,0) = \delta(x), \quad v(0,t) = v(l,t) = 0.$$

If we now, by means of separation of variables, formally construct the Fourier series for solution of this stability problem, we will find that for each term of the series the limit as $t \to \infty$ is zero, while the limit as $t \to -\infty$ does not exist (is infinite) because of the occurrence of a factor $e^{-k^2 t}$, $k \in R^1$, in each term.

EXERCISE

Perform formally the Fourier series construction indicated above. (The resulting Fourier series converges to the solution under very general conditions, but proof of this is not a part of the exercise.)

In computational practice, we need to solve the equation (9.1) for $u_1, \cdots, u_n$. Because of the tridiagonal nature of matrices B and C, it is possible to generate a convenient n-step procedure for doing this, using Gaussian elimination and back substitution on (9.1). We can then scan from left to right and up, determining each successive point on a line $j + 1$ from the four known points of the basic six-point cluster:

$$
\begin{array}{cccc}
\text{scan} & & & \\
\rightarrow & x & \circled{x} & 0 - j + 1 \\
 & x & x & x - j.
\end{array}
$$

EXERCISE

Obtain the indicated n-step iteration formula for solving the 'implicit equations' at each new time line.

Other implicit methods are sometimes used, but, for the slab problem at least, the techniques of analysis are identical to the above.

3. METHODS OF LINES

We classify as a method of lines any one of several discretizations where partial derivatives in all but one variable are approximated by difference quotients, thus replacing a boundary value problem for a partial differential equation by a finite sequence of initial or two-point boundary value problems for ordinary differential equations. Not nearly so much is known of convergence of solutions as for the algebraic systems associated with the more usual finite-difference discretizations. Of course, neither type of discretization is as well adapted to computation of error bounds as is the least squares procedure given earlier. Our analogue computer techniques, proposed earlier for use in connection with least squares procedures, seem superficially similar to some methods of lines, since they require solving a system of initial value problems for ordinary differential equations. However, the systems utilized are entirely different, and only asymptotic values of the solution, not values for every argument, are required. Moreover, error bounds can be computed for linear problems by using our analogue least squares procedure.

For the slab problem of Chapter 9, Sec. 1, we have either to solve the initial value problem for the system of ordinary differential equations,

$$\frac{du_i}{dt} = \frac{1}{h^2}(u_{i+1} - 2u_i + u_{i-1}) \wedge u_i(0) = f(x_i) \; \forall \; i = 1, \cdots, n$$

$$\text{where} \quad u_0(t) = g_0(t) \wedge u_{n+1}(t) = g_1(t)$$

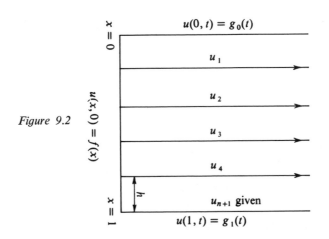

Figure 9.2

obtained by putting $u(x_i,t) = u_i(t)$ and deleting a function $O(h^2)$ in the differential equation, or to solve sequentially the set of two-point boundary value problems,

$$\frac{d^2 u}{dx^2} = \frac{1}{k}(u_j - u_{j-1}) \wedge u_j(0) = g_0(t_j),\, u_j(l) = g_1(t_j) \; \forall\, j = 1,\cdots, m$$

$$\text{where} \qquad u_0(x) = f(x)$$

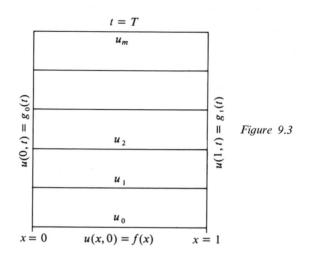

Figure 9.3

obtained by putting $u(x,t_j) = u_j(x)$ and deleting a function $O(k)$ in the differential equation.

These are typical of methods of lines, especially for parabolic equations, even when the equations are nonlinear. The first is generally open to doubt if, as usually anticipated for this method, analogue computing equipment is used to solve the initial value problem for a system of differential equations, without any checks provided by error bounds.

The second method is clumsy for nonlinear problems. The student has seen what difficulties the two-point boundary value problem for nonlinear equations offers, and that this method requires, rather than marching, say, by an implicit method, from one line to the next, the solving of a sequence of such problems. It happens in a large variety of problems (e.g., stellar structures [3], boundary layers [1]) that no initial data (like $u(0,x) = f(x)$ above) but only side data (like $u(0,t) = g_0(t)$,

$u(l,t) = g_1(t))$, with some system of differential equations of parabolic type, are given. If the coefficients of derivatives in any timelike[2] direction are zero on some line, so that on this line the partial differential equation becomes ordinary (a contrived example would be $u_{xx} = xu_t$, which becomes $d^2u/dx^2 = 0$ on $x = 0$), it then becomes possible to generate initial data by solution of a two-point boundary value problem on the singular line. *This is one of the most important reasons for our taking care to provide a good technique for the two-point problem.* However, if one has obtained a good approximation of such a solution, he would ordinarily choose to use an implicit marching scheme to solve at later times t, and it would seem to satisfy only a desire for self-torture to repeat sequentially the solution of a nonlinear two-point boundary value problem.

However, the history of methods of lines (at least those like our second above) has been greatly influenced by the fact that the processes of thought involved in deriving the mathematical model from physical principles have often induced scientists to think of their more intricate parabolic equations as arising physically from a sequence of two-point boundary value problems of ordinary differential equations in a spatial variable whose parameters are dependent on time. The deception is deepened by the mathematical fact that lines t constant are usually characteristic. This syndrome has been evident in work on stellar structures where gigantic quantities of computing time were once used in approximating solutions of exceedingly intricate parabolic problems (without testing on the time step size) by the second method indicated above. At the time, in fact, no really reliable method was available for the two-point problem for ordinary equations. Once again, we stand awed before the crushing weight of evidence against thinking that computation is a physical process, or that a mathematical model is an actual process of nature.

Of course, methods of lines when accompanied by finite-difference methods like Runge-Kutta become simply another type of finite-difference discretization. These changes in finite-difference replacement of the differential equation can be justified when, as very often happens, high-order accuracy is required in one variable, due to large gradients pointed in that direction, while very low-order accuracy is tolerable in another variable. We do not express objection to the change in finite-difference replacement, but only to clumsy or inaccurate methods of solving it.

---

[2] Of course, timelike for a parabolic system is simply a variable along a vector pointed in a noncharacteristic direction.

REFERENCES

[1] R. F. Kramer and H. M. Lieberstein, 'Numerical solution of the boundary-layer equations without similarity assumptions,' *J. Aero. Space Sci.* **26** (1959), 508–514.

[2] J. Crank and P. Nicolson, 'A practical method for numerical evaluation of solutions of partial differential equations of the heat conduction type,' *Proc. Camb. Phil. Soc.*, **43** (1947), 50–67.

[3] Marshall H. Wrubel, 'Stellar Interiors,' in *Handbuch Der Physik*, **51**, *Astrophysics II, Stellar Structure*, 1958, pp. 1–74.

CHAPTER 10

SOME ILLUSTRATIONS ON FLUID DYNAMIC PROBLEMS

1. THE CONVERGING-DIVERGING NOZZLE

Adopting a continuum model, we consider the flow of a gas (compressible fluid—where p is pressure and ρ is density, $\partial \rho / \partial p \neq 0$) through a tube of cross-section area that first diminishes and then increases. Such devices, it will be found, with proper adjustment of inlet and outlet pressures, allow subsonic entrance flow to be converted to a supersonic exit flow. In rocketry it is found that thrust is roughly proportional to average velocity in the exit plane so that it becomes essential that rockets be provided with an exit nozzle in order that appropriate efficiencies be obtained.

Let x be the distance to any position in the tube measured from the entrance plane $x = 0$. Where the exit plane is given by $x = 1$, let $A : [0,1] \to R^1$ be $\ni A(x)$ is the cross-section area of the tube at position x and let $A \in C^2[0,1]$. Moreover, let $\exists$ one and only one $\xi \in (0,l) \ni$ $A'(\xi) = 0$ and let ξ be a point of minimum for A. It is known that for large Reynold's number $\rho v L / \mu$, where v is the velocity, μ is the coefficient of viscosity, and L is a characterizing length (taken here to be minimum radius), the viscous, or shear drag, forces between layers of fluid or a layer of fluid and the wall are negligible.[1] Then, assuming a large minimum radius for the tube, it follows that the wall must be a streamline; i.e., that the wall is at all points tangent to a velocity vector. Furthermore, assuming the existence of flows independent of time,

---

[1] Physical phenomena depend on their dimensionless parameters. Since $\rho v L / \mu$ is dimensionless, a large value of the minimum radius L has the same effect as a large value of the reciprocal viscosity coefficient $1/\mu$ in making the viscous forces small.

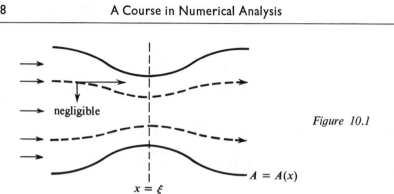

Figure 10.1

and studying only such flows, it is apparent that the wall streamline has the largest curvature of all streamlines across the tube. We assume with the originator of such problems, a Swedish engineer named Delaval (1850), that A'' is small enough—and, therefore, that the curvature of all streamlines is small enough—that radial components of velocity are negligible. We thus ignore radial motions in equating forces, but recognize that the cross-section area is a function of x in accounting for mass conservation.

Let $p: [0,l] \to R^1$, $p \in C^1[0,l] \wedge v: [0,l] \times [0,T] \to R^1$, $v \in C^1([0,l] \times [0,T])$ have functional values representing pressure and velocity, respectively. Letting $p(0) \gg p(l)$, the driving force x in the fluid is the negative of dp/dx, while the acceleration is

$$\frac{dv}{dt} = v_t + x'(t)v_x = v_t + vv_x.$$

Equating force to mass times acceleration, we have

$$\rho(vv_x) = \rho(v_t + vv_x) = -\frac{dp}{dx},$$

where, as agreed, only flows such that $v_t = 0$ are studied. In general, thermodynamically speaking, one must specify a function $\varphi \ni \varphi(p,\rho,S) = 0$, where S is entropy,[2] but, assuming that there are no sources or losses of energy in the flow, the entropy is constant; so we put $p = \Gamma(\rho)$, and note that the speed of sound is given by $c = \sqrt{d\Gamma/d\rho}$.[3] Then

---

[2] Defined by $\dfrac{dS}{dt} = \dfrac{1}{T}\dfrac{dQ}{dt}$, where Q is heat energy and T is temperature.

[3] This is taken as a definition or derived by considering small perturbations of pressure in the compressible flow equations, linearizing and deriving a wave equation with characteristics slope $\sqrt{d\Gamma/d\rho}$.

$$v \frac{dv}{dx} = -\frac{1}{\rho}\frac{dp}{dx} = -\frac{1}{\rho}\frac{d\Gamma}{d\rho}\frac{d\rho}{dx} = -\frac{c^2}{\rho}\frac{d\rho}{dx},$$

or, for $v^2 \neq 0$,

$$\frac{1}{v}\frac{dv}{dx} = -\frac{c^2}{v^2}\frac{1}{\rho}\frac{d\rho}{dx} = -\frac{1}{M^2}\frac{1}{\rho}\frac{d\rho}{dx},$$

or

$$\frac{d(\ln \rho)}{dx} = -M^2 \frac{d(\ln v)}{dx},$$

where M is the mach number v/c. It may already be noted why it is that low-speed subsonic ($M \approx 0$) compressible flow problems may sometimes be successfully treated with incompressible models, since a large change in ln v is reflected as a small change in ln ρ, while such a technique cannot be successful for high-speed supersonic ($M \gg 1$) problems, where small changes in ln v reflect large changes in ln ρ.

For conservation of mass,

$$\rho v A = \text{constant},$$

or

$$\ln \rho + \ln v + \ln A = \text{constant},$$

or

$$\frac{1}{\rho}\frac{d\rho}{dx} + \frac{1}{v}\frac{dv}{dx} + \frac{1}{A}\frac{dA}{dx} = 0.$$

Substituting from above,

$$-M^2 \frac{1}{v}\frac{dv}{dx} + \frac{1}{v}\frac{dv}{dx} + \frac{1}{A}\frac{dA}{dx} = 0,$$

or

(10.1) $$(M^2 - 1)\frac{1}{v}\frac{dv}{dx} = \frac{1}{A}\frac{dA}{dx}.$$

We now note the following:

(1) $M = 1 \Rightarrow A' = 0 \Rightarrow A$ is a minimum (the sonic velocity can be obtained at the throat only).

(2) $A' = 0 \Rightarrow (M = 1) \vee \left(\frac{dv}{dx} = 0\right)$ (at the throat either the velocity is sonic or stationary).

(3) (a) Since $v(0)$ is specified subsonic, and sonic velocities can be obtained at the throat only, and $v \in C\,[0,l]$,

$$v'(\xi) = 0 \wedge M(\xi) \neq 1 \Rightarrow M(\xi) < 1$$

(if the velocity is stationary at the throat and not sonic, it is subsonic).

(10.1)

(b) By continuity $\exists\, \varepsilon > 0 \ni x = \xi + \varepsilon \Rightarrow M(x) < 1 \wedge A'(x) > 0 \Rightarrow v'(x) < 0$ (if the velocity is stationary at the throat and not sonic, it is maximum there, so that $v(l)$ is subsonic).

(4) (a) $M(\xi) = 1 \wedge v'(\xi) < 0 \Rightarrow v(l)$ is subsonic.

(b) $M(\xi) = 1 \wedge v'(\xi) > 0 \Rightarrow \exists\, \varepsilon > 0 \ni x = \xi + \varepsilon \Rightarrow M(x) > 1$
(10.1)
$\wedge A'(x) > 0 \Rightarrow v'(x) > 0$.

It is thus possible by appropriate choice of $p(0) \wedge p(l)$ to achieve a high supersonic value of $v(l)$.

Completing the exhaustion of cases,

(c) $M(\xi) = 1 \wedge v'(\xi) = 0$ is a case that can go either way, depending on the sign of d^2v/dx^2.

A more penetrating analysis is possible if one uses the theory of critical points [2], Chapter 6, Sec. 8, for nonlinear differential equations. Any student specifically interested in this theory, and not merely in an illustration (as follows) of the use of the method characteristics, is advised to study such an analysis. A statement of the results of such an analysis can be found in [5], Chapter 2, Sec. 2(c).

Note that, without the nonlinearity introduced by utilizing a gas rather than a liquid, no such device would be possible. Delaval's analysis dispelled for all time the contention of authorities that fluids could not pass from subsonic to supersonic velocities. The very con-servative authorities of the day had only lately and vaguely acknow-ledged that problems existed where viscosity could become important (as in small channel flow), and they were still so dedicated to incom-pressible models that could be treated with the theory of analytic functions of a complex variable that they could not conceive of a phenomenon where compressibility played a dominant role. If a fluid is considered incompressible, the velocity of sound $\sqrt{d\Gamma/d\rho} = 1/\sqrt{d\rho/d\Gamma}$ must be considered infinite and all (finite) velocities are subsonic. Thus incompressible flows cannot become supersonic and the artificial insistence on the incompressibility assumption prevented scientists prior to Delaval's time from understanding how a subsonic flow could become supersonic. To this day some of our leading mathematical scholars want to believe that, because a 'structure' can be displayed (so far) only for linear problems, nonlinear problems are outside the realm of mathematics. But this implies that all of nature is to be explained in terms of linear models. We have here a striking example of a phenomenon that cannot be so explained, and the biological sciences would seem to be rich in other such examples.

By way of a warning to the student not to flaunt authority without cause, it should be mentioned, however, that Prandtl showed that classical inviscid models cannot explain that a fluid should go from supersonic to subsonic velocities. The explanation requires insertion of a shock, which many people regard as a viscous adaptation of the model.

The Delaval effect, as we have seen, is subject to really very simple analysis if close attention is paid to the relevant formulas. It is not subject, so far as we can understand, to treatment by purely intuitive discussion, unless the results of the analysis are allowed to become a part of intuition.

2. COMPUTATIONAL PROCEDURES FOR THE CLASSICAL NOZZLE PROBLEMS

The Euler equations of motion for inviscid, steady-state, three-dimensional flow can be derived as above, but by equating forces in the three coordinate directions. The mass conservation condition, now called the continuity equation,[4] is derived in a somewhat different, though still elementary, manner from the above. We do not include the derivation here. If entropy is assumed to be constant, and if axial symmetry is introduced, the equations can be written

(Continuity) $\qquad (\rho u r)_r + (\rho v r)_z = 0$

(Motion) $\qquad u u_r + v u_z + \dfrac{1}{\rho} p_r = 0$

$$u v_r + v v_z + \frac{1}{\rho} p_z = 0,$$

and we assume that $p = \Gamma(\rho) = K\rho^\gamma$. If we introduce a streamfunction Ψ by the equations

(10.2) $\qquad \Psi_r = \rho v r, \qquad \Psi_z = -\rho u r,$

----

[4] It assumes that the transformation of a given volume of fluid with time is a topological transformation—one to one and bicontinuous.

then the continuity equation is automatically satisfied by asking that $\Psi \in C^2(D)$, where D is some domain of E^2.

EXERCISE

Show that on any streamline Ψ is constant.

One combination of the momentum equations gives that the Bernoulli quantity $h + (1/2)q^2$ is constant on a streamline. This is a compatibility equation, in fact, derived in a previous problem where it was noted that the quantity h called enthalpy is given by

$$\frac{dh}{dt} = T\frac{ds}{dt} + \frac{1}{\rho}\frac{dp}{dt}.$$

We assume that this quantity is constant across streamlines in the approach flow (or entrance plane of a nozzle), so we have

(10.3)
$$\frac{\gamma}{\gamma - 1}\frac{p}{\rho} + \tfrac{1}{2}(u^2 + v^2) = h + \tfrac{1}{2}q^2$$

$$= h_0 \in R^1, \qquad \text{where} \qquad q^2 = u^2 + v^2.^{5}$$

Another combination (see Appendix E) of the momentum equations gives the vorticity equation

(10.4)
$$A\Psi_{rr} + 2B\Psi_{rz} + C\Psi_{zz} = D$$

where $\quad A = \left(1 - \dfrac{u^2}{c^2}\right), \quad B = -\dfrac{uv}{c^2}, \quad C = \left(1 - \dfrac{v^2}{c^2}\right), \quad D = \rho v$

$$\left(c^2 = \frac{d(K\rho^{\gamma})}{d\rho} = \frac{\gamma p}{\rho}\right),$$

which is the desired streamfunction equation.

In dealing with nozzle flows, we can work either with the Euler first-order system or with equations (10.3) and (10.4), where, putting

$$P = \Psi_r \quad \text{and} \quad Q = \Psi_z,$$

(10.4) will be replaced by the usual first-order system. Advantages in the use of the streamfunction equation are in expressing boundary conditions where we simply have that $\Psi_r + A'\Psi_z = 0$, and in avoiding

---

[5] It can be shown under our conditions that $h = \dfrac{\gamma}{\gamma - 1}\dfrac{p}{\rho}$.

third-leg characteristic (one is the streamline) computations. The direct finite-difference method might be utilized, except that the irregular wall boundary will offer some difficulties. Note, however, that for use of the streamfunction equation, in the step-by-step procedure suggested below, it will be necessary to evaluate A, B, C, and D at every step, and this will involve evaluation of the density ρ from knowledge of Ψ_r and Ψ_z at each step. Equation (10.3) gives on appropriate substitutions an implicit relation between ρ and Ψ_r and Ψ_z, which must be solved numerically at each step for ρ by an iterative method. We suggest the Newton method.

EXERCISES

Assuming that h_0, Ψ_r, and Ψ_z are known, show that (10.3), represented as $F(\rho) = 0$, is such that $M \neq 1 \Rightarrow F'(\rho) \neq 0$.

Of course, the function Ψ is defined by (10.2) only up to a constant. In setting up a nozzle problem, we put $\Psi = 0$ on the axis of the nozzle tube, thus specifying the constant. We now intend in some way to approximate the values of Ψ and Ψ_r (or, equivalently, Ψ_r and Ψ_z) on some line of constant mach number $M = 1 + \varepsilon$, where ε is small and positive. In the words of T. M. Cherry, who has determined infinite series solutions for the two-dimensional nozzle problem (subsonic and supersonic portion [3], without the necessity to determine such a 'post-sonic line') this can be accomplished only with 'some skulduggery.' A transformation (hodograph) of (10.4) is performed, giving a differential system for r and z in terms of $v = \Psi_r/\rho r$ and $u = -\Psi_z/\rho r$ as independent variables, which is, strictly speaking, only valid for two-dimensional flow, but is presumed valid outside some large neighborhood of the axis. An asymptotic series solution is then assumed for r and z in powers of

$$M^2 - 1 = \frac{u^2 + v^2}{c^2} - 1.$$

Letting $M^2 - 1 = \varepsilon$, only the term containing the first power of ε is retained. This provides a first-order differential equation for a curve given by $z = z(r)$ on which $M^2 = 1 + \varepsilon$. Starting from a wall position, this equation is then integrated toward the axis by finite-difference methods. Near the axis the equation is invalid, and some (possibly higher-order) extrapolation is used (see Appendix B or [4], pp. 69–73). Assuming the density to be its sonic value, Ψ_r and Ψ_z are then determined on this curve by simultaneous solution of the equations

$$\frac{\Psi_r{}^2 + \Psi_z{}^2}{\rho^2 r^2 c^2} = 1 + \varepsilon$$

and (10.3).

We intend to design a nozzle where the wall curvatures would be too large for a Delaval analysis to be appropriate[6] and where our $M = 1 + \varepsilon$ curve $z = z(r)$ will no longer be straight, as in one-dimensional theory. However, it will be close to straight, and the above crude techniques probably will not really give very bad results. Moreover, since a hyperbolic equation (which is presumed to be continuously dependent on the data) is involved in the supersonic region, some errors can be tolerated in estimation of the 'post-sonic line' and initial values on it.

We now proceed, using the usual method of characteristics for all interior points. For a last point adjacent to the wall boundary and not

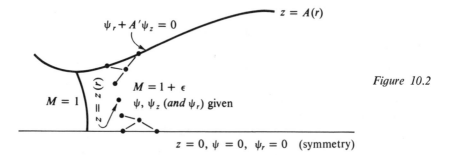

Figure 10.2

on it, a characteristic is intersected with the curve represented by $z = A(r)$ to give a first point on the next line. The equation $\Psi_r + A'\Psi_z = P + A'Q = 0$, then, replaces one compatibility relation in determining Ψ_r and Ψ_z at the intersection of a characteristic with the wall. A similar technique is used to determine points on the axis where $\Psi = 0$ replaces a compatibility equation. In using the differential equation at points of the axis, since the coefficient $D = \Psi_r/r$, it is necessary to note that

$$P_r(0,z) = \Psi_{rr}(0,z) = \frac{1}{h}(\Psi_r(h,z) - \Psi_r(0,z)) + O(h) = \frac{1}{h}\Psi_r(h,z) + O(h),$$

since symmetry requires $\Psi_r(0,z) = 0$.

---

[6] For example, a Polaris missile must be stowed vertically in a submarine where total length is a critical factor. Since a long nozzle cannot be tolerated, large curvature walls are required. Of course, in the supersonic region, even for large curvature walls the axial component of velocity will be so large that one-dimensional analysis would give correct gross features; but for these and other designs, it is desirable for efficiency to shape the walls so that radial components of velocity in the exit plane are as small as possible.

The general versatility of the method of characteristics, as opposed to the direct finite-difference replacement of (10.4), when there are boundaries other than just initial lines, is now in evidence. This will be further illustrated as we proceed, but it should not discourage the student from seeking methods to utilize the direct difference procedure with such boundaries.

In modern technology, requirements to consider burning in the nozzle, which alters (10.3) and adds an entropy equation to (10.4) involving chemical reactions, or requirements of thrust vector control for solid propellant rockets, where motor gimbeling is unthinkable and where one may wish to consider nozzles when axial symmetry of the flow is violated, or requirements to consider interactions of the hot and therefore ionized fluid with a strong magnetic field provided by exterior magnetos, can almost hopelessly complicate the method of characteristics as applied to this class of devices. Also, in modern technology there is often a shift in emphasis on design specifications to be met. Simply providing parallel exit flow may not be all that is required. Wall temperatures may have to be kept below a critical value or it may be required to keep the thrust vector directed according to the prescription of a guidance device. Actually these kinds of demands will ultimately make obsolete the kind of computational procedures outlined here. We cherish the hope that development of our 'continuous' methods, now in their infancy, will in the future allow approximation of the entire subsonic and supersonic classical nozzle problem and be capable of including some of the exotic requirements mentioned. However, direct iterative methods, as envisioned in an earlier research exercise, which would use machine algebra to iterate to solutions of boundary value problems without discretization, should also be investigated.

RESEARCH EXERCISE

Find an appropriate 'least squares or Galierkin approximating family' for the classical nozzle problem.

3. DISCUSSION OF JET PROBLEMS

Assuming that a nozzle has been designed, and that Ψ, Ψ_z (and Ψ_r) are known at the exit plane (one usually assumes the flow to be uniform in the exit plane since the attainment of this is an objective of classical nozzle design), we can compute the flow in the exhaust by again using the method of characteristics. We utilize as an outside boundary a curve where the pressure in the jet flow is equal to the ambient pressure. Of course, this curve (which will be a streamline), unlike a wall, is not fixed in advance by a formula $z = A(r)$, but must be generated step by step. If a line of data is known from axis to free streamline, with one point known on the free streamline, the next point on the free streamline is obtained by intersecting the line $dz/dr = -\Psi_r/\Psi_z$ (which is the direction of the jet boundary) with a characteristic from a point adjacent to the boundary. Replacing one compatibility relation with $p = p_0$ on the jet boundary where p_0 is ambient pressure, we obtain our flow data there.

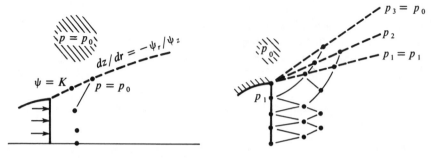

Figure 10.3

At other points, to get data on the next line, we can use the same program that was used for the nozzle, with the exception of complications noted below.

The values of Ψ_r and Ψ_z at the first point on the free steamline are not those at the wall of the nozzle end because they depend on the pressure at this boundary, which is p_0, and not on the pressure at the nozzle exit. To obtain these values (i.e., Ψ_r and Ψ_z), refining the mesh in a neighborhood of the nozzle end point, we recommend that one march around to a fan of fictitious straight walls, using the method of characteristics program for a nozzle, until one obtains a wall direction where the pressure at the wall is p_0. If this final direction is virtually unchanged with further mesh refinement, the direction and the values of Ψ_r and Ψ_z (Ψ is known) are those at the nozzle end point. The usual advice given here is to use a Prandtl-Meyer expansion at this point, but, strictly speaking, the derivation of that technique is based on finding the solutions lost in a hodograph transformation by the Jacobian vanishing, and is valid only for two-dimensional, irrotational ($\Leftarrow S$ constant) flow. It also requires an entirely independent program, whereas this method does not.

As the computation proceeds, however, it will usually become quite complicated, for it will be found that characteristics of the same family soon coalesce requiring, as indicated earlier (see Chapter 8, Sec. 2), the introduction of a shock (see Chapter 12, Sec. 1), along this

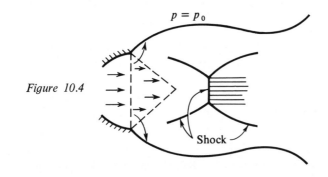

Figure 10.4

envelope. This now also must be followed as a free interface, just as the jet boundary was followed. If it is followed step by step, as we suggest, there now develops a complicated shock reflection pattern, which we are not, at this point, prepared to discuss.

Jet flow problems are typical of a certain class of 'free-boundary' problems where the boundary on which some conditions are satisfied must be generated by the solution. Notice, however, that this is accomplished step by step here—at least, to the extent that one finds finite-differences satisfactory—which makes the computational task far easier than it is in some other problems we will have occasion to discuss later (see Chapter 12, Sec. 4).

But again, modern requirements are tending to make obsolete current techniques for jet computation. In space, ambient pressure being negligible, the jet boundary expands far around the nozzle end to form a configuration better described as a 'plume' than a jet. Now if one wishes to telemeter data through this ionized cloud back to an earth-bound station or to another space object, he would have to know at least the temperature distribution in this field. For soft landings in low-pressure atmospheres, problems of pilot visibility of the surface or of the amount of possibly lethal debris kicked up from the surface are of interest. The decisions that are required in these cases may not be considered as particularly sensitive to the flow field in the plume, and crude approximations or even educated guesses at the form of functions involved (e.g., bell-shaped pressure distribution across the plume, etc.) seem adequate. Still curiosity and a lurking fear that we will one day get so far from what is firmly known that we have no foothold on intuition drives us to ask about the details of the flow field, but we have virtually nowhere to look for a beginning. Near the edge of the plume we have a rarefied flow where the continuum model is no longer valid, while presumably in the plume center a continuum model is all we know how to handle. In between lies a region where almost nothing is known about appropriate models.

The Boltzmann integro-differential equations are supposed to apply for the entire plume, but although there is an astute theory of asymptotic solutions giving rarefied theory at one extreme, and the Euler and Navier-Stokes equations, as successive approximations, at the other extreme [1], very little is known about how to pose boundary conditions for the full integro-differential equations, and nothing is known about methods of approximation. A development of numerical methods and relevant mathematical theory should be undertaken. Once again, iterative methods, presumably starting this time from solutions of the rarefied problem where the integral part of the equation is deleted, seem to be indicated.

RESEARCH EXERCISE

Develop a convergent iterative method for solving boundary value problems of the Boltzmann equations that can be used to approximate the flow in an exhaust plume expanded around to negligible presures. Use the iterative method to provide existence.

4. DISCUSSION OF COMPUTATION TECHNIQUE ON LATERAL EDGES OF CLOSED BODIES

As it will develop in Chapter 12, it is often possible, though sometimes quite difficult, to determine the flow in a neighborhood of the nose of a body facing a supersonic uniform stream, leaving the values of flow variables specified in a hyperbolic region, on a characteristic touching the body on one side and a shock on the other. It is possible, then, to generate the shock step by step, and along with the method of characteristics, to use the shock relations (see Chapter 12, Sec. 1) like a compatibility relation. As with a nozzle wall, the lateral edge of the body may be used as a line where $\Psi = 0$, and intersected successively with characteristics, thus following the given body and generating the shock. The only computationally difficult problem, in purely classic contexts, is to find the flow in the nose region, and this will be discussed later as indicated.

In modern contexts, the flow may be heated to dissociation temperatures by passing it across a strong shock, thus making intricate the thermodynamic state relation $\varphi(p,\rho,s) = 0$. One may hope to include effects of ablation of materials from the nose into the flow or effects of finite rates of dissociation. Even large yaw would introduce enough complication to excite the calmest computor.

In the recent past, it was thought that knowledge of the details of the afterflow of closed bodies was essential. This is not the case for drag considerations for high-speed bodies in air, since base pressures for bodies in supersonic flow have been found to be negligible. In the phenomenon of afterflow for high-speed bodies in gases considered dense enough that continuum models are used for nose and lateral flow, there is no clear line of demarcation between 'wake' and ambient flow, as there is for the case of cavitation behind bodies towed at high speed through a liquid (see Chapter 12, Sec. 4). Since the flow expands around and in on the aft end of the body to virtually zero pressure, a continuum model does not apply here, just as it does not apply for an exhaust plume expanding out to negligible pressure. Schlierin photographs of the afterflow of high-speed bodies in gas reveal diffuse radially fanned regions of darkness well to the aft of the body, indicating broad areas not subject to shock approximation where there are large gradients of density and pressure. The only solution for this problem lies in a model based on the Boltzmann equation, which, as mentioned above, is supposed to include effects for all levels of density. Once again, however, an appropriate boundary value problem must be posed.

It seems questionable that detailed knowledge of the afterflow—especially including effects of ablation, material impurities washed in from the nose, large yaw, and a number of possible chemical effects—is of immediate import. However, the problem is there, virtually untouched, for someone who is willing to take an interest in formulating the basic scientific problems involved.

5. THE LAGRANGE INTERIOR BALLISTIC PROBLEM

We consider a right circular cylinder of mass m and cross section A that slides with negligible friction inside a tube of the same cross section. The tube is closed at one end only. Where x is measured from the closed end of the tube, the cylinder is held at a position $x = X_0$, while the gas pressure is raised to a value p_0 in the chamber to the rear of the cylinder. After waiting until equilibrium is obtained in the

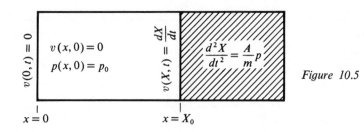

Figure 10.5

chamber (i.e., until the fluid velocity or average particle velocity $v = 0$ at all points in the chamber), the cylinder is released to travel the tube on a time trajectory $x = X(t)$. It is assumed that $\exists\, T \in R^1 \ni X : [0,T] \to R^1 \wedge X \in C^2[0,T]$. Assuming that pressure inside the chamber is given by functional values of $p = p(x,t)$ (i.e., assuming one-dimensional, time-dependent flow), since the cylinder is driven down the tube by the fluid pressure at its base, we have the relation

$$\frac{d^2 X}{dt^2} = \frac{A}{m} p(X,t).$$

Further, we assume that any point where the fluid meets the wall, traveling normal to the wall, must be a point of stagnation relative to the wall, so that

$$(v(0,t) = 0) \wedge (v(X,t) = dX/dt).$$

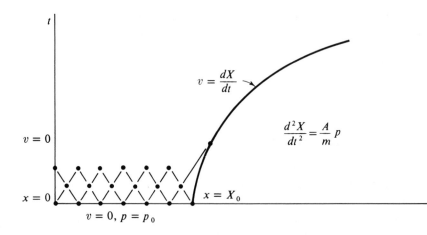

Figure 10.6

The inviscid equations of continuity and fluid motion in the chamber are

$$\rho_t + (\rho v)_x = 0$$

$$\rho v_t + \rho v v_x + p_x = 0.$$

The system is hyperbolic.

EXERCISE

Find the differential equations of the characteristics.

Computationally, one starts on the line $t = 0$ and generates v and p on successively higher curves. For any point other than the first or last on such a curve, the ordinary method of characteristics can be used. For a first point not on the line $x = 0$, a line of characteristic slope from that point is intersected with the line $x = 0$, and the boundary condition $v = 0$ is used to replace a compatibility relation. For a last point not on the trajectory $x = X(t)$, a line of characteristic slope is intersected with a line of slope $dX/dt = v$ from the last point on the trajectory. The relation

$$\frac{dv}{dt} = \frac{d}{dt}\left(\frac{dX}{dt}\right) = \frac{A}{m}p$$

is used to replace a compatibility relation. Once more it has been possible to devise a computational procedure capable of step-by-step generation of a free boundary. This is an example where the method is more easily grasped in detail than in other examples, and this is our principal reason for including it in this text.

Physically, when the cylinder is released and pushed forward by its base pressure, a local temporary decrease of pressure is felt at the base, creating a pressure gradient toward the cylinder that drives fluid into the partial vacuum thus created. But this lowers the pressure farther back, and a rarefaction wave thus travels toward the rear or breach of the chamber. At the breach, where $v = 0$, this is reflected as a compression wave that now travels back toward the cylinder and may overtake it. Most designers would cut the tube to a length that now 'ended' the problem before the returning wave had hit the cylinder, for then relatively simple formulas that avoid extensive calculation can be given for the solution. But if this is not done, regions occur in the (x,t) plane of nonlinear interactions of waves arriving from fore and aft. Each of these regions may be easily identified by tracing successive reflections

of the first characteristic issuing from the base of the cylinder. If some
compression waves of much larger magnitude than others should be
generated, they will by virtue of the nonlinearity involved (notice that
the slope of characteristics derived in the exercise depends on pressure)
propagate at much higher rates. If a succession of such compression
waves, which will be seen in the computations as 'right-running'
characteristics, overtake each other, a shock will be formed. This will
be seen as a coalescence of right-running characteristics. Such a shock
would be handled as suggested for the jet; only it is more apparent
here why it might form. We are not aware if calculations have been
made extensively, in order to find out whether or not such shocks do
indeed occur. Intuitively, it would seem more likely that such shocks do
indeed occur if a large drag on the cylinder were included in its differential equation of motion. The model could be modified for studying the
operation of a reciprocating engine by closing the other end of the
cylinder and providing an alternating pressure $p = p_1 \sin \omega t$ on the right
end to subtract from the base pressure in the equation of motion of the
cylinder. It would then become

$$\frac{d^2 X}{dt^2} = \frac{A}{m} (p - p_1 \sin \omega t).$$

Here one would be almost certain to develop shocks for some values of
p_1 and ω.

Since the Lagrange problem is a highly idealized model of a gun, it
has been valuable in interior ballistics principally as a point of departure
for thought rather than as a source of reliable quantitative information.
The necessity to seal the high-pressure gases behind the projectile, and
perhaps to spin the projectile for yaw stability and controlled Magnus
moments in flight, requires the use of devices like rotating bands on
the projectile to be cut through by lands and grooves in the barrel.
These produce large friction drag on the projectile, which is highly variable from one firing to the next. Other effects, moreover, are not so easy
to include—effects of nonequilibrium start, continued burning, and
even the presence in the fluid of many unburned grains of 'powder.'
For efficient design, a gun chamber will rarely be a cylinder either, so
even our one-dimensional flow equation will have to be replaced by two
axially symmetric ones. Thus there are three independent variables,
and if the gas passes through a constriction in the chamber at supersonic
velocity, a shock may be formed. If, in addition to all this, a rocket is to
be fired from the gun in order to decrease time to target[7]—the rocket's

---

[7] A critical parameter for countermeasure devices.

motor ignited by the heat in the chamber gas—the problem is too far removed from the Lagrange model for that model even to be considered a legitimate point of departure.

Thus it is that almost all the well-known problems, when taken into modern context, carry us into areas where almost nothing is known about how to proceed with basic formulation, let alone with computations. It seems to us that systems-minded administrators in their preoccupation with hardware production have been far too impatient with the development of basic scientific formulations relating to their devices. How long then can we expect to be able to build such devices by intuitive and empirical extrapolations from models far removed from their context?

References

[1] J. B. Keller, 'On the solution of the Boltzmann equation for rarefied gases,' Comm. Appl. Math., **1**, (1948), 275–284,.

[2] G.-C. Rota and G. Birkhoff, *Ordinary Differential Equations*, Ginn and Company, Boston, 1962.

[3] T. M. Cherry, 'Transonic nozzle flow found by the hodograph method,' in *Partial Differential Equations and Continuum Mechanics*, R. Langer, ed., University of Wisconsin Press, Madison, Wisc., 1949, pp. 69–73.

[4] W. E. Milne, *Numerical Calculus*, Princeton University Press, Princeton, N.J., 1949, pp. 69–73.

[5] Shih-I Pai, *Fluid Dynamics of Jets*, D. van Nostrand, Inc., Princeton, N.J., 1954.

CHAPTER 11

INITIAL VALUE PROBLEMS
OF SECOND-ORDER
EQUATIONS IN E^2

1. THEORY OF THE LAPLACE EQUATION

In variation of the problem of Chapter 8, Sec. 3, and as promised in the numerical stability discussion of Chapter 8, Sec. 4, we consider the problem

$$\Psi_{xx} + \Psi_{yy} = 0$$

$$\Psi(x,0) = f(x) \wedge \Psi_y(x,0) = g(x),$$

where f and g are defined on (a,b), and we will inquire into what continuity conditions insure existence of a regular solution. Putting $\xi = \frac{1}{2}(x + iy)$ and $\eta = \frac{1}{2}(x - iy)$, for regular solutions, Ψ, we have that $\Psi_{\xi\eta} = 0$, so that all regular solutions, Ψ, are of the form

$$\Psi(x,y) = F(x + iy) + G(x - iy)$$

From the initial conditions, we have

$$f(x) = F(x) + G(x)$$

$$\wedge \; g(x) = i[F'(x) - G'(x)] \quad \text{or} \quad -ig(x) = F'(x) - G'(x),$$

and it follows immediately that any regular solution of the initial value problem is of the form

(11.1) $\Psi(x,y) = \frac{1}{2}[f(x + iy) + f(x - iy)] - \frac{1}{2}i \int_{x-iy}^{x+iy} g(\xi)d\xi.$

It has thus become necessary to extend the domain of f and g to some region R of the complex plane containing (a,b). In order that $\Psi \in C^2$ in some region of E^2 containing (a,b), we ask that $f \in C^2(R)$ and $g \in C^1(R)$. But since the domain R is in the complex plane, our functions f and g must be analytic there; i.e., the existence of a derivative in a complex neighborhood of a point of (a,b) implies the existence of all derivatives in that neighborhood, and it implies that the function has a convergent Taylor series there. But then, since a quick argument shows that our solution (11.1) for Ψ is unique, we find that all regular solutions for Ψ are analytic, and, moreover, that a solution of our initial value problem can exist in an E^2 neighborhood of (a,b) only if f and g are analytic in (a,b) (not, as was sufficient for the wave equation, just for $f \in C^2 \wedge g \in C^1$). We become suspicious of numerical approximation, since even approximation by terminating decimals of functional values of the presumably analytic data functions may involve a replacement by functions that are not analytic. Even if the replacing functions are analytic on the real interval (a,b), it is unlikely that their extension into the complex region R would approximate faithfully the complex analytic extension of the original functions f and g.

Let us consider the stability problem; i.e., replace $f(x)$ by $f(x) + \delta(x)$, $g(x)$ by $g(x) + \eta(x)$ and consider solutions $\Psi(x,y) + v(x,y)$, where $\Psi(x,y)$ is given by (11.1). Then, $v_{xx} + v_{yy} = 0 \wedge v(x,0) = \delta(x) \wedge v_y(x,0) = \eta(x)$, so that the displacement v resulting from perturbation δ and η of the data functions has the form

(11.2) $v(x,y) = \frac{1}{2}[\delta(x + iy) + \delta(x - iy)] - \frac{1}{2}i \int_{x-y}^{x+y} \eta(\xi)d\xi$

if its exists. If δ and η are analytic in a neighborhood of the complex point $(x + iy)$, then v exists in a neighborhood of the point $(x,y) \in E^2$; otherwise, unless there are some very special relations, as will be developed here, between functions δ and η, no regular solution v exists, and no regular solution $\Psi + v$ of the problem with perturbed data exists.

We give an example to demonstrate the possible disastrous implications of this for numerical work. Let $f(x)$ be perturbed by the amount

$$\delta(x) = \frac{\varepsilon}{x^2 + \Delta^2},$$

and let $g(x)$ be perturbed by the amount $\eta(x) = 0$ on $(-1,1)$. Both perturbation functions are analytic on $(-1,1)$ and

$$\max_{x \in (-1,1)} \frac{\varepsilon}{x^2 + \Delta^2} = \frac{\varepsilon}{\Delta^2},$$

which, for any given choice of Δ, can be made arbitrarily small by selection of ε. The resulting displacement function is

$$v(x,y) = \tfrac{1}{2}[\delta(x + iy) + \delta(x - iy)] = \operatorname{Re} \delta(x + iy)$$

$$= \operatorname{Re} \frac{\varepsilon}{(x + iy)^2 + \Delta^2}$$

(by the Schwartz reflection principle[1]), and we see that it is unbounded in a neighborhood of the point $(0, \Delta) \in E^2$, which can be made arbitrarily close to the data line by choice of Δ. The solution of the perturbed problem does not exist in a neighborhood of this point, but what is more important is that perturbations that are analytic on the real data interval and arbitrarily small in maximum norm can yield displacements of the solution that are arbitrarily large in maximum norm and arbitrarily close to the data interval.

The student should now review the discussion in Chapter 8, Sec. 4 on stability for the Laplace equation, where it is seen that for the finite-difference approximation studied there, he can expect reasonably good answers for large mesh close to the data line, but that large errors will develop closer to the data line as the mesh is refined, and this is precisely what is observed in computational practice. In the next paragraph, we show how, for a data set that is analytic, as it must be for existence, one may control the perturbation functions so that they are small in the requisite region of the complex plane and thus give rise to small displacement functions. In Chapter 10, Sec. 5, it will be seen that this same technique carries over to the treatment of quasilinear second-order equations of elliptic type in E^2 when they are written in a certain canonical form.

Before undertaking this, we remark that singularity occurrence in the solution of the initial value problem for the Laplace equation depends to some minor extent at least on whether or not a solution is sought in the upper- or lower-half plane. Since this remark can be applied

---

[1] For this we need that δ is analytic in a complex region containing $(-1,1)$ and has real functional values for real arguments. Then $\delta(\bar{z}) = \overline{\delta(z)}$. The latter hypothesis is true, since δ is obtained by extension of a real-valued function on $(-1,1)$.

as well to the stability problem posed above, a sense of direction exists for stability of the initial value problem for the Laplace equation. Thus we write (11.1) in the form

$$\Psi(x,y) = \operatorname{Re} f(x + iy) - \tfrac{1}{2}i\left[\int_x^{x+iy} g(\xi)d\xi - \int_x^{x-iy} g(\xi)d\xi\right]$$

$$= \operatorname{Re} f(x + iy) - \tfrac{1}{2}i\left[i\int_0^y g(x + it)dt + i\int_0^y g(x - it)dt\right]$$

$$= \operatorname{Re} f(x + iy) + \tfrac{1}{2}\int_0^y [g(x + it) + g(x - it)]dt$$

or

(11.3) $$\Psi(x,y) = \operatorname{Re} f(x + iy) + \int_0^y \operatorname{Re} g(x + it)dt,$$

where a path x constant has been chosen for the complex integral and the Schwartz reflection principle applied. If either f or g, but not both, have a singularity in the complex plane at $x + i\Delta$, then so does the function Ψ as defined by (11.1) at the point $(x, \Delta) \in E^2$, and a regular solution of the initial value problem does not exist in a neighborhood of this point. However, if both f and g have singularities at the complex point $x + i\Delta$, the solution may still exist at $(x, \Delta) \in E^2$ if

(11.4) $$\operatorname{Re} f(x + i\Delta) + \int_0^\Delta \operatorname{Re} g(x + it)dt$$

exists (i.e., if singularities in f and g subtract when the formula (11.1) for Ψ is formed). But then

$$\operatorname{Re} f(x - i\Delta) + \int_0^{-\Delta} \operatorname{Re} g(x + it)dt$$

(11.5) $$= \operatorname{Re} f(x + i\Delta) - \int_0^\Delta \operatorname{Re} g(x - i\xi)d\xi$$

$$= \operatorname{Re} f(x + i\Delta) - \int_0^\Delta \operatorname{Re} g(x + it)dt,$$

which is the expression (11.3) for $\Psi(x, -\Delta)$, does not exist, for if it did, adding (11.4) and (11.5), we see that f has no singularity at $x + i\Delta$, contrary to assumption.

Thus the occurrence of a singularity in the extended complex domain of the data will cause the occurrence of a singularity in the solution in either the top- or bottom-half plane but not necessarily in both. An example is

$$\Psi_{xx} + \Psi_{yy} = 0$$

$$\Psi(x,0) = \varepsilon \ln \Delta(\Delta^2 + x^2)^{-1/2}, \quad \Psi_y(x,0) = \varepsilon \Delta(\Delta^2 + x^2)^{-1},$$

for which the unique solution is

$$\Psi(x,y) = \varepsilon \ln \Delta[(y - \Delta)^2 + x^2]^{-1/2}.$$

Here the data f and g are both singular at $x = 0 + i \Delta$, while the solution Ψ has a singularity at $(0, \Delta)$ only, not at $(0, -\Delta)$. If now we interpret f and g as perturbations δ and η, while we interpret Ψ as a displacement v, we see that arbitrarily small perturbations of the data can produce arbitrarily large displacements of the solution in the upper-half plane arbitrarily close to the data line and cause only small displacements in the lower-half plane. Of course, this can also be reversed.

A similar sense of direction for stability considerations arising from other sources and relevant to asymptotic rather than finite stability has already been demonstrated for the case of the equation $dy/dt = y$ and for finite-difference replacements of the heat equation $u_{xx} = u_t$.

2. A STABLE FINITE-DIFFERENCE TECHNIQUE FOR THE LAPLACE EQUATION

In using an approximation procedure for the initial value problem for the Laplace equation in E^2 where the data is analytic, the above indicates that we must take steps to insure that these data are closely approximated, not just on a real line segment, but in some appropriate region of the complex plane. Conforming to the above, we make the extension to the complex domain in one variable only; i.e., let $x = x_1 + ix_2$, but let y remain real. In planes $x_1 = \text{constant}$, the Laplace equation

$$\Psi_{xx} + \Psi_{yy} = 0$$

becomes the wave equation

$$\Psi_{yy} - \Psi_{x_2 x_2} = 0.$$

The data

$$\Psi(x,0) = f(x), \quad \Psi_y(x,0) = g(x)$$

become

$$\Psi(x_1 + ix_2, 0) = f(x_1 + ix_2)$$

$$\Psi_y(x_1 + ix_2, 0) = g(x_1 + ix_2),$$

where *it is assumed that formulas are available for the analytic functions f and g so that complex extensions can be made without instabilities being relevant to this process* by simple substitution of the complex variable $x_1 + ix_2$ for the real variable $x = x_1$. We now solve, in each of several planes $x_1 = \text{constant}$, the requisite well-posed initial value problems with complex data by the method of characteristics (or by using the so-called direct finite-difference method for hyperbolic type). We retain

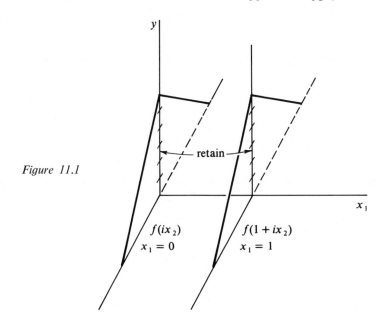

Figure 11.1

data only on the lines generated in the real plane. Essential here is the fact that no computing numbers (terminating decimals) replace real numbers—in fact, no approximations are made—until a stable problem has been posed. The solution vector $\begin{pmatrix} u_1 \\ u_2 \end{pmatrix}$ of the problem written in matrix form, as in Chapter 8, Sec. 4, is now complex in any $x_1 = \text{constant}$ plane (where computations are made), but the matrix B remains real, and it is this matrix only that determines stability. Instead of that for the Laplace equation $\begin{pmatrix} 0 & 1 \\ -1 & 0 \end{pmatrix}$, we now have the one for the wave equation $\begin{pmatrix} 0 & 1 \\ 1 & 0 \end{pmatrix}$. More important, since the direct finite-difference replacements were asymptotically stable for both cases, assuming that we did not allow perturbations that obviated existence, *we have managed to keep perturbations small in an appropriate region of the complex plane.* Of course, the region in which this is possible depends on how far an analytic extension that can be made by substitution in a formula is possible in the complex plane. Substitution in a formula is an essential feature of this computational procedure. The region of E^2, then, where it is possible to keep displacements of the solution Ψ small, depends on where the extended complex domain of the data functions is reflected along characteristics onto the real plane. Of course, as we have shown, singularities in both f and g together may not propagate forward, but will propagate either fore or aft.

We see no reason why our least squares 'continuous' procedure using harmonic polynomials should not be used here. One must be careful to fit the extended data over a region R of the complex plane containing the real interval (a,b) on which the data are given, and not just over (a,b) alone. The solution will then be well approximated in the region of E^2, which is a reflection of R by the characteristics.

The pessimist's refrain, 'If anything can go wrong, it will,' becomes, in computing, an incontrovertible law of nature that the modern computor may not ignore if he wants his calculations to be successful. Without taking positive steps to control the size of perturbations in the complex extensions of the data that we know will in turn control the size of displacements in solution of the Cauchy problem for the Laplace equation, we cannot expect them to be small, and they are not.

3. THE H. LEWY LOCAL CANONICAL FORM

We consider again the quasilinear equation

$$(11.6) \qquad a\Psi_{xx} + 2b\Psi_{xy} + c\Psi_{yy} = d.$$

That it is of basic importance in fluid dynamics, where it may be a streamfunction equation, has already been demonstrated and will again be demonstrated in the next chapter.[2]

First consider only the hyperbolic case, $b^2 - ac > 0$. In Chapter 8, Sec. 2, it was seen that the two real characteristic families are given by

$$\left.\frac{dy}{dx}\right|_1 = \alpha \quad \text{and} \quad \left.\frac{dy}{dx}\right|_2 = \beta$$

---

[2] See Chapter 9, Sec. 2, and Appendix E. Also, see Chapter 12, Sec. 1.

and that the compatibility equations with $P = \Psi_x$ and $Q = \Psi_y$ can be given by

$$
\begin{vmatrix}
d - a\dfrac{dP}{dx}\Big|_1 - b\dfrac{dQ}{dx}\Big|_1 & c - b\alpha \\[4mm]
\dfrac{dQ}{dx}\Big|_1 & \alpha
\end{vmatrix} = 0
$$

$$
\begin{vmatrix}
d - a\dfrac{dP}{dx}\Big|_2 - b\dfrac{dQ}{dx}\Big|_2 & c - b\beta \\[4mm]
\dfrac{dQ}{dx}\Big|_2 & \beta
\end{vmatrix} = 0.
$$

We adopt the characteristic curves

$$
\lambda(x,y) = \text{constant}, \quad \mu(x,y) = \text{constant}^3
$$

as local (if a, b, c depend on Ψ, Ψ_r, or Ψ_z) coordinates where λ is constant on the 1-characteristic and μ is constant on the 2-characteristic. With

$$
\frac{dy}{dx}\Big|_1 = \frac{y_\mu}{x_\mu}, \quad \frac{dy}{dx}\Big|_2 = \frac{y_\lambda}{x_\lambda}, \quad \frac{dP}{dx}\Big|_1 = \frac{P_\mu}{x_\mu}, \quad \text{etc.,}
$$

we have

(11.7)
$$
\begin{aligned}
y_\mu - \alpha x_\mu &= 0 \\
y_\lambda - \beta x_\lambda &= 0 \\
\alpha dx_\mu - a\alpha P_\mu - cQ_\mu &= 0 \\
\beta dx_\lambda - a\beta P_\lambda - cQ_\lambda &= 0 \\
-Px_\mu - Qy_\mu + \Psi_\mu &= 0
\end{aligned}
$$

where the last equation derives from

$$
\frac{\Psi_\mu}{x_\mu} = \frac{d\Psi}{dx}\Big|_1 = \Psi_x + \frac{dy}{dx}\Big|_1 \Psi_y = P + \frac{y_\mu}{x_\mu} Q.
$$

---

[3] One may think of integrating the equations $\dfrac{dy}{dx}\Big|_1 = \alpha$ and $\dfrac{dy}{dx}\Big|_2 = \beta$, obtaining constants of integration λ and μ, respectively, and then solving for λ and μ in terms of x and y.

This is the equation (11.6) in characteristic coordinates. It must be noted that we have introduced x and y as dependent variables (this accounts for the system being homogeneous), which allows an arbitrary choice of each x and y as functions of μ and λ on an initial data line. One of these functions is allowed to remain arbitrary. The other is implied in the selection of an arbitrary relation between λ and μ on the data line, since x and y are related on the data line by the equation of that curve. For convenience, we put $\lambda + \mu = 0$ on the data line. This transforms any (noncharacteristic) initial data curve in the (x,y) or physical plane into the line $\lambda + \mu = 0$ in the characteristic plane.

For the purpose of examining an initial value problem then, it is suggested that coordinates

$$\xi = \lambda + \mu \quad \eta = \lambda - \mu$$

be adopted. Since the equations (11.7) are homogeneous, they are invariant with respect to stretching. Thus our transformation amounts to a rotation of the characteristic coordinates through $45°$ so that a form similar to the matrix form of the wave equation is to be expected if we solve for derivatives with respect to ξ in terms of derivatives with respect to η. The requisite manipulations accomplishing this that follow (where no attempt is made to invent different symbols for different functions of different variables whose functional values can be identified), being simple uses of the chain rule of differentiation, are self-explanatory:

$$\begin{cases} y_\xi - \alpha x_\xi = y_\eta - \alpha x_\eta \\ y_\xi - \beta x_\xi = -(y_\eta - \beta x_\eta) \end{cases}$$

$\Rightarrow$

$$x_\xi = \frac{1}{\alpha - \beta}[-2y_\eta + (\alpha + \beta)x_\eta] = \frac{\alpha + \beta}{\alpha - \beta}x_\eta - \frac{2}{\alpha - \beta}y_\eta$$

$$y_\xi = \frac{1}{\alpha - \beta}[-(\alpha + \beta)y_\eta + 2\alpha\beta x_\eta] = \frac{2\alpha\beta}{\alpha - \beta}x_\eta - \frac{\alpha + \beta}{\alpha - \beta}y_\eta$$

$\Rightarrow$

$$\begin{cases} x_\mu = x_\xi - x_\eta = \frac{2\beta}{\alpha - \beta}x_\eta - \frac{2}{\alpha - \beta}y_\eta \\ x_\lambda = x_\xi + x_\eta = \frac{2\alpha}{\alpha - \beta}x_\eta - \frac{2}{\alpha - \beta}y_\eta \end{cases}$$

$$\begin{cases} -a\alpha P_\xi - cQ_\xi = -\dfrac{2\alpha\beta}{\alpha - \beta} d \cdot x_\eta + \dfrac{2\alpha}{\alpha - \beta} d \cdot y_\eta - a\alpha P_\eta - cQ_\eta \\[4mm] -a\beta P_\xi - cQ_\xi = -\dfrac{2\alpha\beta}{\alpha - \beta} d \cdot x_\eta + \dfrac{2\beta}{\alpha - \beta} d \cdot y_\eta + a\beta P_\eta + cQ_\eta \end{cases}$$

$\Rightarrow$
$$\begin{cases} a(\alpha - \beta)P_\xi = -2d \cdot y_\eta + a(\alpha + \beta)P_\eta + 2cQ_\eta \\[2mm] c(\alpha - \beta)Q_\xi = 2\alpha\beta d \cdot x_\eta - 2\alpha\beta a P_\eta - c(\alpha + \beta)Q_\eta \end{cases}$$

$\Rightarrow$
$$\boxed{\begin{aligned} P_\xi &= -\frac{2}{a(\alpha - \beta)} d \cdot y_\eta + \frac{\alpha + \beta}{\alpha - \beta} P_\eta + \frac{2}{a(\alpha - \beta)} cQ_\eta \\[3mm] Q_\xi &= \frac{2\alpha\beta}{c(\alpha - \beta)} d \cdot x_\eta - \frac{2\alpha\beta}{c(\alpha - \beta)} a P_\eta - \frac{\alpha + \beta}{\alpha - \beta} Q_\eta \end{aligned}}$$

$$\Psi_\mu = \Psi_\xi - \Psi_\eta = P x_\mu + Q y_\mu$$

$$= \frac{2\beta}{\alpha - \beta} P x_\eta - \frac{2}{\alpha - \beta} P y_\eta + \frac{2\alpha\beta}{\alpha - \beta} Q x_\eta - \frac{2\alpha}{\alpha - \beta} Q y_\eta$$

$\Rightarrow$
$$\boxed{\Psi_\xi = \left(\frac{2\beta}{\alpha - \beta} P + \frac{2\alpha\beta}{\alpha - \beta} Q\right) x_\eta - \left(\frac{2}{\alpha - \beta} P + \frac{2\alpha}{\alpha - \beta} Q\right) y_\eta + \Psi_\eta}$$

$$\left(\alpha + \beta = \frac{2b}{a}\right) \wedge \left(\alpha - \beta = \frac{2\sqrt{b^2 - ac}}{a}\right) \wedge (\alpha\beta = c/a)$$

$\Rightarrow$
$$\boxed{\begin{aligned} x_\xi &= \frac{1}{\sqrt{b^2 - ac}} (bx_\eta - ay_\eta) \\[3mm] y_\xi &= \frac{1}{\sqrt{b^2 - ac}} (cx_\eta - by_\eta) \\[3mm] P_\xi &= \frac{1}{\sqrt{b^2 - ac}} (-dy_\eta + bP_\eta + cQ_\eta) \\[3mm] Q_\xi &= \frac{1}{\sqrt{b^2 - ac}} (dx_\eta - aP_\eta - bQ_\eta) \\[3mm] \Psi_\xi &= \frac{1}{\sqrt{b^2 - ac}} (\overline{\Lambda} x_\eta - \Gamma y_\eta \qquad + \sqrt{b^2 - ac}\, \Psi_\eta) \end{aligned}}$$

where $\bar{\Lambda} = P(b - \sqrt{b^2 - ac}) + cQ \wedge \Gamma = aP + Q(b + \sqrt{b^2 - ac})$.

With

$$R = \begin{pmatrix} x \\ y \\ P \\ Q \\ \Psi \end{pmatrix} \quad \text{or} \quad \begin{pmatrix} x \\ y \\ \Psi_x \\ \Psi_y \\ \Psi \end{pmatrix} \quad \text{we have} \quad \boxed{R_\xi = BR_\eta}$$

where

$$B = \frac{1}{\sqrt{b^2 - ac}} \begin{pmatrix} b & -a & 0 & 0 & 0 \\ c & -b & 0 & 0 & 0 \\ 0 & -d & b & c & 0 \\ d & 0 & -a & -b & 0 \\ \bar{\Lambda} & \Gamma & 0 & 0 & \sqrt{b^2 - ac} \end{pmatrix},$$

which is the Lewy local canonical form. Multiplication of B by itself shows that

$$B^2 = I,$$

where I is the unit matrix. In characteristic coordinates rotated through 45°, all the eigenvalues of B with respect to I in the system $IR_\xi - BR_\eta = 0$ would have to be one, a fact consistent with this result. Of course, B is its own inverse. Group elements with this property are called involutory.

EXERCISE

Show, as contended, that B is involutory.

If we now allow that $b^2 - ac < 0$, the same manipulations apply.[4] Quantities α and β are complex conjugates and the equations $dy/dx = \alpha$, $dy/dx = \beta$, solved with real initial values, will give λ and μ as complex conjugates. Then, although $\xi = \lambda + \mu$ is real and $\eta = \lambda - \mu$ is pure imaginary, we still have

$$R_\xi = BR_\eta = BR_{i\bar\eta},$$

---

[4] Difficulty arises only for $b^2 - ac = 0$. Besides the formally obvious division by zero, the tacit assumption of inversion of the function $\begin{pmatrix} \lambda \\ \mu \end{pmatrix}: D \to E^2$, where $D \subset E^2$, would be invalid since $J\left(\frac{\lambda,\mu}{x,y}\right) = 0$.

where $\bar{\eta}$ is real, but if we insist that the equation be expressed so as to make evident that R is a vector of functions of real variables, we have

$$R_\xi = \mathscr{B}R_{\bar{\eta}} \quad \text{where} \quad \mathscr{B} = -iB$$

and $\qquad\qquad \mathscr{B}^2 = -I.$

Summarizing, the equation (11.6) may be written locally as

$$R_\xi = BR_\eta,$$

where $B^2 = +I$, if (11.6) is of hyperbolic type, $B^2 = -I$, if (11.6) is of elliptic type, and the equation does not apply if (11.6) is of parabolic type. If coefficient functions a, b, c, d of (11.6) do not depend on Ψ (but only on x, y, Ψ_x, Ψ_y), then the fifth element of R and the fifth row and column of B are understood to be deleted. Then if coefficients a, b, c, d of (11.6) also do not depend on Ψ_x and Ψ_y (but only on x and y), the canonical form is global: i.e., it exists not just in the neighborhood of a point but over any purely hyperbolic or purely elliptic region where the functions α and β satisfy, let us say, an appropriate Lipschitz condition. Initial data for the equation (11.6) in canonical form are always given on $\xi = 0$. The value of x on this line may be specified as any function of η (with appropriate smoothness properties so that a solution of the canonical problem exists), and y is given as the function of x that represents[5] the initial data curve in x,y coordinates. The initial data then takes the form

$$R(0,\eta) = R_0(\eta) \qquad \text{given},$$

where $R_0 : E^1 \to E^5$ (or E^4 if a, b, c, d do not depend on Ψ).

4. D'ALEMBERT SOLUTION IN CANONICAL FORM

If a, b, c, $d \in R^1$ are simply real numbers, then B is a matrix of constants. Consider then the initial value problem

$$R_\xi = BR_\eta, \quad R(0,\eta) = R_0(\eta).$$

In case $B^2 = I$, hyperbolic type, the unique solution is

$$R(\xi,\eta) = \tfrac{1}{2}[R_0(\eta + \xi) + R_0(\eta - \xi)] + \tfrac{1}{2}B[R_0(\eta + \xi) - R_0(\eta - \xi)].$$

---

[5] Of course, the curve may be represented in the form $\varphi(x,y) = 0$, in which case we have required that $\varphi_y \neq 0$.

EXERCISE

Verify the above by differentiation and substitution.

In case $B^2 = -I$, elliptic type, the unique solution is

$$R(\xi, \eta) = \tfrac{1}{2}[R_0(\eta + i\xi) + R_0(\eta - i\xi)] - \tfrac{1}{2}iB[R_0(\eta + i\xi) - R_0(\eta - i\xi)]$$

$$= \operatorname{Re} R_0(\eta + i\xi) + B \operatorname{Im} R_0(\eta + i\xi)$$

provided, of course, that R_0 is analytic.

EXERCISE

Verify the above by differentiation and substitution.

The manipulations in classic texts showing that equations in E^2 of hyperbolic and elliptic type with coefficients dependent on x and y alone can be transformed into the wave equation and Laplace equation, respectively, are subsumed in the derivation of Chapter 11, Sec. 3 of the Lewy canonical form. Likewise, the solutions given above are the D'Alembert solution—and its modification discussed earlier for the Laplace equation—given in a form where it is not necessary to include as a separate computation a transformation of the initial data segment to an axis.

5. FINITE-DIFFERENCE PROCEDURES

Utilizing the canonical form,

$$R_n = BR_\xi,$$

we recall that initial data was given for $\xi = 0$. The analysis, formulas, statements, conclusions, and picture in Chapter 8, Sec. 4, can be taken over for the case where B is a matrix of real numbers (*constants*) by simply replacing

$$U \text{ by } R, \quad x \text{ by } \xi, \quad y \text{ by } \eta$$

and, of course, $B = \begin{pmatrix} 0 & 1 \\ 1 & 0 \end{pmatrix}$ by the appropriate canonical form matrix. The student is advised to reread Chapter 8, Sec. 4, in this new light.

The case of nonlinear equations is not nearly so simple, and, even if our original second-order equation is linear but has variable coefficients, its canonical form will be nonlinear because the matrix B will depend on x and y, which are the first two components of the solution vector R. To indicate that components of B depend on components of R, we write $B(R)$ in place of B. Then in the finite-difference replacement (8.7) of Chapter 8, Sec. 4, modified as indicated, in place of B we write for nonlinear cases

$$\tfrac{1}{2}[B(R_i{}^j) + B(R_{i+1}{}^j)].$$

With A_N in (8.8) appropriately modified, we now write $A_N(R^J)$, and (8.8) of Chapter 8, Sec. 4, becomes

$$(11.8) \qquad \begin{pmatrix} R_1 \\ R_2 \\ \vdots \\ R_{N-1} \end{pmatrix}^{J+1} = A_N(R^J) \begin{pmatrix} R_1 \\ R_2 \\ \vdots \\ R_{N-1} \end{pmatrix}^J + \begin{pmatrix} 0 \\ 0 \\ \vdots \\ ((\tfrac{1}{2})I + sB)R_N{}^J \end{pmatrix}.$$

Investigating stability as in Chapter 8, Sec. 4, we have

$$\begin{pmatrix} \delta_1 \\ \delta_2 \\ \vdots \\ \delta_{N-1} \end{pmatrix}^{J+1} = A_N(R^J + \delta^J) \begin{pmatrix} \delta_1 \\ \delta_2 \\ \vdots \\ \delta_{N-1} \end{pmatrix}^J + [A(R^J + \delta^J) - A(R^J)] \begin{pmatrix} R_1 \\ R_2 \\ \vdots \\ R_{N-1} \end{pmatrix}^J =$$

$$= G(\delta_i{}^J),$$

where G is a function of the perturbation vector $\delta_i{}^J$ that depends on R^J; i.e., a more complete but perhaps less suggestive notation would be $G(\delta_i{}^J, R_i{}^J)$. We see then that, strictly speaking, numerical stability of the difference equation (11.8) depends upon convergence of Picard iteration for a function G that depends on that solution R^J whose stability is examined. One can properly speak then only of the stability of a given solution, and the stability of one solution does not imply stability of another.

The von Neumann criterion argues that either we should accept the analysis above for B constant, which gives the well-known condition $s \le \tfrac{1}{2}$ for stability[6] for hyperbolic type or, giving a localized rationale, accept an analysis like that at the end of Chapter 8, Sec. 4, which gives the same result for hyperbolic type. In spite of the demonstrated practicality of such advice, the instincts of a mathematician cause him

---

[6] If one is willing to accept as a criterion of stability that the asymptotic factor of reduction of the perturbations is one, then $s = \tfrac{1}{2}$ is acceptable (see Chapter 8, Sec. 4).

to seek a criterion that is more clearly based on rigorous logic. On the
other hand, to examine for numerical stability in the strict sense displayed above seems tortuous and, perhaps, not even worthwhile
because of the form of G, which is especially complicated, since it
depends on the solution whose stability is to be examined.

We propose here that the following criterion for numerical stability
of marching schema for nonlinear equations be adopted to replace, on
the one hand, the von Neumann criterion and, on the other hand, the
definition—being asymptotic stability—of the relevant difference
equation. The criterion is evidently sufficient but not necessary for
numerical stability.

*Let V be a normed finite-dimensional vector space and let $F: A \to A$,
$A \subset V$. The marching schema*

$$u \in A, \quad u^{j+1} = F(u^j)$$

*will be judged stable in a neighborhood $N \subset A$ if $\exists\, u \in V \ni \forall\, u^0 \in N$,
$\{u^j\} \to u$. In particular, if A is a complete normed finite-dimensional
vector space and F is contractive, then the marching schema will be judged
stable in A.* An obvious extension to the case where A is a complete
metric space is possible.

In order to apply the criterion, it is first necessary to formulate a
marching schema that is expressed by a function F mapping a subset of
an n-dimensional vector space into itself. For many examples, such as
slab-type problems for parabolic equations or vibrating string-type
problems for hyperbolic equations, this is arranged simply by regarding
the side data as fixed, so that the n-new values on the $j + 1$-line are
expressed as a function of n-values only (not $n + 2$) on the j-line. Of
course, this avoids the question of stability with respect to perturbations
of side data. For a Cauchy problem, say, for a hyperbolic equation,
application is more difficult. We assume that we have a solution
$u^j = (u_1{}^j, u_2{}^j, \cdots, u_n{}^j, \cdots)$ of the Cauchy problem, and in order to examine
stability of the solution, we fix all values $u_i{}^j$ except for all $m < i \le m + n$
and $\forall\, j$. Then the march does indeed express $(u_{m+1}{}^{j+1}, \cdots, u_{m+n}{}^{j+1})$ as a
function of $(u_{m+1}{}^j, \cdots, u_{m+n}{}^j)$. Of course, stability with respect to any
interval of data can then be examined.

For purposes of computation, it will be necessary to express the
vector-valued function F in component form, such that each of the
components is a rational function of the components of u^j. Then to
apply the restricted form of the criterion, it will only be necessary to
examine conditions on coefficients of the component rational functions

that force F to be contractive. This will supply a somewhat restricted, but hopefully useful, class of stable nonlinear marching schema. In the case at hand, we require that in (11.8) the vector-valued function $A_N(R^j)R^j$ be contractive in some L^p or Tchebychev norm.

RESEARCH EXERCISE

Find coefficient conditions, useful in stability analysis for marching schema, such that a function on a finite-dimensional vector space (complete in some norm) into itself has components that are expressed as rational functions of components where the function is contractive.

We would not hold with a criterion of numerical stability of a march that would simply require that $\forall$ J the vector U^J on the line J be a continuous function in some norm (or norms) of the initial vector U^0. Although this may be a desired property of the difference equation (one guaranteed by the contraction condition), it says nothing about the properties of the march that proceeds $\forall$ J $\in \Omega_N$ from J to J + 1, not from $j = 0$ to $j = J$.

EXERCISE

Select the basic cluster

$$
\begin{array}{c}
\overset{4}{\times} \\[4pt]
2\times \qquad \times 3 \qquad \Big\uparrow \quad k \quad s = k/h \\[4pt]
\overset{\times}{1}
\end{array}
$$

$$\xleftarrow{\hspace{1.5cm}}\overset{}{h}\xrightarrow{\hspace{1.5cm}}$$

and examine the stability of the difference analogue

$$R_4 = R_1 + s\,\frac{B_1 + B_2}{2}\,(R_2 - R_3) + O(h^2) + O(k^2)$$

using B as constant according to the localized von Neumann criterion.

For elliptic type, we use the same procedure as was used for the Laplace equation in Chapter 10, Sec. 2. It will be recalled that the technique was necessary not for asymptotic stability of the difference equaiton, but for keeping perturbations of the data for the differential equation small in an appropriate region of the complex plane. We extend the domain of the solution vector R in one variable only. Let η remain real and put $\zeta = \zeta_1 + i\zeta_2$. In planes ζ_1 constant, the equation

$$R_\zeta = BR_\eta \qquad \text{becomes} \qquad \frac{1}{i} R_{\zeta_2} = BR_\eta$$

or

$$R_{\zeta_2} = iBR_\eta = \mathscr{B}R_\eta$$

and $\mathscr{B}^2 = (iB)^2 = I$, so that it is of hyperbolic type. The data, if formulas are available for the data functions, are again extended to the complex plane by substitution and the difference methods for hyperbolic type may be used. The difference analogue in the exercise above with $s = 1$, which is $O(h^2)$ may, insofar as one finds the von Neumann criterion adequate, be used here.

CHAPTER 12

THE DETACHED SHOCK PROBLEM

1. THE FLUID EQUATIONS

For purposes of the present discussion, we addend to the considerations of Chapter 10, Sec. 2, relative to equations for axially symmetric, inviscid, steady-state flow the possibility of a variation of entropy S, thus augmenting the Euler equations with the equation

$$uS_r + vS_z = 0, \quad \text{or} \quad \frac{dS}{dr} = S_r + \frac{v}{u} S_z = 0$$

on a streamline (or S is constant on a streamline given by $dz/dr = v/u$). Since the streamfunction Ψ is also constant on a streamline, the addended equation can be expressed by simply stating that S is a function of Ψ. In the thermodynamic or state law, we must now include the variation of S, and we do this by putting $p = K(S)\rho^\gamma$; i.e., we let K be a function of S. But, since S is to be regarded as a function of Ψ, we may write

$$p = A(\Psi)\rho^\gamma.$$

The streamfunction equation remains as before, except that

$$D = \rho v - \rho^2 r^2 \frac{1}{\gamma} \frac{d}{d\Psi} \ln A(\Psi) \cdot (h + q^2)$$

where

$$q^2 = u^2 + v^2 = \left(\frac{\Psi_z}{\rho r}\right)^2 + \left(\frac{\Psi_r}{\rho r}\right)^2 \wedge h = \frac{\gamma}{\gamma - 1} A(\Psi)\rho^{\gamma - 1}.$$

We recall that the streamfunction equation was derived from a vorticity expression; the absence of the now added term in D in our earlier considerations expresses the fact that isentropic flows are such that the vorticity is zero at every point (irrotational). Since manipulations required to arrive at the new formula for D are lengthy, we relegate them to an appendix (see Appendix E), in spite of their instructional value. We are content here to remark that between the theory of numerical analysis and its application to a problem of science (as opposed to mathematics), even ignoring programming, a burden of work and reasoning exists that is almost never appreciated by those who are satisfied merely to study the pure aspects of the subject.

When discontinuities of the first kind (jumps or saltus discontinuities), called 'shocks,' occur in the fluid, then the equations of continuity, momentum, and energy take on the following form (first posed by Rankine and then corrected by Hugoniot), where q_t and q_n are components of the velocity, tangent and normal, respectively, to the curve on which the shock occurs:

$$q_{1t} = q_{2t}$$

$$\rho_1 q_{1n} = \rho_2 q_{2n}$$

$$p_1 + \rho_1 q_{1n}^2 = p_2 + \rho_2 q_{2n}^2$$

$$h_1 + \tfrac{1}{2} q_{1n}^2 = h_2 + \tfrac{1}{2} q_{2n}^2.$$

We specify that the velocity of flow is directed from the 1-side to the 2-side in order not to violate the entropy law of thermodynamics. Of course, such jumps can be thought of as corresponding physically to large gradients, and a derivation of the last three equations is possible if solutions of the compressible one-dimensional, steady-state, viscous-flow equations are considered, and if the limit of solutions is examined as the viscosity coefficient goes to zero. Thus insertions of shocks into an inviscid model are sometimes considered viscous adaptations. Were we now to derive the inviscid Euler equations from the Hamilton principle, we would have no right (for phenomena where it has been judged that discontinuities of the flow variables should be included in the model) to assume that all flow variables have a continuous derivative. We need to assume this at a certain particular step in the derivations in order to arrive at the Euler equations from the Hamilton principle. However, before performing this step, linearizing locally about a line of suspected discontinuity, we are able to perform a certain integration by parts and arrive at the above Rankine-Hugoniot equations. Actually, the procedure amounts to the use of a generalization of the Hamilton principle even in the linear cases, as is discussed in Appendix D. The procedure is often referred to in physics as a Gauss or divergence technique and is known to physicists and engineers as a procedure for deriving interface conditions for electromagnetic phenomena. Mathematically, we speak of obtaining weak solutions of the inviscid equations, but this possibly could be strictly justified only if our equations were linear.

Von Neumann and other distinguished modern scientists have dreamed of being able to approximate weak solutions of the inviscid equations directly and have labored effectively toward a definition (since the equations are nonlinear) of their concept and the realization of their dream. Certainly we too cherish this prospect, but for the present it still seems most proper to treat shock problems numerically by dividing the flow into regions where the Euler equations are valid and then inserting boundaries, across which the shock conditions are assumed.

2. NOSE FLOWS

Prandtl has shown that supersonic flow can become subsonic in the context of inviscid models only by passing through a shock. Thus if a plane face is presented head-on to a supersonic flow, a shock will form somewhere in front of the plane if an inviscid model is adequate. If a half (considered infinite) cone is placed in a relatively low mach number supersonic flow, a straight oblique shock attaches to the nose; if the cone is replaced by a wedge, the shock simply bends or refracts the flow outward and parallel to the body.

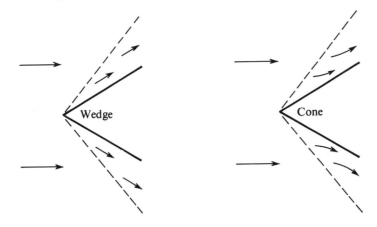

Figure 12.1

Thus the flow for an infinite wedge is trivially determined.[1] For an infinite cone, because no characteristic lengths are involved (in radius of cone, radius of curvature of sides, or length of cone), the flow variables at a point are seen to depend only on the angle of a radius vector drawn from the nose to the point, not on its distance from the nose. Moreover, It can be shown that if the entropy is constant in the approach flow, it is also constant after passing through a straight shock. With these simplifications, the Euler equations can be written as ordinary differential equations and are known as the equations of Taylor-Maccoll flow [1], [2]. We need, then, only to solve a two-point boundary value problem in order to describe the flow over an infinite cone. But as discussed in Chapter 9, Sec. 4, if the flow variables on a ('right') characteristic between body and shock are known, we can then follow a given body and generate a corresponding shock step by step as a free

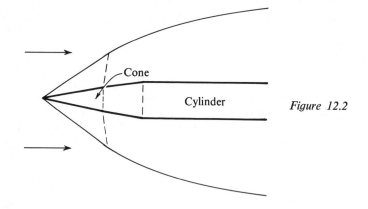

Figure 12.2

boundary. The body may then be turned back, although there are limitations, as indicated in Chapter 9, Sec. 5. For sharp-nosed bodies of any convex shape in relatively low mach number approach flows, we approximate the flow in a neighborhood of the nose point by Taylor-Maccoll flow and generate the rest of the approximation as indicated.

If the angle of the infinite cone is opened out or if the approach flow mach number is increased, the shock detaches from the nose. No solutions of the detached shock problem have been attempted for sharp noses, although this kind of configuration was approached in [3]. There has been no demand for such flows, since it is usually felt that for high mach number approach, the temperature, which also jumps at the

[1] For any given wedge there are actually two shock solutions, one weak and one strong, and both have been seen in nature, but the strong (corresponding to large jumps of pressure) shock is rare, usually occurring only when the flow faces another larger angle wedge or 'flange' farther down the stream.

shock line, would be very high and the point would melt anyway. At mach 20 approach, in the earth's atmosphere at 100,000 feet, the temperature behind a shock would be between 7500° and 8500° Rankine. Moreover, a theory shows that the rate of heat transfer to a sharp point on the body is infinite. Re-entry bodies are thus often deliberately designed to be blunt, which sacrifices immensely in drag efficiencies, in order to alleviate heat transfer. The heating problem is of far larger magnitude for a ballistic missile, which may re-enter on a vertical path at speeds in the vicinity indicated, than it is for a satellite, which decelerates comparatively slowly on a low-angle trajectory in thin air. However, since the satellite may be a space vehicle carrying a human cargo and may need to preserve its control capacity for landing, design criteria are far more stringent. To assess the heating of the body, we need to know the pressure distribution on the body as given by inviscid models, in order to use it in boundary layer calculations ([1] of Chapter 9).

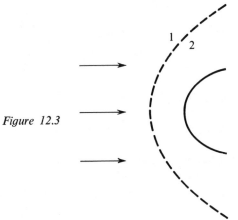

Figure 12.3

If the body is blunt, a region of subsonic flow must exist near the nose, since a stagnation point must occur at the nose. Since the approach is supersonic, a shock normal to the flow at the line of axis of the body occurs detached from the body. This shock must bow back asymptotic to a characteristic direction for the approach flow, so that the flow may return at infinity to the assumed uniform flow.

EXERCISE

Prove from the material of Appendix G that as the shock angle to streamline approaches the mach angle $\alpha = \sin^{-1} \dfrac{1}{M}$, $P_2 - P_1$ approaches zero; e.g., $M \simeq 20 \Rightarrow \alpha \simeq 3°$. 'Old shocks never die; they just bow in and fade away.'

Thus a curved or bowed shock is obtained for a blunt body in a supersonic stream behind which, near the nose, there is a region of

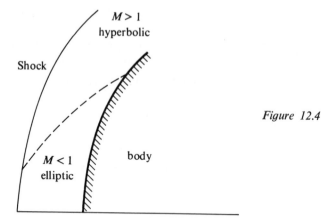

Figure 12.4

subsonic flow, where the streamfunction equation is of elliptic type, and there is a sonic line and a region of supersonic flow beyond, where the streamfunction equation is of hyperbolic type.

3. NUMERICAL ASPECTS

Were we to prescribe a finite-difference equation in the elliptic region using, say, a five-point analogue, and, given the body, try to solve the resulting set of nonlinear algebraic equations by iteration as we would for a Dirichlet problem, we would find ourselves trapped vis à vis the shock and sonic line into an unmanageable free-boundary correction problem. Unlike the free-boundary problems discussed in the last chapter, there is no possibility in such a context for generating the free boundaries step by step. We would face solving the system and, then, successively, correcting the boundaries. Not only are the boundaries curved and irregular (even apparently containing a cusp), making for small mesh size and intricate programming, but the accuracy of the finite-difference replacement degenerates near the boundary exactly where the accuracy would be critical for boundary corrections. There is no assurance, beyond intuition, of convergence of such a boundary iteration.

Most workers, other than those trying to approximate weak solutions directly, or those such as in one Russian school which uses crudely devised adaptations of methods of lines and cone theory, have investigated the possibilities of the inverse problem; namely, *given the shock, find the body and its corresponding flow.* If an analytic shock is given together with a uniform supersonic approach flow in front (region 1) of the shock, it is possible to solve the shock relations for Ψ and Ψ_z on the shock (in region 2), thus obtaining analytic functions that serve as initial data (see Appendix F). Also, from the shock relations, it is possible to obtain the analytic function A (see Appendix G) appearing in the equation $P = A(\Psi)\rho^\gamma$, which is necessary for evaluation of the coefficient D appearing in our streamfunction equation (unless the shock is straight, A is not constant so that the flow is rotational). We thus obtain a Cauchy problem for an elliptic quasi-linear second-order equation in E^2 with analytic coefficients and analytic data. The Cauchy-Kovalevsky theorem guarantees the existence (uniqueness is trivial) of an analytic solution in a neighborhood of the data line. The Lewy paper [5] guarantees convergence of the finite-difference techniques, suggested in our last chapter, in a neighborhood of the data line. We have, moreover, in the last chapter delineated a finite-difference technique that is numerically stable, when judged according to the von Neumann criterion, and that controls numerical perturbations in such a way that existence of analytic solutions will not be canceled by these perturbations. The body and pressure on the body are found by interpolation (see Appendix B) to $\Psi = 0$.

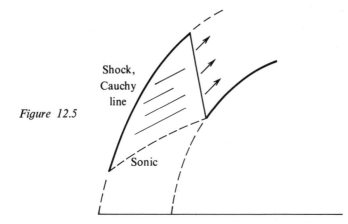

Figure 12.5

Many more details are of importance in approximating the solution of the detached shock problem by this method. For example, the arbitrariness of one of the data functions, when the equation is expressed in the Lewy canonical form, can be used to control which lines will be generated by each computation in the real plane with ξ_1 constant. A sufficiently interested student will obtain these details by reading the references quoted below. An approximate state law appropriate for the nose region only (see Appendix G) is used to accommodate gas dissociation effects caused by high temperatures. A number of bodies are generated, and the modified Newtonian pressure distribution of Lester Lees [4] for rounded (not 'square-faced') bodies is verified to about 3 percent accuracy for $M = 5.8$ and about 7 percent accuracy for $M = 20$ in air (see Appendix H). This then serves well as a design criterion for appropriate bodies.

Up to the last characteristic from the sonic point on the body, an initial value problem for hyperbolic equations can now be solved by the method of characteristics, starting from an interval above the sonic point on the shock. From this characteristic it is possible to proceed by methods described in Chapter 10, Sec. 4, with a given body and generating the shock step by step. We may then 'corner or turn' the body in the supersonic region, giving a procedure for some finite bodies.

4. CAVITATION, A RELATED PROBLEM

We feel inclined to justify some of the above contentions concerning the difficulty in correction of free boundaries with a quick discussion of a procedure used by P. R. Garabedian [6] to approximate the solution of a free-boundary problem for a linear equation of elliptic type where it is possible to solve a Dirichlet-type problem and, successively, to adjust the boundary.[2] A least squares procedure, not a finite-differences, approximation was used, which entails an intense specialized knowledge of the functions relevant to cavitation [7], but the least squares fit was made to a discrete set of points on the boundary, not to all points of a boundary, as was done in our previous discussion. We discuss here only Garabedian's very striking technique of boundary adjustment. It would seem to have deserved wider appreciation by numerical analysts.

The study is of the Riabouchinsky ('mirror image') model for cavitation where, instead of conceiving of a body of rotation being towed rapidly through a liquid with a free-end cavity forming (and foaming and fussing) aft, one conceives of two parallel discs being towed so that the approach flow is normal to their faces. As the speed of the two is

---

[2] However, we refer the reader to works by D. Fisher [9] and D. Gilbarg and M. Shiffman [10] on another cavitation problem that is nonlinear but where a two-dimensional problem is involved, and a hodograph transformation makes it possible to use accelerated successive replacements to solve a finite-difference analogue of a linear problem in a rectangular region.

increased, the liquid—which at first clings to the boundaries of the discs so that front and back sides and tow axis are all a single streamline— separates from the first disc and attaches to the second, forming the

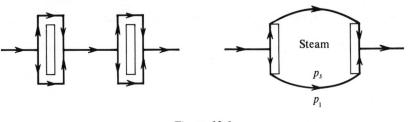

Figure 12.6

steam-filled cavity to be studied. The free streamline position is determined by the balance of exterior liquid pressure and steam pressure in the cavity.

For a liquid, our streamfunction equation (10.4) of Chapter 10, Sec. 2 becomes

$$\Psi_{rr} + \Psi_{zz} - \frac{\Psi_r}{r} = 0$$

when the velocity of sound as it is expressed in Chapter 10, Sec. 2 is taken to be infinite[3] in a fluid considered to be incompressible. If the

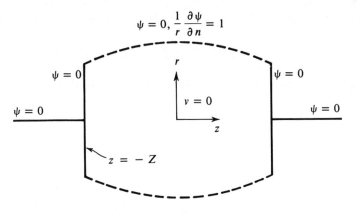

Figure 12.7

planes of the discs are given by $z = \pm Z$, then on the z-axis for $z < -Z \wedge z > Z$, on the discs, and on the boundary of the cavity, $\Psi = 0$.

---

[3] Actually, the cavity acts as an elastic wall providing a lateral pressure relief to a pressure perturbation so that the sound velocity, strictly speaking, is not even theoretically infinite (see [8]) in this particular case, but is very large.

We assume that the motions of the steam inside the cavity are negligible so that there are negligible pressure gradients in the steam-filled cavity. Because of this we are content to require somewhat less than pressure balance at the cavity boundary and only that the liquid pressure $\dfrac{1}{r}\dfrac{\partial \Psi}{\partial n}$ on the boundary be constant.[4] Normalizing, on the free streamline we require

$$\frac{1}{r}\frac{\partial \Psi}{\partial n} = 1.$$

To complete the description of the problem, we also say that the stream-function has a specific form in a neighborhood of infinity and that with this condition it has been possible to establish existence and uniqueness [7] for the boundary value problem. This condition, of course, is needed also in the least squares fits that are to be made before each boundary correction, but here, as we have indicated, our sole purpose is exposition of the free-boundary iteration technique. The two conditions on the free-boundary are regarded as together determining the location of the boundary and providing the requisite boundary data there.

If the streamfunction equation is written in intrinsic coordinates—i.e., if the streamlines and a family normal to the streamlines are adopted as coordinates—on the free streamline, by virtue of the condition $\Psi = 0$, we may eliminate any term containing a factor Ψ or its tangential derivative. This gives that on the free streamline the differential equation is

$$\frac{\partial}{\partial n}\frac{1}{r}\frac{\partial \Psi}{\partial n} + \frac{\kappa}{r}\frac{\partial \Psi}{\partial n} = 0,$$

where κ is the curvature of the free streamlines.

EXERCISE

Derive the above equation.

Using again the condition $\Psi = 0$, on the free streamline we have

$$\frac{\partial}{\partial n}\frac{1}{r}\frac{\partial \Psi}{\partial n} + \frac{\kappa}{r}\frac{\partial \Psi}{\partial n} + \Psi \cdot \frac{\partial}{\partial n}\frac{\kappa}{r} = 0 \quad \text{or} \quad \frac{\partial}{\partial n}\left(\frac{1}{r}\frac{\partial \Psi}{\partial n} + \frac{\kappa}{r}\Psi\right) = 0.$$

Thus at the free streamline, it is seen that the quantity

$$\frac{1}{r}\frac{\partial \Psi}{\partial n} + \frac{\kappa}{r}\Psi$$

---

[4] The Gilbarg, Shiffman, Fisher problem is for a gas, and the free streamline is assumed to be sonic.

is stationary with respect to normal displacements of the boundary. According to the two boundary conditions, this quantity must be equal to one on the free streamline.

Taking an initial guess now at the location of the free boundary, the solution of the boundary value problem, with

(12.1)
$$\frac{1}{r}\frac{\partial \Psi}{\partial n} + \frac{\kappa}{r}\Psi = 1$$

on the assumed boundary, is now approximated by using a least squares procedure. Of course, if it develops that $\Psi = 0$ from the approximation at every point on the assumed boundary, our computation is completed. Otherwise, in difference approximation, the normal shift to the correct boundary where it is necessary both that $\Psi = 0$ and $\frac{1}{r}\frac{\partial \Psi}{\partial n} = 1$, is computed by putting

$$\frac{1}{r}\frac{\Psi - 0}{-\delta n} = 1 \quad \text{or} \quad \delta n = -\frac{\Psi}{r}.$$

This shift is now computed for the guessed boundary, where the quantity (12.1) is already approximated $0(\delta n^2)$ by the available approximation of Ψ. The new approximation of Ψ using (12.1) on the new free boundary can therefore be expected to change very little, and hence a newly computed shift of the boundary will be small. Then assuming a very good approximating family for the iterative least squares fitting, the boundary iteration can certainly be expected to converge rapidly (and there is computational verification of this fact), though no complete analysis of convergence is available.

We regard our discussions of fluid dynamic illustrations of the use of numerical methods as completed. We have emphasized the need for mathematical development in the area of numerical analysis, and we hope the discussions serve to intensify interest in that subject.

REFERENCES

[1] J. W. Maccoll, 'The conical shock wave formed by a cone moving at high speed,' *Proc. Royal Soc. (London)*, **A159**, (1937), 459–472.
[2] Z. Koqal, 'Tables of supersonic flow around cones,' M.I.T. Tech. Rept. No. 1 (1949).

[3] P. R. Garabedian and H. M. Lieberstein, 'On the numerical calculation of detached bow shock waves in hypersonic flow,' *J. Aero. Sci.*, **25**, 2, (1958), 109–118.

[4] H. M. Lieberstein, 'Further numerical data on blunt bodies,' *J. of Aero. Sci.*, **25**, (1958).

[5] H. Lewy, 'Neuer Beweis des analytischen Charakters der Loesungen elliptischer Differentialgleichungen,' *Math. Ann.*, **101**, (1929), 609–619.

[6] P. R. Garabedian, 'The mathematical theory of three-dimensional cavities and jets,' *Bull. Am. Math. Soc.*, **62**, (1956), 219–235.

[7] P. R. Garabedian, H. Lewy and M. Schiffer, 'Axially symmetric cavitational flow,' *Ann. Math.*, **56**, (1952), 560–602.

[8] H. M. Lieberstein, 'Determination of the tension-stretch relation for a point in the aorta from measurement in vivo of pressure at three equally spaced points,' *Acta Biotheoretica, Leiden*, **XVII**, (1965).

[9] D. D. Fisher, 'Calculation of subsonic cavities with sonic free streamlines,' *J. Math. Phys.*, **42**, (1963), 14–26.

[10] D. Gilbarg and M. Shiffman, 'On bodies achieving extremal values of the critical Mach number, I', *J. Rat, Mech. Anal.*, **3**, (1954), 209–230.

CHAPTER 13

A COMPUTATIONAL PROCEDURE FOR RANDOM WALKS WITHOUT A PRODUCT CONVENTION[1]

We will assume that a machine is available that is equipped with a fast analogue binary decision unit, activation of which may be thought of as 'flipping a coin.' The sequence of activations will be utilized in such a way that it will not matter if the equipment is biased toward one decision or the other so long as the variation of bias is small over short intervals.

1. A MONTE-CARLO METHOD FOR A BOUNDARY VALUE PROBLEM OF A PARTIAL DIFFERENCE EQUATION

We toss a batch of beetles onto a checkerboard where a barrier to their egress has been erected on the boundary. Assuming that the squares are large enough or the beetles few (and small) enough that no crowding occurs, we reason that any given beetle at any given time is equally likely to stay in the square he occupies or to move to one of the adjacent squares of another color. To ensure this, in fact, we place pegs at line intersections inside the playing board to prevent diagonal movements. Using the notation of Chapter 2, Sec. 2, the probability that at any time any beetle will remain where he is will be denoted by U_c, while the probabilities that he will go to the north, south, east, or west squares are U_N, U_S, U_E, and U_W. Since these must all be equal, the equation

---

[1] See [2], Appendix A.

$$U_c = \frac{U_N + U_S + U_E + U_W}{4}$$

must be satisfied at any time for any position on the board. But this is the five-point finite-difference analogue of the Laplace equation. Moreover, the conditions prevailing at the barrier seem to imply there the difference analogue of $\partial U / \partial n = 0$. Thus we have the five-point finite-difference analogue of a Neumann problem for the Laplace equation on a square, solution of which is uniquely determined up to a constant. If we think of a probability distribution over the whole board, the solution is uniquely determined by requiring the sum of probabilities to be one. Assuming that a steady state develops, we might expect that eventually probability distributions will be realized as proportions of beetles in the squares to the total, provided, as we have said, that no crowding takes place in any square.

Such considerations have led to the formulation of some highly questionable methods, called Monte Carlo methods,[2] for solving boundary value problems of partial difference equations. We give one such method without any argument for its validity: To discover the value of a solution at a point P of a Dirichlet problem for the five-point finite-difference analogue of the Laplace equation, perform a random walk with a counter on a checkerboard to C, N, S, E, W and keep the counter walking until (if ever) it hits a boundary point. Then record the given value at the boundary and repeat, walking again from P to the boundary point, and forming a cumulative average of boundary values obtained at the ends of successive walks to the boundary from P. This sequence is said to converge to the solution of the boundary value problem at P. We can only give a probability that the solution (at one point) is 'correct.' On the other hand, the method of accelerated successive replacements allows efficient solution to any desired accuracy of exactly the same set of difference equations. Moreover, using least squares together with harmonic polynomials, we can approximate the solution of the boundary value problem for the differential equation (if that is desired) to high accuracy and with computable error bound. It is in view of these considerations that we have said we regard as of questionable value Monte Carlo methods for 'solving' boundary value problems.

It may be noted that even the walks used in such methods, when they

---

[2] Not to be confused with methods involving random choices of values of independent variables in certain probability formulations of quadratures for integrals—also called Monte Carlo.

are done on the computing machines, are often not really random. Either pseudorandom number generators are utilized or a table is used. Strictly speaking, once such a list has been used, it is no longer random, but is, in fact, the same list used before.[3] If we used the beetle box experiment as such to approximate solutions of the Neumann problem where there is no flux across the boundary, at least it would be evident that an analogue device had been used and there would be no computation pretense or expense involved. We presume that beetles, when they are not the performing English variety, are cheaper than electricity!

On the other hand, random walks properly managed on a computer seem to play a legitimate role of their own in science, quite independent of problems of differential or difference equations. One can find some of the differential equations of mathematical physics out of random walk considerations, but sometimes the mechanical processes studied are so intricate that derivation of the relevant differential equation, if there is one, is beyond the capacities of the investigator. In these cases, performance of a random walk simulation (also referred to by physicists as a Monte-Carlo method) is indicated, and the task of performing a random walk with rigorous adherence to the concept of 'equally probable' becomes an important and, moreover exciting, consideration for a modern computor.

In such usage we find the concept of probability (or really 'equally probable') too abstract, and too important, to justify the usual product convention [2] with respect to probabilities of independent events. We utilize instead a certain technique suggested by von Neumann to avoid the use of any but the weakest sort of assumptions about assignments of probabilities to independent events and still form random walks. As stated earlier, it is assumed that the machine is equipped with a fast analogue binary decision unit, activation of which may be thought of as 'flipping a coin.' The sequence of activations will be utilized in such a way that it will not matter if the equipment is biased toward one decision or the other so long as the variation of bias is small over short intervals.

2. A SUGGESTION OF VON NEUMANN

Approximately a decade ago, Professor von Neumann suggested, in a casual public comment [1] on the task of generating from binary bits a list of numbers of given digit length that are random in the sense of

---

[3] Unless, of course, some random process in selection of the list has been involved.

being equally probable to occur, that one could generate, even from a 'weighted' binary-decision element, a binary decision that is equally probable to occur by applying the decision element twice, ignoring those cases where the results of two applications agree, and assigning the decision of the first application when they do not. We have been impressed by the fact that the result is not only independent of 'weighting' of binary decision elements, but depends only on assignment of a probability to 'independent' events occurring together, which is a symmetric function of the probabilities of each of the separate events. Therefore, an 'equally probable' decision from such handling of binary decision elements is independent of any special assumptions of probability theory. In fact, the decision depends only on the assumption, absurd to deny, that the probability assigned to independent events is independent of the order of occurrence. Of course, there are other simple properties one would like a probability assigned independent events to have. We lay down these properties as axioms defining independent events and then generate a large class of functions, called probability products, having these properties. We expect that enough axioms could be found to insure that the classical product rule holds, but we prefer to lay down only the absolutely essential axioms so that probability 'just' retains its meaning, and then indicate how to manage random walks without making further assumptions.

3. A NONSTOCHASTIC PROBABILITY PRODUCT FOR n-ARY EVENTS

The elements $X_1, X_2, \cdots, X_n$ of an arbitrary set A of order $n \geq 2$ are said to be n-ary events. Numbers $x_1, x_2, \cdots, x_n \in [0,1]$ assigned to n-ary events $X_1, X_2, \cdots, X_n$, respectively, such that

$$\sum_{i=1}^{n} x_i = 1$$

are said to be probabilities of n-ary events, $X_1, X_2, \cdots, X_n$. Where x and y are any two elements of $[0,1]$, let l_1 be the subset of the Cartesian product space $[0,1] \times [0,1]$ such that $x - y = 0$, and let l_2 be the subset such that $x + y \leq 1$.

A function f mapping $l_1 \cup l_2$ into $[0,1]$ such that

$\quad$ (i) on $l_1 \cup l_2$, $\quad f(x,y) \leq x$
$\quad$ (ii) on $l_1 \cup l_2$, $\quad f(x,y) = f(y,x)$
and $\quad$ (iii) on l_2

$$2f(x,y) + 2f(x,1 - x - y) + 2f(y, 1 - x - y)$$
$$+ f(x,x) + f(y,y) + f(1 - x - y, 1 - x - y) = 1$$

will be said to be a probability product.

Elements (a,α) of the Cartesian product space $A \times A$ are said to be independent events for n-ary events $X_1, X_2, \cdots, X_n$, if for x the probability of $'a'$ and y the probability of α, a number called the probability of event (a,α) is assigned to the element (a,α) by a probability product f.

From (i) and (ii) it follows that

(iv) $f(x,y) \le y$

and   (v) $f(0,0) = f(1,0) = f(0,1) = 0,$

and, from (iii) and (v), that

$$f(1,1) = 1.$$

Conditions (i) and (iv) require that the probability of independent events occurring together be less than that of either occurring separately. Condition (ii) requires that the order of occurrence of events be irrelevant and (iii) that at least one event occurs.

Some serious students will insist on adopting a bimonotone condition, $x_j > x_k$ implies $f(x_i, x_j) > f(x_i, x_k)$, but we seek a minimal set of axioms and can imagine probabilities not obeying this rule.[4] The associative property

$$f(x, f(y,z)) = f(f(x,y), z)$$

would ordinarily be required for treatment of probability of n independent events using compositions of a probability product. However, we will show how to manage a random walk without having to consider the probability of more than two events using an arbitrary probability product and, therefore, how requirements that force associativity can be bypassed.

Let $b \in [0,1]$. Then

$$f(x,y) \begin{cases} = \tfrac{1}{2}(1 + b)xy & \text{for} & x > \tfrac{1}{2} \text{ or } y > \tfrac{1}{2}, x + y \le 1 \\ = xy & \text{for} & x \le \tfrac{1}{2} \text{ and } y \le \tfrac{1}{2} \\ = bx^2 + (1 - b)x & \text{for} & x = y > \tfrac{1}{2} \end{cases}$$

---

[4] We see no need to interpret probability as relative frequency of occurrence in a sample, and it does not help for applications to introduce a (Venn) limit that we cannot assess, although this interpretation is still allowed here. However, even if one insists on an interpretation of relative frequency, the frequency record in the event space A gives no information about the frequency record in the event space $A \times A$, so that 'nature' does not demand monotonicity, and we delete it.

is a probability product for n-ary events not identical to the classical rule $f(x,y) = xy$ unless $b = 1$. Note here that $f(x,y)$ has discontinuities of the first kind with saltus made arbitrarily small by appropriate choice of the parameters b. This example for the general n-ary case we regard as sufficient to demonstrate that the probability of independent events in a sufficiently abstract interpretation of probability need not be assigned by the classical stochastic law, and we proceed to give a more general, in some ways more satisfying, class of solutions for the binary $(n = 2)$ case. The binary case, then, is basic to our random walk considerations.

Note that for cases where one does not wish to assume that at least one event occurs, a probability pseudoproduct, defined by allowing

$$\sum_{i=1}^{n} x_i \le 1$$

and setting the left side of (iii) to be less than or equal to one is relevant. The function f, defined by $f(x,y) = x^{\alpha}y^{\alpha}, \alpha \ge 1$, is always a probability pseudoproduct—one which, moreover, is both associative and bimonotone. In contrast, the above example of a probability product is associative, but not bimonotone.

4. PROBABILITY PRODUCTS FOR BINARY EVENTS

Assume that $n = 2$. Since $x_1 + x_2 = 1$, we may, without loss of generality, define l_2 as the subset of the Cartesian product space $[0,1] \times [0,1]$ such that $x + y = 1$ where x and y are any two elements of $[0,1]$. Our axioms, then, defining a probability product for the special case of binary events, become

(i) on $l_1 \cup l_2$, $f(x,y) \le x$
(ii) on $l_1 \cup l_2$, $f(x,y) = f(y,x)$
and (iii) on l_2, $2f(x,y) + f(x,x) + f(y,y) = 1$.

Theorem

Let p be a real number such that $\tfrac{1}{2} \le p \le \tfrac{3}{4}$ and let $\alpha(x)$ be any function mapping $[0,1]$ into $[0,1]$ such that $\alpha(\tfrac{1}{2}) = \dfrac{1}{4(1 - p)}$.

Let

$$F(x)\begin{cases} = (1 + 2(p - 1)\alpha(x))x & \text{for} \quad 0 \le x \le p \\ = (1 + 2p\alpha(x))x - 2p\alpha(x) & \text{for} \quad p \le x \le 1. \end{cases}$$

Then the functions $f: l_1 \cup l_2 \to [0,1]$ defined by

$$f(x,x) = F(x)$$
$$f(x,1-x) = \tfrac{1}{2} - \tfrac{1}{2}[F(x) + F(1-x)]$$

are probability products.

Proof

We provide functions f that are such that (i) and (ii) are satisfied and such that (iii) is satisfied except at $x = y = \tfrac{1}{2}$, imposing only as a last step that (iii) be satisfied at $(\tfrac{1}{2},\tfrac{1}{2})$.

For $x + y = 1$, $x \neq \tfrac{1}{2}$, from (iii)

(13.1) $f(x,y) = \tfrac{1}{2} - \tfrac{1}{2}[f(x,x) + f(y,y)] = \tfrac{1}{2} - \tfrac{1}{2}[F(x) + F(y)]$

where

$$F(x) = f(x,x), \quad F(y) = f(y,y) \qquad \text{for all} \qquad x,y \in [0,1].$$

Of course, from (i), $F(x) \leq x$. For $\tfrac{1}{2} \leq p \leq 1$ let $F_1(x)$ be defined by

(13.2) $F_1(x)\begin{cases} = (2p - 1)x & \text{for} \quad 0 \leq x \leq p \\ = x - 2p(1 - x) & \text{for} \quad p \leq x \leq 1. \end{cases}$

Then, for $F(x) \geq F_1(x)$, $f(x,y)$ defined by (13.1) satisfies (i);

for $0 \leq x \leq (1 - p)$, $\quad f(x,y) \leq \tfrac{1}{2} - \tfrac{1}{2}[(2p - 1)x + (1 - x) - 2px] = x$,

for $(1 - p) \leq x \leq p$, $\quad f(x,y) \leq \tfrac{1}{2} - \tfrac{1}{2}[(2p - 1)x + (2p - 1)(1 - x)]$
$$= 1 - p \leq x,$$

for $p \leq x \leq 1$, $\quad f(x,y) \leq \tfrac{1}{2} - \tfrac{1}{2}[x - 2p(1 - x) + (2p - 1)(1 - x)]$
$$= 1 - x \leq x.$$

Any F, then, that is defined by interpolation of the functional values of the identity function and those of F_1 will be such that f defined by (13.1) satisfies (i). For arbitrary $\alpha: [0,1] \to [0,1]$, we have then that

(13.3) $F(x) = [1 - \alpha(x)]x + \alpha(x)F_1(x).$

Noting finally, that in order for (iii) to be satisfied at $x = \tfrac{1}{2}$ we must have that $F(\tfrac{1}{2}) = \tfrac{1}{4}$, and that this in turn restricts $\alpha(x)$ so that $\alpha(\tfrac{1}{2}) = \dfrac{1}{4(1 - p)}$, we require that $p \leq \tfrac{3}{4}$ in order that $0 \leq \alpha(\tfrac{1}{2}) \leq 1$. The theorem follows. ∎

For a simple geometric statement of the theorem, let the set of points of the closed triangle $(0,0)$, $(p,p(2p-1))$, $(1,1)$, $\frac{1}{2} \leq p \leq \frac{3}{4}$ be denoted by T_p where it is noted that the locus of vertices $(p,p(2p-1))$ is the parabola through $(0,0)$, $(\frac{1}{2},0)$, $(1,1)$. Let F be any function represented by a 'curve' passing through the point $(\frac{1}{2},\frac{1}{4})$ whose points are elements of T_p for some (fixed) p. Then the function f defined by (13.1) is a probability product, and, in fact, the class of functions so defined are those given by the theorem. Sets T_p cannot be augmented by accretion of some points without deletion of others because functions F such that

$$
\begin{aligned}
F(x) &= F_1(x) &&\text{for} && 0 \leq x \leq p \\
F(x) &< F_1(x) &&\text{for} && \text{some } x \ni p \leq x \leq 1
\end{aligned}
$$

or

$$
\begin{aligned}
F(x) &< F_1(x) &&\text{for} && \text{some } x \ni 0 \leq x \leq p \\
F(x) &= F_1(x) &&\text{for} && p \leq x \leq 1
\end{aligned}
$$

are not such that (i) and (iv) are satisfied. On the other hand, F defined by

$$
\begin{aligned}
F(x) &= x &&\text{for} && 0 \leq x < \tfrac{1}{2} \\
F(\tfrac{1}{2}) &= \tfrac{1}{4} \\
F(x) &= x(2x-1) &&\text{for} && \tfrac{1}{2} < x \leq 1
\end{aligned}
$$

is such that (13.1) defines a probability product f not covered by the theorem.

In the theorem let $p = \frac{1}{2}$ and let

$$
\alpha(x) \begin{cases} = 1 - x &\text{for} & 0 \leq x \leq \tfrac{1}{2} \\ = x &\text{for} & \tfrac{1}{2} \leq x \leq 1 \end{cases}
$$

Then the probability product given by the theorem is the classical stochastic one, f, defined by

$$
f(x,y) = xy.
$$

If f is continuous on $l_1 \cup l_2$, we say that the probability $f(x,y)$ of independent events is continuously dependent on the probability of the events, and this often will be desirable in applications. For instance, although we may not wish to assume that the probability of head or tail in the toss of a coin is always one half, we still may wish to assume that results for a slightly 'weighted' coin are not grossly different than for an 'unweighted' coin. Probability products given in the theorem are continuously dependent on the probability of the events if $\alpha(x)$ is continuous.

5. CONSTRUCT SPACES AND THE CLASSICAL PRODUCT RULE

Consider a binary event space A with elements identified with 0,1 and call it a binary primordial event space. Utilizing the von Neumann suggestion, form now a new binary event space composed of elements $(0,1)$, $(1,0)$ by deleting from $A \times A$ the elements $(0,0)$ and $(1,1)$ and call it the construct space C (of A). Since elements of C now constitute all recognized events, we assign to elements of C probabilities such that the sum is one. Noting that under any assignment of probabilities to the primordial space A and any choice of a probability product f, the elements $(0,1),(1,0)$ of the construct space (which we now identify with 0 and 1, respectively) have equal probabilities, we assign each element of C the probability $\frac{1}{2}$. Now each element of the cross space $C_1 = C \times C$ under any assignment of a probability product f has the same probability $f(\frac{1}{2},\frac{1}{2})$, which, since there are four elements in C_1, must be $\frac{1}{4}$ (also, $f(\frac{1}{2},\frac{1}{2}) = F(\frac{1}{2}) = \frac{1}{4}$ for any probability product). Consider cross spaces $C_{m+1} = C_m \times C_m$, $n = 1,2,\cdots$, and by way of an induction hypothesis suppose that all elements of C_m have equal probability $1/n$ where n is the number of elements in C_m. Then all elements of C_{m+1}, n^2 in number, are assigned the same probability $f(1/n,1/n)$, which then must have the value $1/n^2$, regardless of the choice of a probability product f, and our hypothesis has been established. But now for $X_1 \in C_m$ and $X_2 \in C_m$, $P(X_1)P(X_2) = 1/n \cdot 1/n = 1/n^2 = P(X_1,X_2)$, and the required assignment of probabilities (to both the space and the cross space) demands the classical product rule for probabilities assigned the occurrence of two independent events. The classical product being associative, we may now define by using composition, probabilities of more than two independent events occurring together. We have $P(X_1)P(X_2)\cdots P(X_k) = P(X_1,X_2,\cdots,X_k)$.

Next consider an n-ary space A and identity the $n > 2$ elements with integers $0,1,2,3,\cdots,n - 1$. We express these integers in binary form $0\cdots000,0\cdots001,0\cdots010,0\cdots011,\cdots,n - 1$ and call this set of integers so expressed the primordial n-ary event space, using again the notation A to represent that set. The elements of the 0,1 sequences that are used to represent elements of A can be thought of as elements of a primordial binary event space. Arbitrary assignment of probabilities in the primordial binary spaces gives rise to arbitrary assignment of probabilities in the primordial n-ary space (not uniquely determined by those in the binary space), by considering elements of the n-ary primordial space as elements of some cross spaces of the binary primordial space, with probabilities assigned by an arbitrary probability product. We now replace elements of the binary primordial space used in defining the above sequences $0\cdots000, 0\cdots001, 0\cdots010, 0\cdots011, \cdots, n-1$ by elements of the binary construct space and call this set of sequences the construct space C (of A) for n-ary events. Since elements of C are conjunctions of events belonging to some successive cross spaces of the binary construct space, above considerations demand use of the classical product rule over equal numbers of binary events of equal probability in assigning probabilities to elements of C. Thus if C has n elements, each element has probability $1/n$. Again an induction shows that elements of C_m defined by $C_1 = C \times C, C_{m+1} = C_m \times C_m$ have probability $1/n$ if C_m has n elements, and the product rule is demanded for the n-ary as for the binary case.

One sees then that, if proper care is taken, it is possible to avoid consideration of an arbitrary probability product, except for binary events. Consequently, the need to assume associativity in defining a probability product is wholly obviated for applications where it is possible to form the construct space. Further, whether the property of bimonotonicity is assumed becomes almost unimportant, since it will apply anyway (as a property of the classical product rule) after formation of the construct space.

Obviously, all of the many applications where it is required only to obtain decisions that are equally probable are completely resolved by utilizing the 'double penny toss' technique. This embraces, then, all random walk processes. Suppose, for example, our beetle motions are to be simulated by a random walk conducted on the intersection points of a rectangular grid. At each step we require the choice of one of the five numbers $0,1,2,3,4$, in such a way that the choice of any one of them is equally probable. We perform the 'double penny toss' to decide on each of three binary digits, reading, say, from left to right. Any of these three digit binary numbers (being elements of the construct space) have equal probability of occurring—in particular, $000,001,010,011,100$, in our group, are equally probable[5]—regardless of the choice of a probability product or of semantic agreements as to a meaning of probability. We thus have constructed a computational procedure for random walks without a product convention.

---

[5] Sequences of tosses resulting in other combinations are ignored.

REFERENCES

[1] J. von Neumann, 'Role of computing machines,' *Bull. Am. Math. Soc.*, (1953), 332. (Delivered at, but not printed in the *Proc. Symp. Appl. Math.* in conjunction with the April meeting in New York, 1953).
[2] I. J. Good, *'Probability and the Weighing of Evidence,'* Griffin, London, 1950.

APPENDIXES

COMMENTS ON
QUADRATURE FORMULAS

Some apologies are offered for not having included chapters in the text on quadrature formulas (i.e., formulas for finite-difference approximation of integrals) and interpolation formulas. The reasons are both technical and pedagogical.

In the systematic development of theories of convergence of iterative methods and stability of marching schema, together with their motivations in approximate solution of boundary value problems, there seemed no logical place for the development of quadrature formulas and interpolation formulas. Moreover, the student will have had a course in calculus and almost certainly will have studied the approximation of an integral on a real interval by replacing the area under a curve with a set of trapezoids (with two vertices on the curve) or by replacing it with a set of areas under parabolas (with three points on the curve). If, by some oversight, he has not been exposed to these materials before, he is here instructed to derive such formulas, called the trapezoid rule and Simpson's rule, respectively, for himself.

It is our experience that *at this level* students find these studies and those of the simpler ones of the interpolation formulas excessively dull, and the intensive study of this material sometimes sours their all too tentative tastes for numerical analysis. Except possibly for the study of the Gaussian quadrature formula, which we have omitted because of the former consideration of finding a proper place for its development, we feel that the student should delay any further study of quadrature and interpolation until he takes a graduate course in real variables and integration. In the context of integration theory, such studies can once again become vital, pulsating subjects. Numerical analysts, as such, simply cannot take the responsibility of training young mathematicians in numerical methods for all of mathematics and should probably confine themselves, wherever possible, to those areas where difficulties of analysis special to numerical treatment are of overriding importance. Quadratures are probably rarely in this category. To some minor degree this may justify our not treating integral equations, although for the most part that devolves on an unwillingness to require or develop still more prerequisite material.

With respect to quadrature formulas for integrals on real intervals, it should be noted that the material on Runge-Kutta methods in Chapter 7, Secs. 4, 5, offers an extremely efficient method for forming finite-difference approximation of integrals especially if combined, when appropriate, with the material on 'finite form' in Chapter 7, Sec. 6. If one wishes the value of

$$\int_a^b f(x)dx,$$

he simply integrates to $x = b$, the initial value problem

$$\frac{dy}{dx} = f(x), \quad y(a) = 0.$$

As to integrals over regions in R^n, $n > 1$, one can, theoretically, always treat them as iterated integrals over R^1, and actually one is usually driven to that procedure. We are not aware of any efficient quadrature formulas that arise from direct finite-difference approximation of integrals over R^n for $n > 1$. If they could be provided, they would prove very useful, for example, in connection with the least squares methods treated here for boundary value problems. Of course, if only polynomial functions are to be integrated, we (or the student) could provide some formulas, but this only suggests that 'continuous methods' may after all be more efficient in generating approximate formulas for integrals over R^n, $n > 1$ than are finite-difference methods.

A quadrature formula is defined as a formula of the form

(A.1) $$\sum_{i=1}^{N} a_i f(x_i),$$

which is intended to give an approximate value of the integral

(A.2) $$\int_A f \, dA, \quad (A \subset R^n),$$

where

$$({\{x_i \mid i = 1,\cdots,N\}} \subset A) \wedge (f: A \to R^1),$$

and
$$\{a_i \mid i = 1,\cdots,N\} \subset R^1$$

specifies the quadrature formula to be used. The computor, if he is planning the programming of a problem where a quadrature is to be used, is advised to choose N as large as he might deem necessary, to reserve two pairs of N consecutive word locations for storage of vectors (a_i)[1] and $f(x_i)$, and to call for the scalar product of these two vectors to give (A.1) as an approximation to (A.2). Then he will be free later to select the quadrature formula he may wish to utilize by reading his selected numbers a_i into the reserved word locations, and this, of course, allows him to experiment easily with the quadrature appropriate to his purposes.

In quadratures where the integrand is tabulated at a discrete set of points,[2] or worse, where the functional values of the integrand are obtained from experiments and the accuracy is unknown, one must decide what 'model' he will use in extending the integrand function so that it is defined on all of $A \subset R^n$.

If $A \subset R^1$, we will often prefer to obtain f at all points of A (including the points where it is originally tabulated) by a moving least squares average polynomial over a number of points—say, by taking least squares parabola fits over eight surrounding points to define f at a single point. But we do not treat such smoothing procedures here. This is an area where numerical analysis and statistics reach a common domain, and we think it can be better treated by statisticians. The same comment is more important when applied to interpolation formulas, since the act of summing, which one must somehow[3] perform in the process of evaluating a quadrature, is itself a smoothing operation.

We are not convinced of the overwhelming practical role ordinarily assigned the study of quadrature formulas. We cannot, from our own experience, recall a single example where such a formula was actually used in a practical problem.

---

[1] Of course, the values a_i are to be thought of as read in directly from cards or other equipment such as tape, while values $f(x_i)$ are thought of as generated from formulations programmed in the machine or transferred from other locations in core, drum, disc, or tape.

[2] i.e., B is a finite set and $B \subset A$, while r_n is an n-terminating subset of R^1 and $f: B \to r_n$.

[3] The summation is with some weights. If consecutive values of $a_i f(x_i)$ in (A.1) differ in sign and in absolute value are large compared to their difference, then, of course, large losses of accuracy could occur. Quadratures may not be strictly summing, and differencing is a roughing operation.

B

COMMENTS ON
INTERPOLATION FORMULAS

The student should read here the last paragraphs of Appendix A. Quadrature formulas and interpolation formulas are bound together in an inseparable theoretical, and therefore pedagogical, marriage. Having given our views, in Appendix A, on the teaching and theoretical stature of the studies of quadrature formulas, we now confine ourselves to the practical aspects of the computation of (exact, not least squares) polynomial interpolation only.

We have found the layout of computation for interpolation, given by Milne[1] as Aitken's method, extremely practical for use on a digital computer. It gives only a format for obtaining successively higher-order Lagrange polynomial interpolants. However, one can easily look down the list of interpolants it provides and note a convergence in the higher digits with a start of oscillation in the lower-order digits. The appropriate choice of order of interpolation is then quite easily and efficiently made. Anyone who has ever faced head-on the problem of actually carrying out reliable interpolations will recognize the great value of having such a technique readily available as a subroutine.

Let $I_{0,1,\cdots,n}(x)$ represent the value at the real number x of the polynomial of degree n passing through the $n + 1$ points $(x_0,y_0),(x_1,y_1),\cdots,(x_n,y_n)$. We have that

(B.1)
$$I_{0,p}(x) = \frac{1}{x_p - x_0} \begin{vmatrix} y_0 & x_0 - x \\ y_p & x_p - x \end{vmatrix}$$

---

[1] Milne, W. E., *Numerical Calculus*, Princeton University Press, 1949, pp. 68–78.

is the linear interpolating polynomial between x_0 and x_p, $p = 1, \cdots, n$, as can quickly be seen from the fact that $I_{0,p}(x_0) = y_0$ and $I_{0,p}(x_p) = y_p$. Further, it is then evident from the same argument that

(B.2)
$$I_{0,1,p}(x) = \frac{1}{x_p - x_1} \begin{vmatrix} I_{0,1}(x) & (x_1 - x) \\ I_{0,p}(x) & (x_p - x) \end{vmatrix}$$

is the quadratic interpolating polynomial between x_0, x_1, and x_p, $p = 2, \cdots, n$, and that

(B.3)
$$I_{0,1,2,p}(x) = \frac{1}{x_p - x_2} \begin{vmatrix} I_{0,1,2}(x) & (x_2 - x) \\ I_{0,1,p}(x) & (x_p - x) \end{vmatrix}$$

is the cubic interpolating polynomial for x_0, x_1, x_2, x_p where $p = 3, \cdots, n$, etc. Of course, it is possible to get alternate forms of the interpolating polynomials of each degree higher than one by reordering the values $x_1, \cdots, x_n$. Also, the polynomials themselves in (B.1), (B.2), and (B.3) are never computed. Only the functional values are computed, so that successively higher-order interpolants are found by utilizing only successive linear interpolations. This, in turn, can be utilized on a modern digital computer by programming *just one representative equation* and using it repeatedly as for an iterative scheme. In fact, the Aitken's method (according to Milne) can be described as an iterative method of computing successively higher-order Lagrange interpolants.

If one requires interpolation to a value x on a digital computer, he simply arranges his computation and output format as follows:

x_i	y_i	1st order	2^d order	3^d order
x_0	y_0			
x_1	y_1	$I_{0,1}(x)$		
x_2	y_2	$I_{0,2}(x)$	$I_{0,1,2}(x)$	
x_3	y_3	$I_{0,3}(x)$	$I_{0,1,3}(x)$	$I_{0,1,2,3}(x)$

We believe that every computing laboratory should keep on hand a subroutine of this nature and one for inverse interpolation (Neville).

ON COMPUTATION
WITH REAL INTERVALS

Throughout this text we have assumed that computing would be done with terminating decimals. The error bounds for approximate solution of boundary value problems have usually been achieved here by ignoring temporarily the difficulty in replacing real numbers by terminating decimals and then computing an error bound from an algorithm that is independent of the source of the approximation. Of course, such an algorithm must include the careful assessment of the loss of accuracy in using terminating decimals in (the smaller) calculation of the error bound itself. In analysis of computation procedures, so important to the subject of numerical analysis as distinguished from approximation theory, we have been forced to utilize real number analysis and then to call on relatively crude properties of terminating decimals that arise by embedding them in the real number system.

This is not the only possibility. Instructions used to be given to every elementary physics student to consider, before computing with a terminating decimal, what the largest and smallest terminating decimal of one digit longer length would be that would round off to the number at hand. The student, on proceeding with the computation of a dependent number, was then to consider what the largest and smallest result—to one higher digit —would be. In modern form, this has been developed to a computation system of 'interval numbers.' It provides a method for assessing the error due to round-off, and when cleverly used in connection with convergent iterative methods or stable marching schema—especially if they are contractive—it could, presumably, be effective. In fact, there is little doubt that the system has already been carried to a further stage of development than had been expected by most workers in the field of numerical analysis. We still cannot see real hope that it will, of itself, ever provide the possibility of determining bounds for errors of approximation of boundary value problems, but the systemization it provides, for assessment of the error made in using terminating decimals, may be extremely useful in the act of computing bounds according to formulas prescribed by analysis. This will be especially true in cases where this last computation is excessively long. Someday we would like to discover that it is possible to perform an analysis with the objects with which we compute, but the only real hope we have seen for this, however dim, is in the real interval system. We give its description essentially according to a survey article by Ramon E. Moore,[1] except that we take care to assure that the pairs of numbers with which one needs to compute are represented by terminating decimals. We understand that this material was developed from its earliest stages with the encouragement of Professor George Forsythe of Stanford University.

Let r_n be the set of real numbers that can be represented by n-digits regardless of the position of the decimal point. To perform computations that in the system used in this text would be in r_{n-1}, we now compute with elements of the cross space $r_n \times r_n$. We wish, in fact, to interpret these elements as closed intervals of real numbers where the end points are in r_n. The arithmetic is as follows:

(C.1) $[a,b] + [c,d] = [\max\{A \mid (A \in r_n) \wedge (A \le (a + c))\}, \min\{B \mid (B \in r_n)$
$\wedge (B \ge (b + d))\}]$

(C.2) $[a,b] \cdot [c,d] = [\max\{A \mid (A \in r_n) \wedge (A \le ac) \wedge (A \le ad) \wedge (A \le bc)$
$\wedge (A \le bd)\}, \min\{B \mid (B \in r_n) \wedge (B \ge ac) \wedge (B \ge ad)$
$\wedge (B \ge bc) \wedge (B \ge bd)\}]$

(C.2) $([c,d] \ne [0,0]) \Rightarrow ([a,b] \div [c,d] = [a,b] \cdot [(1/d),(1/c)]).$

The class of pairs used in the interval number system, together with the property, not included in the above symbolic statement, that they form a bounded set because of the occurrence of exponent overflow and underflow, should be studied with special attention to algebraic and topological properties. The student should understand that this is the statement of a research exercise.

[1] Moore, Ramon E., 'The Automatic Analysis And Control Of Error In Digital Computation Based On The Use of Interval Numbers,' in B. Rall ed., *Errors In Digital Computers*, Vol. I, John Wiley, 1965, pp. 61–130.

D

THE WEAK SENSE OF
THE HAMILTON PRINCIPLE
FOR A VIBRATING STRING

One may not always clearly understand, when seeking a generalized solution (weak sense, sense of distributions, sense of completion by ideal vectors, sense of an element of a ring extension) of a differential equation in a problem where a physical phenomenon is to be represented by the solution, that he may view this act as invoking a generalization of a basic

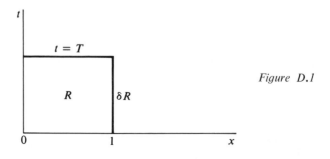

Figure D.1

physical principle such as that enunciated by Hamilton. To demonstrate this, we give an example of the derivation of the differential equation for the vibrating string from Hamilton's principle and, alternately, a derivation of the functional equation that defines a weak solution of this equation.

Let the horizontal distance to a point of the string be denoted by x measured from the origin, let t denote time, assume that the mass density ρ is uniform on the string and that particles move only in a vertical direction, so that there is a uniform tension τ. Let the displacement of a point of the string at position x and time t be given by $u(x,t)$. We consider only displacement functions $u: R \rightarrow R^1$ such that $\partial u / \partial x$ is small and

$$\forall n > 1, \quad \frac{\partial^n u}{\partial x^n} \ll \frac{\partial u}{\partial x}.$$

Under these conditions, the Hamilton principle requires that we seek a function for which the integral

$$I = \int_0^T L \, dt = \int_0^T (V - P) \, dt = \int_0^T \left(\int_0^1 (\tfrac{1}{2}\rho u_t^2 - \tfrac{1}{2}\tau u_x^2) \, dx \right) dt^1$$

(D.1)
$$= \tfrac{1}{2} \int_R (\rho u_t^2 - \tau u_x^2) \, dR$$

is stationary with respect to a certain class of perturbations subject to the constraints[2]

$$\begin{array}{ccc} u(0,t) = 0 & & u(x,0) = f(x) \\ u(1,t) = 0 & \text{and} & u(x,T) = g(x). \end{array}$$

The constraints will be briefly written

(D.2)
$$u(x,t) = u_\delta(x,t) \; \forall \; (x,t) \in \delta R.$$

Assuming that $u = \bar{u}(x,t)$, where $\bar{u}, \bar{u}_x, \bar{u}_y \in C(R \cup \delta R)$, is a function for which I is stationary with respect to variations of the real parameter ε among the class of functions

(D.3)
$$u = u(x,t,\varepsilon)$$

(D.4)
$$\ni (u(x,t,0) = \bar{u}(x,t)$$

(D.5)
$$\wedge \, (u(x,t,\varepsilon) = u_\delta(x,t) \; \forall \; (x,t) \in \delta R \wedge \forall \, \varepsilon \in R^1)$$

we find the equation that $u = \bar{u}(x,t)$ must satisfy under the conditions that

$$u_x, u_t, u_\varepsilon, u_{x\varepsilon}, u_{t\varepsilon} \in C(R \cup \delta R).$$

---

[1] This is the action, the kinetic minus potential energy.
[2] We do not propose that prescription of this data for the resulting differential equation gives a well-posed problem. It does not, but any solution of the problem must take on values of some function of x at $t = 0$ and $t = T$.

Letting $\eta = u_\varepsilon$, we have from (D.5)

(D.6) $\eta(x,t,\varepsilon) = 0 \ \forall \ (x,t) \in \delta R$

Substituting (D.3) in (D.1),

$$I(\varepsilon) = \tfrac{1}{2}\int_R (\rho u_t^2(x,t,\varepsilon) - \tau u_x^2(x,t,\varepsilon)) \, dR,$$

so the condition that $\bar{u}$ be stationary and satisfy (D.4) can be written

(D.7) $0 = I'(0) = \int_R (\rho \bar{u}_t \eta_t - \tau \bar{u}_x \eta_x) \, dR = \rho \int_0^1 dx \int_0^T \bar{u}_t \eta_t \, dt - \tau \int_0^T dt \int_0^1 \bar{u}_x \eta_x dx$

If we now seek to find an equation for functions $\bar{u}$ such that $I(\varepsilon)$ is stationary and such that

(D.8) $(\bar{u}_{xx} \wedge \bar{u}_{tt} \in C(R)) \wedge (\bar{u}_x \wedge \bar{u}_t \in C(R \cup \delta R)$

(i.e., such that $\bar{u}$ is 'second-order regular' in R), then we may integrate (D.7) by parts to obtain

$$0 = \rho \int_0^1 \left[\bar{u}_t \eta \Big|_{t=0}^{t=T} - \int_0^T \eta \bar{u}_{tt} \, dt \right] dx - \tau \int_0^T \left[\bar{u}_x \eta \Big|_{x=0}^{x=1} - \int_0^1 \eta \bar{u}_{xx} \, dx \right] dt.$$

Using (D.6) and putting $c^2 = \tau/\rho$, this becomes

$$\int_R \eta(\bar{u}_{xx} - (1/c^2)u_{tt}) \, dR = 0 \ \forall \ \eta \in C(R).$$

Since the function $\bar{u}_{xx} - (1/c^2)\bar{u}_{tt} \in C(R)$, we conclude that

$$\bar{u}_{xx} - (1/c^2)\bar{u}_{tt} = 0,$$

which is the equation sought.

Our only purpose in developing the material of this Appendix is to point out that if one now returns to (D.7) and, before integrating by parts, he weakens the assumption (D.8) on the smoothness properties for $\bar{u}$ to require only that

(D.8') $\bar{u} \in C(R),$

but strengthens the conditions on the class of admissible functions η so that

(D.9) $\qquad\qquad (\eta_{xx} \wedge \eta_{tt} \in C(R)) \wedge (\eta_x \wedge \eta_t) \in C(R \cup \delta R),$

then the integration by parts—so to speak, in the other direction—yields

(D.10) $\displaystyle \int_0^1 \bar{u}\eta_t \Big|_{t=0}^{t=T} dx - (1/c^2)\int_0^T \bar{u}\eta_x \Big|_{x=0}^{x=1} dt + \int_R \bar{u}(\eta_{xx} - (1/c^2)\eta_{tt})\, dR = 0.$

Thus a function $\bar{u} \in C(R)$, which makes $I(\varepsilon)$ stationary, satisfies the functional equation (D.10) $\forall\ \eta$ satisfying (D.9). Such a function is said to be a weak solution of the wave equation where the condition $\bar{u} \in C(R)$ can obviously be weakened to $\bar{u}$ square integrable (even in the Lebesgue sense) without materially weakening our physical concepts.

If one now observes again that $\bar{u}(x,t)$ is a displacement distance of a particle at position x on the string and time t, and that in order to have existence of a weak solution function, $\bar{u} : R \to R^1 \ni \bar{u} = \bar{u}(x,t)$, one need not require that the velocity $\bar{u}_t(x,t)$ or the spacial gradient $\bar{u}_x(x,t)$ exists, it becomes evident that the use of weak solutions in physical problems is a genuine generalization—and not simply a restatement—of the Hamilton principle. The Hamilton principle, as it was originally formulated for the linearly vibrating string, is given in (D.1), and it surely does require the existence of velocities. The weakening of the principle is a slight one—one that is clearly physically reasonable in other contexts, such as light diffraction where the (three-dimensional) wave equation arises, but we feel it is important for those who are interested in mathematical formulation of physical problems—including numerical analysts—to realize what basic principles are being invoked in the formulation. In contexts where weakening the Hamilton principle as suggested does not do direct violence to physical intuition (as it does for us in some incompressible flow problems), it should certainly be gratefully accepted if it allows the statement of very general existence theorems.

E

DERIVATION OF THE STREAM FUNCTION EQUATION

From the equations of motion of Chapter 10, Sec. 2,

$$(\rho v r/c^2)(uu_r + vu_z + (1/\rho)p_r) - (\rho u r/c^2)(uv_r + vv_z + (1/\rho)p_z) = 0.$$

We have

(E.1) $\quad (p = \Gamma(\rho)) \Rightarrow ((p_r = (d\Gamma/d\rho)\rho_r = c^2\rho_r) \wedge (p_z = (d\Gamma/d\rho)\rho_z = c^2\rho_z)),$

and therefore

(E.2)
$$0 = (\rho v r/c^2)(uu_r + vu_z + (c^2/\rho)\rho_r) - (\rho u r/c^2)(uv_r + vv_z + (c^2/\rho)\rho_z)$$
$$= (1 - (u^2/c^2))(\rho r v)_r + (-uv/c^2)((\rho r v)_z - (\rho r u)_r) + (1 - (v^2/c^2))(-\rho r u)_z$$
$$\quad - \rho v + \rho r(u_z - v_r).$$

Using A, B, C, D as given in Chapter 10, Sec. 2, p. 172,

(E.3) $\qquad A\psi_{rr} + B(\psi_{rz} + \psi_{zr}) + C\psi_{zz} = D - \rho r(u_z - v_r).$

The Bernoulli law is

(E.4) $\quad (\gamma/(\gamma - 1))p/\rho + \tfrac{1}{2}(u^2 + v^2) = (\gamma/(\gamma - 1))K\rho^{\gamma - 1} + \tfrac{1}{2}(u^2 + v^2) = h_0$

(E.5) $\quad \Rightarrow \gamma K\rho^{\gamma - 2}\rho_r + (uu_r + vv_r) = 0$

(E.6) $\quad \Rightarrow (1/\rho)p_r + uu_r + vv_r = 0.$

Combining this with the first equation of motion gives

(E.7) $$v_r - u_z = 0,$$

and this establishes the streamfunction equation quoted in Chapter 10, Sec. 2, p. 172, for the case of isentropic (constant entropy) flow.

The quantity $(u_z - v_r)$ appearing in (E.3) is the magnitude of the curl of a three-dimensional velocity vector in a flow that is axially symmetric, where u is the radial component of velocity and v is the axial component. It is thus that the streamfunction equation is referred to as the vorticity equation. We have shown in (E.7) that if a flow is isentropic, it is also irrotational.

In Chapter 12, Sec. 1, p. 201, where curved shocks are involved, we require the streamfunction equation for cases where the entropy is not constant in the entire flow field, but is, in fact, constant on any streamline. Since the streamfunction is also constant on any streamline, the entropy can be regarded as the functional values $S(\psi)$ of a function S. Our state law is now

$$p = K(S)\rho^\gamma,$$

which can be written

(E.8) $$p = A(\psi)\rho^\gamma,$$

and the derivations of both (E.3) and (E.7) (which is to be used in (E.3)) must be appropriately modified.

Let us turn our attention first to a modified expression for the vorticity in terms of $A'(\psi)$. From (E.8)

$$p_r = \gamma A\rho^{\gamma-1}\rho_r + A'\rho^\gamma\psi_r$$

or

(E.9) $$\gamma A\rho^{\gamma-2}\rho_r = (1/\rho)p_r - A'\rho^{\gamma-1} \cdot \rho v r.$$

Returning to (E.4),

$$(\gamma/(\gamma-1))A(\psi)\rho^{\gamma-1} + \tfrac{1}{2}(u^2 + v^2) = h_0$$

$$\Rightarrow \gamma A\rho^{\gamma-2}\rho_r + (\gamma/(\gamma-1))A'\rho^{\gamma-1} \cdot \rho v r + (uu_r + vv_r) = 0,$$

so that from (E.9)

$$(1/\rho)p_r + (uu_r + vv_r) + (1/(\gamma- 1))A'\rho^{\gamma-1} \cdot \rho vr = 0.$$

Combining this now with the first equation of motion given in Chapter 10, Sec. 2, p. 171,

$$-v(u_z - v_r) = -\rho rv \cdot (1/(\gamma - 1))A'\rho^{\gamma-1}$$
$$= -\rho rv \cdot (1/\gamma)(\gamma/(\gamma - 1))A\rho^{\gamma-1}(A'/A),$$

so that

(E.10) $$-(u_z - v_r) = -\rho rh(1/\gamma)\, d(\ln A)/d\psi.[1]$$

We now modify (E.3) for the state law (E.8). Here, note that if $p = \Gamma(\rho,S)$, then $c^2 = \partial\Gamma/\partial\rho$. From the state law (E.8), then

(E.11) $$(1/\rho)p_r = (c^2/\rho)\rho_r + A'(\psi)\rho^{\gamma-1} \cdot \rho vr$$

$$(1/\rho)p_z = (c^2/\rho)\rho_z - A'(\psi)\rho^{\gamma-1} \cdot \rho ur$$

Using these in (E.2), we obtain

(E.12) $$A\psi_{rr} + 2B\psi_{rz} + C\psi_{zz} = \rho v - \rho r(u_z - v_r) - \rho^2 r^2(u^2 + v^2)$$
$$(1/c^2)(A'/A)A\rho^{\gamma-1}.$$

But $c^2 = (\gamma p/\rho)$ and $A\rho^{\gamma-1} = (p/\rho)$, so that using (E.10) in (E.12), where $q^2 = u^2 + v^2$,

(E.13) $$A\psi_{rr} + 2B\psi_{rz} + C\psi_{zz} = \rho v - \rho r(h + q^2)(1/\gamma)\, d(\ln A)/d\psi,$$

as quoted in Chapter 12, Sec. 1.

If the student requires the streamfunction equation for the thermodynamically general case $p = \Gamma(\rho,S)$, $h = H(p,\rho)$, it will be apparent that by differentiating Γ implicitly with respect to r and z and using

$$S_r(r,z) = S'(\psi)\psi_r = S'(\psi) \cdot \rho vr$$

$$S_z(r,z) = S'(\psi)\psi_z = -S'(\psi) \cdot \rho ur,$$

it will be possible to obtain p_r and p_z in terms of ρ_r and ρ_z, as required

---

[1] Unless v is zero on a set with limit point.

above for (E.11). Next, by differentiating

$$H(p,\rho) + \tfrac{1}{2}(u^2 + v^2) = h_0$$

implicitly with respect to r and z, and putting p_r in terms of ρ_r, as derived from the entropy equation, it will be possible to obtain the general form of (E.10) above. These then will give the desired general streamfunction equation as one may wish to use it, say, in the supersonic region of a high-speed flow past a blunt body (see Chapter 10, Sec. 4) where the gas may be dissociated and large changes of density occur.

DERIVATION OF INITIAL VALUES ψ_r AND ψ_z FOR THE DETACHED SHOCK PROBLEM

The Rankine-Hugoniot shock relations of Chapter 12, Sec. 1, give the flow variables on the downstream side ② of the shock in terms of the flow variables on the approach side ①.[1] Since these relations involve only the tangential and normal components of the velocity vector q on each side, and since all the other flow variables are scalars, in order to determine the flow variables on the downstream side of a shock at a given point (of a curved shock), it is only necessary to know the slope at that point (and, of course, the approach flow values). The first shock relation $q_{1t} = q_{2t}$ gives, in terms of the streamfunction, that $\psi_1 = \psi_2$. Then, assuming a uniform approach flow, we have, with $\rho_1 = 1$, that

$$((\psi_1)_r = \rho_1 q_1 r) \wedge ((\psi_1)_z = 0)) \Rightarrow \psi_1 = \tfrac{1}{2}\rho_1 q_1 r^2 = \tfrac{1}{2}q_1 r^2$$

and, therefore, that

$$\psi_2 = \tfrac{1}{2}q_1 r^2$$

at any point (r,z) on the downstream side of a possibly curved shock given by

(F.1) $$z = f(r).$$

---

[1] A derivation of the more general shock relations for a shock that changes position with time can be found in the expository article T. Y. Thomas, 'The fundamental equations and shock conditions for gases,' *Math. Magazine*, **XXII** (1949), 169. The relations given there are easily seen to reduce to those used here for the case where the shock is stationary.

Therefore, $(\psi_2)_r$ can be obtained from knowledge·of $(\psi_2)_z$ by the equation

$$(\psi_2)_r = d\psi/dr - f'(r)(\psi_2)_z = q_1 r - f'(r)(\psi_2)_z,$$

where $d\psi_2/dr$ is a derivative on the shock. We thus need determine here only $(\psi_2)_z$.

Let a possibly curved shock be inclined at an acute angle β to a normal of the axis of symmetry and let the approach velocity vector q_1 be oriented parallel to the axis of symmetry, while the refracted vector q_2 is inclined at

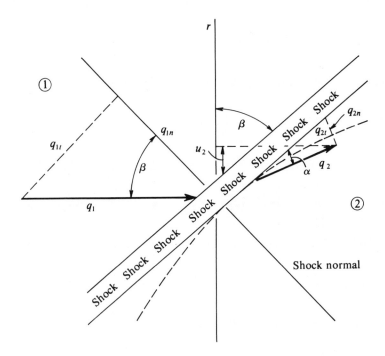

Figure F.1

an acute angle α to the shock. As already indicated, a scaling is selected so that $\rho_1 = p_1 = 1$. Let

(F.2) $$V = 1/\rho_2 \wedge L = (q_1/q_{1n})^2 = 1 + (f'(r))^2,$$

so that from our scaling and the second shock relation, $q_{1n} = \rho_2 q_{2n}$,

(F.3) $$q_{2n} = V q_1/L^{1/2}.$$

Also,

(F.4) $$q_{2t} = q_{1t} = q_1 \sin \beta = q_1 f'(r)/L^{1/2}.$$

But from (F.2), (F.3), and (F.4),

$$
\begin{aligned}
u_2 = q_2 \cos (\alpha + \beta) &= q_2(\cos \alpha \cos \beta - \sin \alpha \sin \beta) \\
&= q_2((q_{2t}/q_2)(q_{1n}/q_1) - (q_{2n}/q_2)(q_{1t}/q_1)) \\
&= q_1 f'(r)(1 - V)/L
\end{aligned}
$$

Then

$$(\psi_2)_z = -\rho_2 u_2 r = u_2 r(-1/V) = (q_1 f'(r)r/L)(1 - (1/V)).$$

For V as a function of ψ, see Appendix G.

DERIVATION OF THE ENTROPY FUNCTION A(ψ) FOR THE DETACHED SHOCK PROBLEM

The student is referred, for an understanding of the general context here, to the first paragraph above of Appendix F. The function $A(\psi)$, which appears in the coefficient D of the streamfunction equation (see

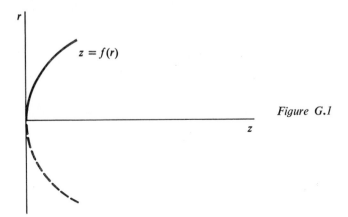

Figure G.1

Chapter 12, Sec. 1, or equation (E.13) of Appendix E) for the anisentropic flow downstream of a curved shock, and which is defined by

$$p = A(\psi)\rho^{\gamma},$$

is here derived for a shock

$$z = f(r).$$

Our shock relations, with $\rho_1 = p_1 = 1$, are written

(G.1)
$$q_{1n} = \rho_2 q_{2n},$$

(G.2)
$$q_{1n}^2 - \rho_2 q_{2n}^2 = p_2 - 1 = A(\psi)\rho_2^\gamma - 1$$

(G.3)
$$\gamma/(\gamma - 1) + \tfrac{1}{2}q_{1n}^2 = (\gamma/(\gamma - 1))A(\psi)\rho_2^{\gamma-1} + \tfrac{1}{2}q_{2n}^2. \text{[1]}$$

Then $2\rho_2 \cdot$ (G.3)–(G.2) yields

$$2\gamma/(\gamma - 1)\rho_2 + \rho_2 q_{1n}^2 - q_{1n}^2 = A(\psi)\rho_2^\gamma(\gamma + 1)/(\gamma - 1) + 1$$

and

(G.4) $A(\psi) = (1/\rho_2)^\gamma[(\gamma - 1)/(\gamma + 1)]$
$$\{\rho_2[(2\gamma/(\gamma - 1)) + (q_{1n}/q_1)^2 q_1^2] - (q_{1n}/q_1)^2 q_1^2 - 1\}.$$

Therefore, our task will be complete when we have determined ρ_2 and $(q_{1n}/q_1)^2$ in terms of ψ.

From (G.2) and (G.1)

$$q_{2n} = q_{1n} - (1/q_{1n})(p_2 - 1)$$

or, again from (G.1),

(G.5)
$$(1/\rho_2) = q_{2n}/q_{1n} = 1 - (\gamma/(\gamma q_{1n}^2))(p_2 - 1) = 1 - (1/(\gamma M_{1n}^2))(p_2 - 1),$$

and we now seek $(p_2 - 1)$.
From (6.3),

$$1 + \tfrac{1}{2}((\gamma - 1)/\gamma)q_{1n}^2 = p_2/\gamma_2 + \tfrac{1}{2}((\gamma - 1)/\gamma))q_{2n}^2$$

or, using again that $M_{1n}^2 = q_1^2/((\gamma p_1)/\rho_1) = q_1^2/\gamma$ and applying (G.5),

$1 + \tfrac{1}{2}(\gamma - 1)M_{1n}^2 = p_2/\rho_2 + \tfrac{1}{2}(\gamma - 1)(q_{2n}/q_{1n})^2 M_{1n}^2$
$$= p_2 - (1/(\gamma M_{1n}^2))p_2^2 + (1/(\gamma M_{1n}^2))p_2 + \tfrac{1}{2}(\gamma - 1)M_{1n}^2$$
$$- ((\gamma - 1)/\gamma)(p_2 - 1) + \tfrac{1}{2}((\gamma - 1)/(\gamma^2 M_{1n}^2))(p_2 - 1)^2.$$

Solving this quadratic for $(p_2 - 1)$, we have

$$p_2 - 1 = ((2\gamma)/(\gamma + 1))(M_{1n}^2 - 1)$$

---

[1] See footnote[1] of Appendix F.

or from (G.5), with $V = 1/\rho_2$

(G.6) $V = 1/\rho_2 = 1 - (2/(\gamma + 1))(1 - (1/M_{1n}^2)) =$
$$1 - (2/(\gamma + 1))(1 - (M_1/M_{1n})^2(1/M_1^2)).$$

Let $L = (M_1/M_{1n})^2 = (q_1/q_{1n})^2$. Then (see Appendix F),

$$L(\psi) = 1 + f'((2\psi/q_1)^{1/2}),$$
(G.7) $V(\psi) = 1 - (2/(\gamma + 1))(1 - L(\psi)/M_1^2),$
$$A(\psi) = (V(\psi))^\gamma((\gamma - 1)/(\gamma + 1))$$
$$\{(1/V(\psi))[(2\gamma)/(\gamma - 1) + q_1^2/L(\psi)] - (q_1^2/L(\psi)) - 1\}.$$

In reference [3] of Chapter 12, in order realistically to treat high mach number (say, $M > 8$) approach flows, it was necessary to utilize a value of γ in the subsonic portion only of the shock layer (i.e., on the downstream side of the shock) as a statistical fitting parameter for enthalpy from thermodynamic tables of hot gases. Such a simple fit—i.e., with only one fit parameter involved—is possible because the density changes by less than 10 percent in the subsonic region, and, in fact, in that region, for $M = 20$ at 100,000 feet altitude, the quantity $h\rho/p$, which is assumed by such a fitting procedure to be constant, actually varies only by less than 1 percent, according to thermodynamic tables for dissociated air.[2] Certainly no fit of this sort would be advisable in a supersonic region of flow, because there are always large changes of density in such a region[3] (see Chapter 10, Sec. 1). Thus at mach 20 and 100,000 feet altitude, whereas we have that in the approach stream $\gamma_1 = 1.4$ from kinetic theory, in the very hot shock layer the statistical fit parameter γ is found to be 1.17.

To accommodate the use of $\gamma \neq \gamma_1$, the formula (G.3) is modified by adding the number

$$k = (\gamma_1/(\gamma_1 - 1)) - (\gamma/(\gamma - 1))$$

to the left-hand side, and this parameter is then carried through the above manipulations and included in our final formulas (G.7) for $V(\psi)$ and

---

[2] F. R. Gilmore, 'Equilibrium Composition and Thermodynamic Properties of Air to 24,000°K,' RM–1543, The RAND Corporation, August, 1955; and J. Hilsenrath, and C. W. Beckett, 'Tables of Thermodynamic Properties of Argon-Free Air to 15,000°K,' TN–56–12, Arnold Engineering Development Center, September, 1956.

[3] Also, no such fit should be attempted in the boundary layer where, through an exceedingly thin 'manifold,' the temperature must adjust from the very hot exterior gas to the relatively cool body surface.

$A(\psi)$. The results are to be seen in reference [3] of Chapter 12, where the student should note carefully that the function f used in describing the given shock there is not quite the same function as used here in describing the shock.

Note that, if one were to utilize the same value $\gamma = 1.4$ on both sides of the shock at an approach flow mach number of 20 at 100,000 feet altitude, the temperature on the reverse side of the shock would be computed at about 40,000° Rankine, whereas actually the energy used in molecular dissociation (as accounted for in adopting a different value of γ in the shock layer to fit the enthalpy) brings this temperature down to around 8,500° Rankine.

BODIES COMPUTED FROM GIVEN DETACHED SHOCKS— THE MODIFIED NEWTONIAN LAW OF LESTER LEES

Pictures are shown below of flows and bodies computed from two different given shocks with an approach flow of mach 5.8 and $\gamma = \gamma_1 = 1.4$. The flow in Figure H.1 is computed from a shock given by

(H.1) $$z = f(r) = -z_0 + ((M^2 - 1)(M^2 + r^2))^{1/2}, \quad M = 5.8,$$

which is asymptotic to the characteristics (or mach lines) for the approach flow. An approximately spherical body is obtained. The flow in Figure H.2 is computed from a body given by

(H.2) $$z = f(r) = -z_0 + (0.8(0.8 + r^2))^{1/2},$$

and a flow is obtained that can be smoothly extended to that about a rounded (finite) cone (see Chapter 10, Sec. 4). The method of varying the shock to obtain approximately a desired body shape involves varying the location of the foci of a given conic section shock. The detachment distance of shock to stagnation point of body is denoted by $\mathbf{h}$ (not to be confused here with the h used for enthalpy above), whereas the curvature of the body at the stagnation point is denoted by κ, and only the dimensionless quantities $\kappa\mathbf{h}$ are quoted in the figures. In (H.1) and (H.2) which follow respectively,

$$z_0 = M(M^2 - 1)^{1/2} \quad \text{and} \quad z_0 = 0.8.$$

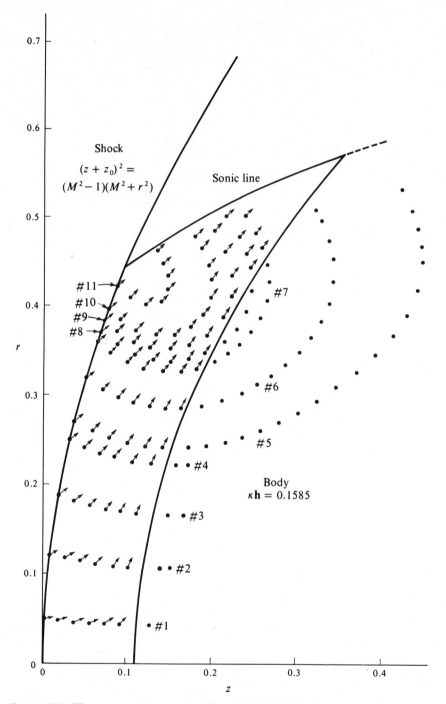

Figure H.1. Flow past an approximately spherical body. (From P. R. Garabedian and H. M. Lieberstein, 'On the numerical calculation of detached bow shock waves in hypersonic flow,' *J. Aero. Sci.*, **25**, 2, (1958), by permission of the American Institute of Aeronautics and Astronautics.)

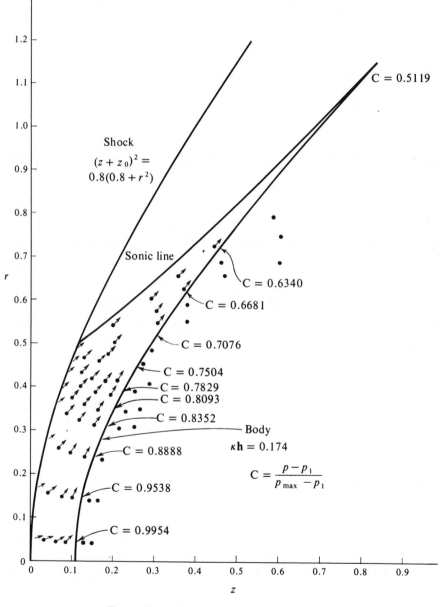

Figure H.2. Flow past a rounded cone. (Ibid.)

The parameter z_0 is chosen, so that $f(0) = 0$ and is introduced in order to avoid a devastating loss of significant digits in computing z for small r—or, really, in computing differences of z for small r.

In the design of a heat-protecting shield (a 'heat sink') for a reentry body, it is important to know the pressure distribution in the neighborhood of the stagnation point where the largest temperature and rate of heat transfer occur. This is used in a boundary layer theory (an adaptation for the viscous effects that are felt very close to the body) to obtain the rate of heat transfer, which, in turn, is used for heat-conduction studies of materials to be used in the nose region of the body. An empirical law for the pressure distribution for flows below dissociation temperatures was developed by Professor Lester Lees of the Guggenheim Laboratories at the California Institute of Technology. It is

$$(H.3) \qquad\qquad (p - p_1) = (p_{max} - p_1)\cos^2 \theta$$

where p_1 is the approach flow pressure, p_{max} is the pressure at the stagnation point of the body,[1] and θ is the inclination of the body to the approach flow normal. Since the law $p = 2 \cos^2 \theta$ (note that p_1 is small compared to p) has been known in the literature as the Newtonian law, (H.3) is called the modified Newtonian law. As reported in reference [4] in Chapter 12, for the case of Figure H.1, the modified Newtonian law is found to be about 3 percent high, and for the case of Figure H.2, the modified Newtonian law is found to be about 3 percent low. Of course, both of these computations are at M = 5.8. A case is reported with M = 20, $\gamma_1 = 1.4$, $\gamma = 1.17$ (see Appendix G), using a shock given by

$$(H.4) \qquad z = -z_0 + ((M^2 - 1)(M^2 + r^2))^{1/2}, \quad M = 20,$$

which gave, as in Figure H.1, an approximately spherical body with a much smaller detachment distance, $\kappa h = 0.0633$, and a sonic line making a much more acute angle to the r-axis direction. The modified Newtonian law was then 6 to 7 percent high. As the verification of an engineering design criterion, the agreement is clearly satisfactory, and it serves to extrapolate the modified Newtonian law to large approach flow mach numbers, where it is more difficult to obtain reliable empirical data. Of course, the law is intended to be valid only for bodies with noticeably rounded, not flat, noses. The agreement, of course, provides empirical verification of the theory for a large number of cases.

---

[1] It can be computed from the Bernoulli law.

INDEX

68 69 70   7 6 5 4 3 2 1